ANSWERS TO PROBLEMS

Organic Chemistry
Third Edition

ANSWERS TO PROBLEMS

ROBERT THORNTON MORRISON
ROBERT NEILSON BOYD

New York University

Allyn and Bacon, Inc.   **Boston**

ACKNOWLEDGMENTS

Our thanks to Sadtler Research Laboratories for the infrared spectra labeled "Sadtler" and to the Infrared Data Committee of Japan for those labeled "IRDC."

ABOUT THESE ANSWERS

Properly speaking, this book does not contain answers at all, but rather checks on *your* answers. For perhaps a third of the problems, suitable answers are much longer and more detailed than it would be possible for us to give here. Remember, you do not work problems so that, when you are through, you know the answers; there are more efficient ways of learning facts. You work problems, first, to see if you understand the chemistry underlying them; second, and more important, you work problems to learn the technique of *using* your chemistry in the same practical ways that an organic chemist does.

For a problem on synthesis, we have simply listed a series of reagents — and, in many cases, only one of several acceptable series — whereas your answer should include structural formulas for intermediates (see page 224 in the textbook), and any other details required by the ground rules of your particular course. We do not say what one would do and see in making a chemical test, but *you* should. In accounting for a set of observations, we have given only a key phrase or term; you should include any equations, structural formulas, diagrams, or discussion that are necessary to show that you have figured out what is going on.

For problems on spectra, answers are presented in two stages; names of the unknown compounds are given in their proper sequence along with all the other answers; then, at the end of the Answer Book, spectra are reproduced with infrared bands identified and nmr signals assigned. We suggest you check each of your answers in two stages, too. First, check the name; if your answer is wrong, or if you have not been able to work the problem at all, return to the spectrum in the textbook and, knowing the correct structure, have another go at it: see if you can now identify bands, assign signals, and analyze spin—spin splittings. Then, finally, turn to the back of the Answer Book and check your answer against the analyzed spectrum.

Give yourself a fair chance to work each problem; once you have looked up the answer, much of the purpose of the problem is lost.

Robert Thornton Morrison

Robert Neilson Boyd

1.1 Ionic: a, e, f.

$\qquad\qquad\quad$ H $\qquad\qquad$:F̈: $\qquad\qquad$ H
(a) K⁺:B̈r:⁻ (b) H:S̈: (c) :F̈:N̈:F̈: (d) :C̈l:C̈:C̈l:
$\qquad\qquad\qquad\qquad\qquad\qquad\qquad\qquad\qquad$:C̈l:

$\qquad\qquad$:Ö: $\qquad\qquad\quad$ H $\qquad\qquad\quad$ H $\qquad\qquad$ H
(e) Ca⁺⁺:Ö:S̈:Ö:⁼ (f) H:N̈:H⁺:C̈l:⁻ (g) H:P̈:H (h) H:C̈:Ö:H
$\qquad\qquad$:Ö: $\qquad\qquad\qquad$ H $\qquad\qquad\qquad\qquad\qquad$ H

$\qquad\qquad\qquad\qquad\qquad\qquad\qquad\qquad\quad$:Ö: $\qquad\qquad\qquad$:Ö:
1.2 (a) H:Ö:Ö:H (b) :N:::N: (c) H:Ö:N̈::Ö: (d) :Ö:N̈::Ö:⁻

$\qquad\qquad\qquad\qquad\qquad\qquad\qquad\qquad\qquad\qquad\qquad\qquad$ H H
(e) H:C:::N: (f) :Ö::C::Ö: (g) H:Ö:C:Ö:H (h) H:C̈:C̈:H
$\qquad\qquad\qquad\qquad\qquad\qquad\qquad\qquad\quad$ Ö: $\qquad\qquad\qquad$ H H

1.3 (a) Na   2   8   1
$\quad$ Mg   2   8   2
$\quad$ Al   2   8   2   1
$\quad$ Si   2   8   2   1   1
$\quad$ P   2   8   2   1   1   1
$\quad$ S   2   8   2   2   1   1
$\quad$ Cl   2   8   2   2   2   1
$\quad$ Ar   2   8   2   2   2   2

(b) Elements of same family have same electronic configuration for highest energy level;   (c) metallic elements on left lose electrons to give 2,8 configuration; non-metallic elements on right gain electrons to give 2,8,8 configuration.

1.4   All tetrahedral (sp^3):   (a) about N;   (b) about O, with one 2e lobe;
(c) about C and O, with two 2e lobes;   (d) about C and N, with one 2e lobe.

1.5   Structure (a), not (b).

1.6   Linear.

1.7   (a) Expect zero moment, contrary to fact.
(b) Expect bigger moment for NF_3, contrary to fact.

1.8   H-bonding: a, e, f.

$$
\begin{array}{ccc}
& \overset{\displaystyle H}{\underset{\displaystyle H}{|}} & \overset{\displaystyle H}{\underset{\displaystyle CH_3}{|}} \\
CH_3-O\text{---}H-O & CH_3-N\text{---}H-N & CH_3-N\text{---}H-N \\
\overset{\displaystyle |}{H}\quad\overset{\displaystyle |}{CH_3} & \overset{\displaystyle |}{H}\quad\overset{\displaystyle |}{CH_3} & \overset{\displaystyle |}{CH_3}\quad\overset{\displaystyle |}{CH_3}
\end{array}
$$

1.9   (a) $CH_3OH > CH_3NH_2$;   (b) $CH_3SH > CH_3OH$;   (c) $H_3O^+ > NH_4{}^+$.

1.10   (a) H_3O^+;   (b) $NH_4{}^+$;   (c) H_2S;   (d) H_2O;   (e) positive charge → increased acidity.

1.11   (a) $CH_3{}^- > NH_2{}^- > OH^- > F^-$;   (b) $NH_3 > H_2O > HF$;
(c) $SH^- > Cl^-$;   (d) $F^- > Cl^- > Br^- > I^-$;   (e) $OH^- > SH^- > SeH^-$.

1.12 $CH_3NH_2 > CH_3OH > CH_3F$.

1.13   (a) $OH^- > H_2O > H_3O^+$;   (b) $NH_2{}^- > NH_3$;   (c) $S^= > HS^- > H_2S$;
(d) negative charge → increased basicity.

1.14 $NH_3 > NF_3$.

1.   Ionic: a, d, e, g.

$$
\begin{array}{llll}
\text{(a) } Mg^{++}2\text{:}\ddot{\underset{..}{C}}l\text{:}^- & \text{(b) :}\ddot{\underset{..}{C}}l\text{:}\overset{\displaystyle H}{\underset{\displaystyle H}{\ddot{C}}}\text{:}\ddot{\underset{..}{C}}l\text{:} & \text{(c) :}\ddot{\underset{..}{I}}\text{:}\ddot{\underset{..}{C}}l\text{:} & \text{(d) } Na^+\text{:}\ddot{\underset{..}{O}}\text{:}\ddot{\underset{..}{C}}l\text{:}^-
\end{array}
$$

$$
\begin{array}{llll}
\text{(e) } K^+\text{:}\ddot{\underset{:\ddot{O}:}{\overset{:\ddot{O}:}{O}}}\text{:}\ddot{C}l\text{:}\ddot{\underset{..}{O}}\text{:}^- & \text{(f) :}\ddot{C}l\text{:}\overset{:\ddot{C}l:}{\underset{:\ddot{C}l:}{Si}}\text{:}\ddot{C}l\text{:} & \text{(g) } Ba^{++}\text{:}\ddot{\underset{:\ddot{O}:}{\overset{:\ddot{O}:}{O}}}\text{:}\ddot{S}\text{:}\ddot{\underset{..}{O}}\text{:}^= & \text{(h) } H\text{:}\overset{\displaystyle H}{\underset{\displaystyle H\ H}{\ddot{C}}}\text{:}\ddot{\underset{..}{N}}\text{:}H
\end{array}
$$

$$
\begin{array}{llll}
\text{2. (a) } H\text{:}\overset{\displaystyle H\ H}{\ddot{N}}\text{:}\ddot{\underset{..}{N}}\text{:}H & \text{(b) } H\text{:}\ddot{\underset{..}{O}}\text{:}\overset{:\ddot{O}:}{\underset{:\ddot{O}:}{S}}\text{:}\ddot{\underset{..}{O}}\text{:}H & \text{(c) } H\text{:}\ddot{\underset{..}{O}}\text{:}\overset{:\ddot{O}:}{\underset{:\ddot{O}:}{S}}\text{:}\ddot{\underset{..}{O}}\text{:}^- & \text{(d) :}\ddot{\underset{..}{C}}l\text{:}\ddot{C}\text{::}\ddot{\underset{..}{O}}\text{:}
\end{array}
$$

$$
\begin{array}{llll}
\text{(e) } H\text{:}\ddot{\underset{..}{O}}\text{:}\ddot{N}\text{::}\ddot{\underset{..}{O}}\text{:} & \text{(f) :}\ddot{\underset{..}{O}}\text{:}\ddot{N}\text{::}\ddot{\underset{..}{O}}\text{:}^- & \text{(g) :}\ddot{\underset{..}{O}}\text{:}\overset{:\ddot{O}:}{C}\text{::}\ddot{\underset{..}{O}}\text{:}^= & \text{(h) } H\text{:}\overset{\displaystyle H\ H}{\ddot{C}}\text{::}\ddot{C}\text{:}H
\end{array}
$$

(i) H:C:::C:H   (j) H:C̈::Ö: (k) H:C:Ö:H   (l) H:C̈:C̈:C̈:H

with the H above and :Ö: below for (k), and H H H above and H H H below for (l)

3. a, c: trigonal. Others tetrahedral; b, h with one 2e lobe; d, e, f with two 2e lobes.

4. Octahedral,

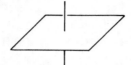

5. (a) Toward Br;   (b) toward Cl;   (c) non-polar;   (d) away from H atoms, bisecting angle between Cl atoms;   (e) 180° away from C–H bond;   (f) similar to water molecule;   (g) similar to water molecule;   (h) toward unshared electron pair on N;   (i) away from Cl atoms, bisecting angle between F atoms.

6. (a) F is more electronegative than Cl; although d is smaller, e is bigger.
    (b) Toward C; that is, D attracts electrons less than H does.

7. Li compound: ionic, salt-like. Be compound: non-ionic, covalent.

8. Alcohol molecules form H-bonds to each other and to water molecules. Ether molecules can form H-bonds only to water, which furnishes H attached to O.

9. (a) H_3O^+ + HCO_3^- $\rightleftharpoons$ H_2CO_3 + H_2O
        Stronger   Stronger   Weaker   Weaker
         acid   base   acid   base

    (b) OH^- + HCO_3^- $\rightleftharpoons$ $CO_3^=$ + H_2O
        Stronger   Stronger   Weaker   Weaker
         base   acid   base   acid

    (c) NH_3 + H_3O^+ $\rightleftharpoons$ NH_4^+ + H_2O
        Stronger   Stronger   Weaker   Weaker
         base   acid   acid   base

    (d) CN^- + H_2O $\rightleftharpoons$ HCN   + OH^-
        Weaker   Weaker   Stronger   Stronger
         base   acid   acid   base

    (e) H^- + H_2O $\longrightarrow$ H_2 + OH^-
        Stronger   Stronger   Weaker   Weaker
         base   acid   acid   base

(f) $C_2^=$ $\quad$ + H_2O $\quad$ ⟶ $\quad$ $2OH^-$ $\quad$ + $\quad$ C_2H_2
$\qquad$ Stronger $\quad$ Stronger $\quad\quad$ Weaker $\quad\quad$ Weaker
$\qquad\quad$ base $\qquad\quad$ acid $\qquad\qquad$ base $\qquad\qquad$ acid

10. (a) H_3O^+;   (b) HCl;   (c) HCl in benzene.

11. Reversible protonation of an unshared electron pair on oxygen atom (Compare page 33).

12. (a)

(b)

(c)

(d)

(e)

(f)

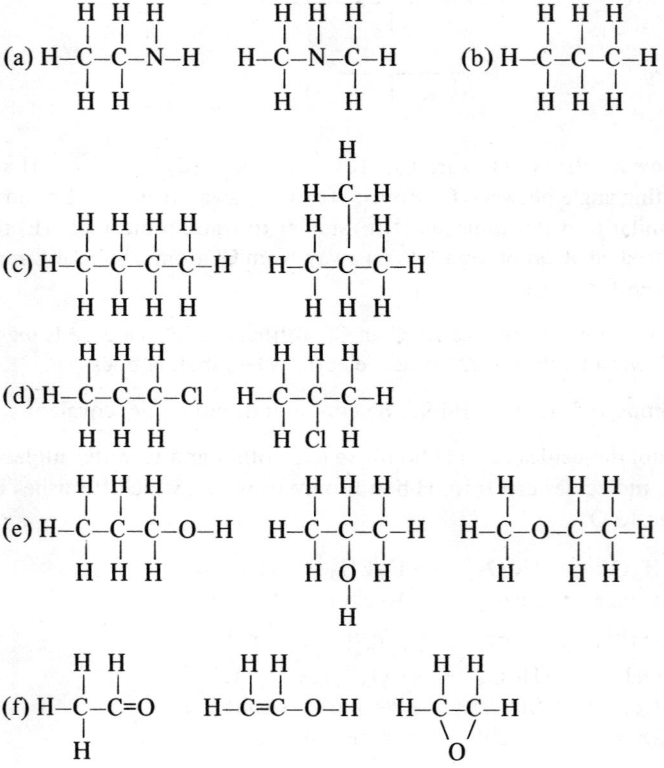

13. To minimize decomposition of unstable compound.

CHAPTER 2

2.1   (a) −8 kcal;   (b) +13 kcal;   (c) −102 kcal.

2.2   (a) +46, +16, −24 kcal;   (b) +36, +33, −20 kcal;
(c) +38, −32, −70 kcal.

2.3 CH_3^+, sp^2, with p orbital empty; flat, trigonal, $120°$ angles. $CH_3:^-$, sp^3, fourth sp^3 orbital occupied by unshared pair of electrons; pyramidal.

2.4 (a) Forms insoluble silver halide, in presence of nitric acid. (b) Boiling removes volatile HCN and H_2S which otherwise would interfere ($AgCN$ and Ag_2S) with halide test.

2.5 (a) ($\%C + \%H$) $< 100\%$; (b) 34.8%.

2.6 (a) 69.6% Cl; (b) 70.4% Cl; (c) 24.85 mg; (d) 26.49 mg; (e) 27.44 mg.

2.7 (a) CH_3; (b) $C_3H_6Cl_2$.

2.8 C_6H_6.

2.9 $C_4H_8O_2$.

1. A, 93.9% C, 6.3% H; B, 64.0% C, 4.5% H, 31.4% Cl; C, 62.0% C, 10.3% H, 27.7% O.

2. (a) 45.9% C, 8.9% H, 45.2% Cl; (b) 52.1% C, 13.1% H, 34.8% O; (c) 54.5% C, 9.1% H, 36.3% O; (d) 41.8% C, 4.7% H, 18.6% O, 16.3% N, 18.6% S; (e) 20.0% C, 6.7% H, 26.6% O, 46.7% N; (f) 55.6% C, 6.2% H, 10.8% O, 27.4% Cl.

3. (a) CH_2; (b) CH; (c) CH_2O; (d) C_2H_5OCl; (e) $C_3H_{10}N_2$; (f) $C_3H_4O_2Cl_2$.

4. $C_{20}H_{21}O_4N$.

5. $C_{14}H_{14}O_3N_3SNa$.

6. (a) 85.8% C, 14.3% H; (b) CH_2; (c) C_6H_{12}.

7. $C_2H_4O_2$.

8. CH_2O.

9. $C_{16}H_{10}O_2N_2$.

10. (a) 942; (b) 6.

11. (a) -130; (b) -44; (c) -26; (d) -2; (e) -13; (f) -8; (g) -1; (h) 1st step $+46$; 2nd steps $+10$, -3, 0; 3rd steps -23, -5, -1 kcal.

12. (a) $+58$, $+20$, -45; (b) E_{act} of a chain-carrying step $\geqslant 20$ kcal.

13. (a) E_{act} of reaction (ii) $\geqslant 16$ kcal; E_{act} of reaction (i) *could* be zero (is actually 13 kcal). (b) Highly improbable, since E_{act} for reaction with Cl_2 is much smaller.

14. (a) $CH_3\cdot$ can react not only with Br_2 but also with HBr (reverse of Step 2, page 60). (b) Reaction of $CH_3\cdot$ with HBr (E_{act} 2 kcal) can compete with (easy) reaction with X_2; reaction of $CH_3\cdot$ with HCl (E_{act} 3 kcal) cannot compete as readily. (c) Halogenation increasingly reversed by HBr that accumulates as reaction product.

15. (a) $Cl-Cl \xrightarrow{h\nu} 2Cl\cdot$; $Cl\cdot + H-H \longrightarrow HCl + H\cdot$; $H\cdot + Cl-Cl \longrightarrow HCl + Cl\cdot$; etc.
    (b) E_{act} of a chain-carrying step $\geqslant 33$ kcal.

16. (a) $(CH_3)_4Pb \xrightarrow{\Delta} \underset{\text{Mirror}}{Pb} + 4CH_3\cdot$; $CH_3\cdot + \cdot CH_3 \longrightarrow CH_3-CH_3$;

    $(CH_3)_4Pb \xrightarrow{\Delta} \underset{\substack{\text{New} \\ \text{mirror}}}{Pb} + 4CH_3\cdot \xrightarrow[\text{old mirror}]{Pb} \underset{\text{Effluent}}{(CH_3)_4Pb}$

    (b) More chance for $CH_3\cdot + \cdot CH_3 \longrightarrow CH_3-CH_3$, and hence fewer $CH_3\cdot$ radicals available for removal of mirror.

17. $(C_2H_5)_4Pb \xrightarrow{140^\circ} Pb + 4C_2H_5\cdot$;
    $C_2H_5\cdot + Cl_2 \longrightarrow C_2H_5Cl + Cl\cdot$;
    $Cl\cdot + CH_4 \longrightarrow HCl + CH_3\cdot$;
    $CH_3\cdot + Cl_2 \longrightarrow CH_3Cl + Cl\cdot$; *etc.*

CHAPTER 3

3.1 (a) $CH_3CH_2CH_2CHCl_2$, $CH_3CH_2CHClCH_2Cl$, $CH_3CHClCH_2CH_2Cl$, $ClCH_2CH_2CH_2CH_2Cl$, $CH_3CH_2CCl_2CH_3$, $CH_3CHClCHClCH_3$;
    (b) $(CH_3)_2CHCHCl_2$, $(CH_3)_2CClCH_2Cl$, $CH_3CH(CH_2Cl)_2$.

3.2 No.

3.3 Van der Waals repulsion between "large" methyls.

3.4 (a)

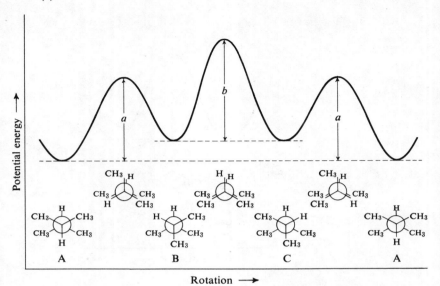

3.4 (b)

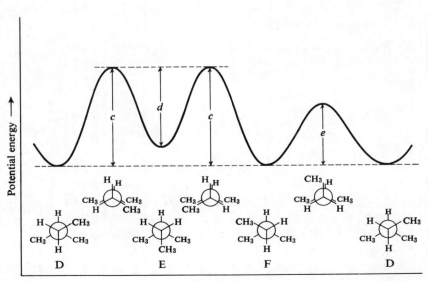

3.4 (c)

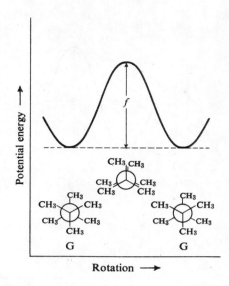

(d) On the assumption of 0.8 kcal per methyl–methyl gauche interaction, and of 3.0 kcal torsional energy plus 0.4 kcal for two methyl–hydrogen eclipsings and 2.2-3.9 kcal per methyl–methyl eclipsing (from Fig. 3.4), one arrives at the following tentative predictions: $b > 4.4$–$6.1 > a > 3.4$; $c > 4.4$–$6.1 > d > 3.4 > e$; size of f depends on value of methyl–methyl eclipsing.

3.5 (a) C–C–C–C–C–C–C, C–C–C–C–$\underset{\overset{|}{\text{C}}}{\text{C}}$–C, C–C–C–$\underset{\overset{|}{\text{C}}}{\text{C}}$–C–C,

C–C–C–$\underset{\overset{|}{\text{C}}}{\overset{\overset{\text{C}}{|}}{\text{C}}}$–C; C–C–$\underset{\overset{|}{\text{C}}}{\underset{}{\text{C}}}$–$\underset{\overset{|}{\text{C}}}{\text{C}}$–C, C–C–$\underset{\overset{|}{\text{C}}}{\text{C}}$–$\underset{\overset{|}{\text{C}}}{\text{C}}$–C, C–C–$\underset{\overset{|}{\text{C}}}{\overset{\overset{\text{C}}{|}}{\text{C}}}$–C–C,

C–C–$\underset{\overset{|}{\text{C}}}{\underset{\overset{|}{\text{C}}}{\text{C}}}$–C–C, C–C–$\underset{\overset{|}{\text{C}}}{\underset{}{\text{C}}}$–$\underset{\overset{|}{\text{C}}}{\overset{\overset{\text{C}}{|}}{\text{C}}}$–C; (b) C–C–C–C–$\underset{\overset{|}{\text{Cl}}}{\text{C}}$, C–C–C–$\underset{\overset{|}{\text{Cl}}}{\text{C}}$–C,

C–C–$\underset{\overset{|}{\text{Cl}}}{\text{C}}$–C–C, C–C–$\underset{\overset{|}{\text{Cl}}}{\overset{\overset{\text{C}}{|}}{\text{C}}}$–C, C–C–$\underset{\overset{|}{\text{Cl}}}{\overset{\overset{\text{C}}{|}}{\text{C}}}$–C, C–C–$\underset{\overset{|}{\text{Cl}}}{\overset{\overset{\text{C}}{|}}{\text{C}}}$–C–C, C–C–$\underset{\overset{|}{\text{Cl}}}{\overset{\overset{\text{C}}{|}}{\text{C}}}$–C , C–$\underset{\overset{|}{\text{Cl}}}{\overset{\overset{\text{C}}{|}}{\text{C}}}$–C;

$$\text{(c) C–C–C–C–Br,} \underset{\text{Br}}{\text{C–C–C–C,}} \underset{\text{Br Br}}{\text{C–C–C–C,}} \underset{\text{Br}}{\text{C–C–C–C,}} \underset{\text{Br Br}}{\text{C–C–C–C,}} \underset{\text{Br}}{\text{C–C–}\overset{\text{Br}}{\text{C}}\text{–C,}}$$

$$\underset{\text{Br Br}}{\text{C–C–}\overset{\text{C}}{\text{C}}\text{–C,}} \underset{\text{Br}}{\text{C–}\overset{\text{C}}{\text{C}}\text{–C–Br,}} \underset{\text{Br Br Br}}{\text{C–}\overset{\text{C}}{\text{C}}\text{–C,}} \underset{\text{Br}}{\text{C–}\overset{\text{C}}{\text{C}}\text{–C.}}$$

3.6 (a) *n*-Hexane, 2-methylpentane, 3-methylpentane, 2,2-dimethylbutane, 2,3-dimethylbutane. (b) Order of isomers identical to Prob. 3.5(a): *n*-heptane, 2-methylhexane, 3-methylhexane, 2,2-dimethylpentane, 2,3-dimethylpentane, 2,4-dimethylpentane, 3,3-dimethylpentane, 3-ethylpentane, 2,2,3-trimethylbutane.

3.7 (a) Order of isomers identical to Problem 3.5(b): 1-chloropentane, 2-chloropentane, 3-chloropentane, 1-chloro-2-methylbutane, 2-chloro-2-methylbutane, 3-chloro-2-methylbutane, 1-chloro-3-methylbutane, 1-chloro-2,2-dimethylpropane. (b) Order of isomers identical to Problem 3.5(c): 1,1-dibromobutane, 1,2-dibromobutane, 1,3-dibromobutane, 1,4-dibromobutane, 2,2-dibromobutane, 2,3-dibromobutane, 1,1-dibromo-2-methylpropane, 1,2-dibromo-2-methylpropane, 1,3-dibromo-2-methylpropane.

3.8 All three graphs show a rate of increase falling off with increasing carbon number.

3.9 (a) $CH_3CH_2CH_3$; (b) $CH_3CH_2CH_3$; (c) $CH_3CH_2CH_2D$; (d) CH_3CHDCH_3.

3.10 (a) $\underset{\text{Br}}{\text{C–C–C–C–C,}} \underset{\text{Br}}{\text{C–C–C–C–C,}} \underset{\text{Br}}{\text{C–C–C–C–C;}}$

(b) $\underset{\text{Br}}{\text{C–C–}\overset{\text{C}}{\text{C}}\text{–C,}} \underset{\text{Br}}{\text{C–C–}\overset{\text{C}}{\text{C}}\text{–C,}} \underset{\text{Br}}{\text{C–C–}\overset{\text{C}}{\text{C}}\text{–C,}} \underset{\text{Br}}{\text{C–C–}\overset{\text{C}}{\text{C}}\text{–C;}}$

(c) $\underset{\text{Br}}{\text{C–}\overset{\text{C}}{\text{C}}\overset{\text{C}}{\text{–C}}\text{–C,}} \underset{\text{Br}}{\text{C–}\overset{\text{C}}{\text{C}}\overset{\text{C}}{\text{–C}}\text{–C;}}$ (d) $\underset{\text{C}}{\text{C–}\overset{\text{C}}{\text{C}}\text{–C–Br}}$

3.11 (a) *n*-PrCl + Li, then CuI, then *iso*-PrCl; or *iso*-PrCl + Li, then CuI, then *n*-PrCl. (b) The second, since *n*-PrCl is a primary halide.

3.12 (a) C–C–C–C–C, C–C–C–C–C, C–C–C–C–C; (b)
$$\begin{array}{c} \text{C} \\ | \\ \text{C–C–C–C,} \\ | \\ \text{Cl} \end{array}$$

with Cl on the respective carbons:

C–C–C–C–C (Cl on C2), C–C–C–C–C (Cl on C3), C–C–C–C–C (Cl on C3);

$$\begin{array}{ccc} \text{C} & \text{C} & \text{C} \\ | & | & | \\ \text{C–C–C–C,} & \text{C–C–C–C,} & \text{C–C–C–C.} \\ | & | & | \\ \text{Cl} & \text{Cl} & \text{Cl} \end{array}$$

3.13 $(CH_3)_3CCH_2X$ is the only possible substitution product.

3.14 (a) 44% 1-Cl, 56% 2-Cl; (b) 64% 1°, 36% 3°; (c) 55% 1°, 45% 3°;
(d) 21% 1-Cl, 53% 2-Cl, 26% 3-Cl; (e) 28% 1-Cl-2-Me, 23% 2-Cl-2-Me,
35% 3-Cl-2-Me, 14% 1-Cl-3-Me; (f) 45% 1-Cl-2,2,3-triMe, 25% 3-Cl-2,2,-
3-triMe, 30% 1-Cl-2,3,3-triMe; (g) 33% 1-Cl-2,2,4-triMe, 28% 3-Cl-
2,2,4-triMe, 18% 4-Cl-2,2,4-triMe, 22% 1-Cl-2,4,4-triMe.

3.15 (a) 4% 1-Br, 96% 2-Br; (b) 0.6% 1°, 99.4% 3°; (c) 0.3% 1°, 99.7% 3°;
(d) 1% 1-Br, 66% 2-Br, 33% 3-Br; (e) 0.3% 1-Br-2-Me, 90% 2-Br-2-Me,
9% 3-Br-2-Me, 0.2% 1-Br-3-Me; (f) 0.6% 1-Br-2,2,3-triMe, 99% 3-Br-
2,2,3-triMe, 0.4% 1-Br-2,3,3-triMe; (g) 0.5% 1-Br-2,2,4-triMe, 9%
3-Br-2,2,4-triMe, 90% 4-Br-2,2,4-triMe, 0.3% 1-Br-2,4,4-triMe.

3.16 40:1; easier to measure accurately ratio of products.

3.17 1.15:1.

3.18 (a) DCl:HCl ratio would have been less than *t*-BuCl:*iso*-BuCl ratio;
(b) same as (a).

3.19 *t*-BuCl, Mg, $Et_2O \longrightarrow$ *t*-BuMgCl $\xrightarrow{D_2O}$ *t*-Bu–D.

3.20 Add DBr, see if unconsumed methane contains deuterium.

3.21 See if $^{35}Cl^{36}Cl$ (mass 71) and/or $^{36}Cl^{37}Cl$ (mass 73) shows up in the
mass spectrum.

3.22 2,2-Dimethylhexane.

1. (a)
$$\begin{array}{cc} \text{C} & \text{C} \\ | & | \\ \text{C–C–C–C–C;} \\ | & | \\ \text{C} & \text{C} \end{array}$$
(b)
$$\begin{array}{c} \text{C–C–C–C;} \\ | | \\ \text{C} \text{C} \end{array}$$
(c)
$$\begin{array}{c} \text{C} \\ | \\ \text{C–C–C–C–C–C–C;} \\ | | | \\ \text{C} \text{C} \text{C} \end{array}$$

```
        C C                    C   C                  C   C
        | |                    |   |                  |   |
(d) C–C–C–C–C–C–C;  (e) C–C–C–C–C–C–C;   (f) C–C–C–C–C–C;
          |                        |                  |   |
          C                        C                  C   C
          |                        |
          C                        C
```

```
                              C
                              |
(g) C–C–C–C–C;   (h) C–C–C–C–C.
        | |              |   |
        C C              C   C
        |
        C
```

2. (a) 2-Methylpentane; (b) 3,3-dimethylpentane; (c) 3-methyl-3-
   ethylpentane; (d) 2,3,4-trimethylhexane; (e) 3-methyl-5-ethyloctane;
   (f) 2,2,4,4-tetramethylpentane; (g) 2-methyl-5-ethylheptane;
   (h) 2,3,5-trimethyl-5-ethylheptane; (i) 2-methyl-3,3-diethylhexane;
   (j) 3-methyl-5-isopropyloctane.

3. (a) 1a, 2b, 2c, 2f; (b) 1d, 1e, 1h, 2a, 2i; (c) 1b, 1c, 1f, 1g, 2e, 2g, 2h;
   (d) 1b; (e) 1a, 1h, 2d, 2f; (f) 2c.

4. (a) 1e, 1g, 1h, 2a, 2d, 2g, 2h, 2i, 2j; (b) 1b, 1f; (c) 1e, 1h, 2a, 2g;
   (d) 1f; (e) 1d, 2d, 2e, 2j; (f) 1c; (g) 1a, 1h; (h) 2f; (i) 2d, 2j;
   (j) 1h; (k) 1d, 2e, 2j.

5. (a) 2,3-Dimethylbutane; (b) *n*-hexane, 2,2-dimethylbutane;
   (c) 3-methylpentane; (d) 2-methylpentane; (e) 6.

6. One monochloro, three dichloro, four trichloro.

7. c, b, e, a, d.

8. (a) Isobutylmagnesium bromide; (b) *tert*-butylmagnesium bromide;
   (c) isobutane; (d) isobutane; (e) 1-deuterio-2-methylpropane,
   $(CH_3)_2CHCH_2D$; (f) lithium di(*sec*-butyl)copper; (g) 3-methylpentane.

9. (a) Mg, anhyd. ether; H_2O. (b) Mg, anhyd. ether; H_2O. (c) Li; CuI;
   ethyl chloride. (d) H_2, Ni, heat, pressure. (e) H_2, Ni, heat, pressure.

10. (a) 1-, 2-, and 3-chlorohexane; (b) 1-, 2-, 3-, and 4-chloro-2-methylpen-
    tane, and 1-chloro-4-methylpentane; (c) 1-, 3-, and 4-chloro-2,2,4-
    trimethylpentane, and 1-chloro-2,4,4-trimethylpentane; (d) 1- and
    3-chloro-2,2-dimethylbutane, and 1-chloro-3,3-dimethylbutane.

11. Order of isomers as in Problem 10: (a) 16, 42, 42%; (b) 21, 17, 26, 26,
    10%; (c) 33, 28, 18, 22%; (d) 46, 39, 15%.

12. Water rapidly destroys a Grignard reagent.

13. Allyl, benzyl $> 3° > 2° > 1° >$ methyl, vinyl.

14. Allylic, benzylic $> 3° > 2° > 1° > CH_4$, vinylic.

15. Rearrangement of initially formed $1°$ radical into more stable $2°$ or $3°$ radical:

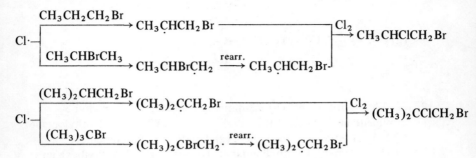

16. (a) 2650 g;   (b) 8710 kcal;   (c) 170 g.

17. Carius: mono, 45.3% Cl; di, 62.8% Cl. Mol.wt. by mass spectrometer: mono, 78.5; di, 113.

18. Try to synthesize it by Corey-House method from isopentyl bromide.

19. (a) Methane, formed by $CH_3OH + CH_3MgI \longrightarrow CH_4 + CH_3OMgI$; 1.49 mg CH_3OH.   (b) 59, *n*-propyl or isopropyl alcohol.   (c) 3; $CH_2OHCHOHCH_2OH$.

20. (a) (1) $(CH_3)_3CO-OC(CH_3)_3 \xrightarrow{130°} 2(CH_3)_3CO\cdot$
      (2) $(CH_3)_3CO\cdot + (CH_3)_3CH \longrightarrow (CH_3)_3COH + (CH_3)_3C\cdot$
      (3) $(CH_3)_3C\cdot + CCl_4 \longrightarrow (CH_3)_3CCl + Cl_3C\cdot$
      (4) $Cl_3C\cdot + (CH_3)_3CH \longrightarrow Cl_3CH + (CH_3)_3C\cdot$
      then (3), (4), (3), (4), etc.

   (b) (1) $(CH_3)_3C-O-Cl \xrightarrow{h\nu} (CH_3)_3CO\cdot + Cl\cdot$
      (2) $(CH_3)_3CO\cdot + RH \longrightarrow (CH_3)_3COH + R\cdot$
      (3) $R\cdot + (CH_3)_3C-O-Cl \longrightarrow RCl + (CH_3)_3CO\cdot$
      then (2), (3), (2), (3), etc.

CHAPTER 4

4.1   2 (mirror images).

4.2   (a) 3;   (b) 2;   (c) 3 (2 are mirror images);   (d) 1.

4.3 (a) $-39.0°$; (b) $-2.4°$; (c) $-0.6°$.

4.4 Use a shorter or longer tube, measure rotation.

4.5 Chiral: b, d, f, g, h.

4.6 Chiral: CH_3CH_2CDCl, $CH_3CHClCH_2D$, CH_3CHDCH_2Cl.
 Achiral: $ClCH_2CH_2CH_2D$, $CH_3CDClCH_3$.

4.7 (a)-(c) Work with models; (d) mirror images, a, b.

4.8 (a)

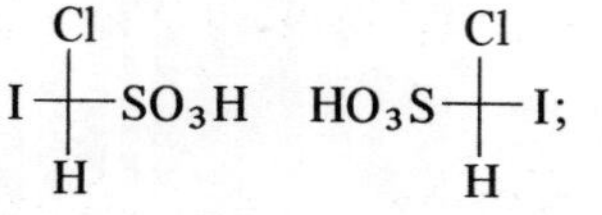

$$\underset{R}{\overset{Cl}{\underset{H}{I-\!\!\!\mid\!\!\!-SO_3H}}} \qquad \underset{S}{\overset{Cl}{\underset{H}{HO_3S-\!\!\!\mid\!\!\!-I}}};$$

(b)

$$\underset{R}{\overset{D}{\underset{H}{CH_3-\!\!\!\mid\!\!\!-Br}}} \qquad \underset{S}{\overset{D}{\underset{H}{Br-\!\!\!\mid\!\!\!-CH_3}}}$$

4.9 $3°, 2°, 1°, CH_3$.

4.10 (a)

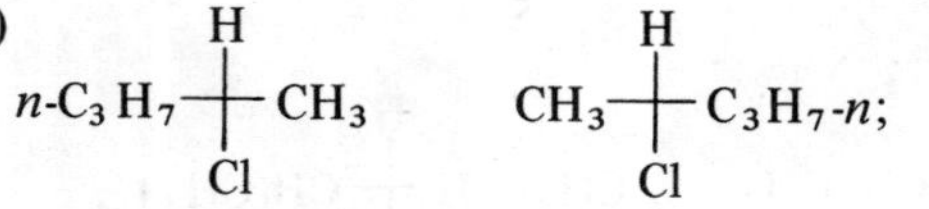

$$\underset{R}{\overset{H}{\underset{Cl}{n\text{-}C_3H_7-\!\!\!\mid\!\!\!-CH_3}}} \qquad \underset{S}{\overset{H}{\underset{Cl}{CH_3-\!\!\!\mid\!\!\!-C_3H_7\text{-}n}}};$$

$$\underset{R}{\overset{CH_3}{\underset{H}{n\text{-}C_3H_7-\!\!\!\mid\!\!\!-CH_2Cl}}} \qquad \underset{S}{\overset{CH_3}{\underset{H}{ClCH_2-\!\!\!\mid\!\!\!-C_3H_7\text{-}n}}};$$

$$\underset{R}{\overset{H}{\underset{Cl}{iso\text{-}C_3H_7-\!\!\!\mid\!\!\!-C_2H_5}}} \qquad \underset{S}{\overset{H}{\underset{Cl}{C_2H_5-\!\!\!\mid\!\!\!-C_3H_7\text{-}iso}}};$$

$$\underset{R}{\overset{H}{\underset{Cl}{iso\text{-}C_4H_9-\!\!\!\mid\!\!\!-CH_3}}} \qquad \underset{S}{\overset{H}{\underset{Cl}{CH_3-\!\!\!\mid\!\!\!-C_4H_9\text{-}iso}}}$$

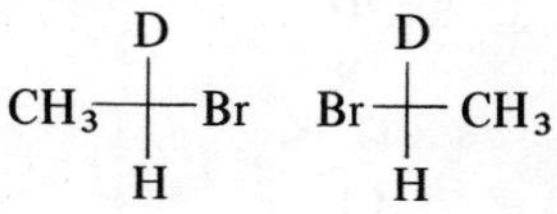

$$\underset{R}{\overset{H}{\underset{Br}{ClCH_2-\!\!\!\mid\!\!\!-C_2H_5}}} \qquad \underset{S}{\overset{H}{\underset{Br}{C_2H_5-\!\!\!\mid\!\!\!-CH_2Cl}}};$$

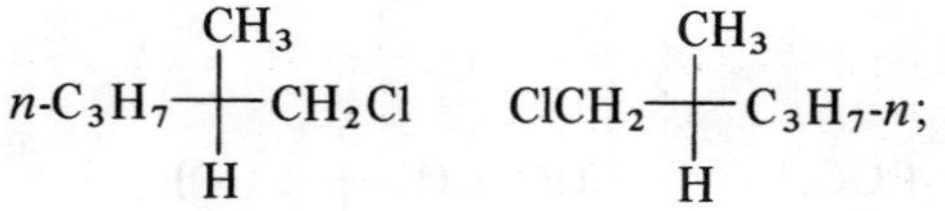

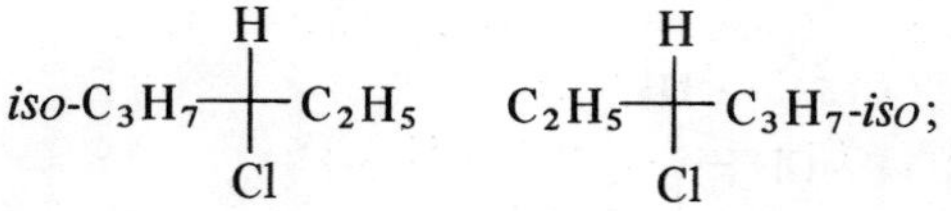

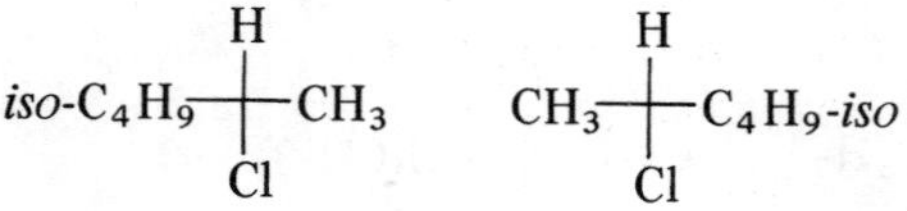

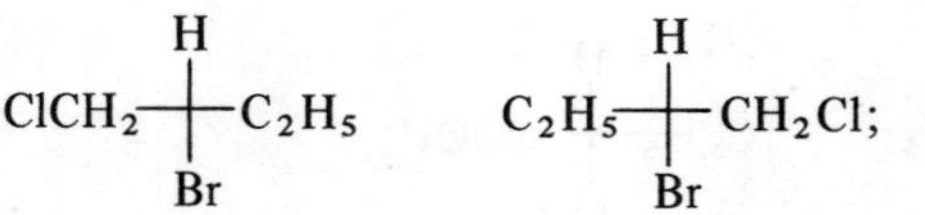

(b)

$$C_2H_5 \overset{\text{H}}{\underset{\text{Cl}}{\rule{1em}{0.4pt}}} D \qquad D \overset{\text{H}}{\underset{\text{Cl}}{\rule{1em}{0.4pt}}} C_2H_5; \qquad DCH_2 \overset{\text{H}}{\underset{\text{Cl}}{\rule{1em}{0.4pt}}} CH_3 \qquad CH_3 \overset{\text{H}}{\underset{\text{Cl}}{\rule{1em}{0.4pt}}} CH_2D;$$

R   S   R   S

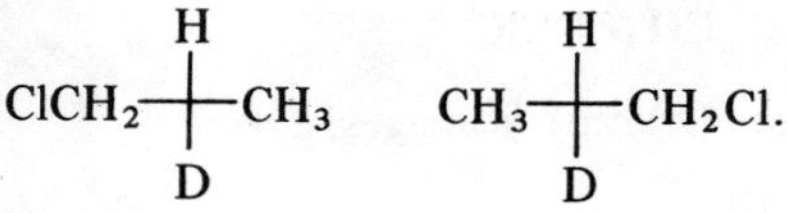

$$ClCH_2 \overset{\text{H}}{\underset{\text{D}}{\rule{1em}{0.4pt}}} CH_3 \qquad CH_3 \overset{\text{H}}{\underset{\text{D}}{\rule{1em}{0.4pt}}} CH_2Cl.$$

R   S

4.11 (a)

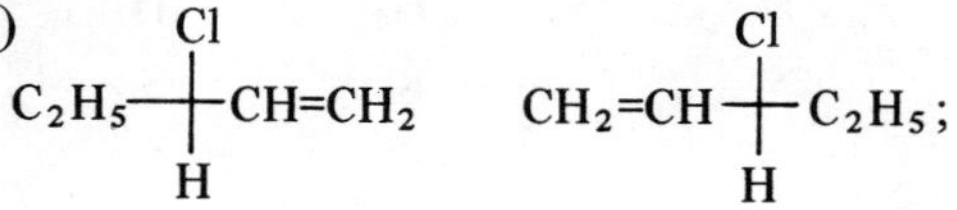

$$C_2H_5 \overset{\text{Cl}}{\underset{\text{H}}{\rule{1em}{0.4pt}}} CH=CH_2 \qquad CH_2=CH \overset{\text{Cl}}{\underset{\text{H}}{\rule{1em}{0.4pt}}} C_2H_5;$$

R   S

(b)

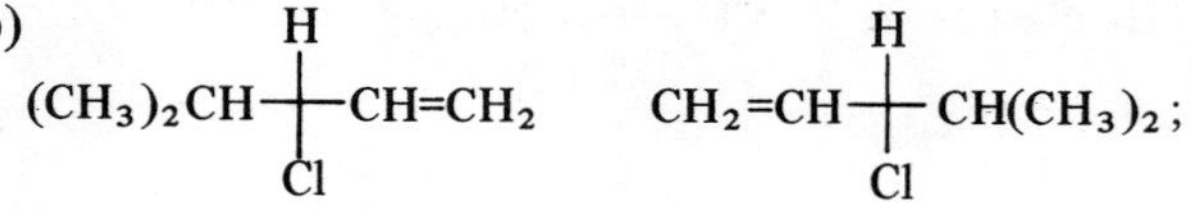

$$(CH_3)_2CH \overset{\text{H}}{\underset{\text{Cl}}{\rule{1em}{0.4pt}}} CH=CH_2 \qquad CH_2=CH \overset{\text{H}}{\underset{\text{Cl}}{\rule{1em}{0.4pt}}} CH(CH_3)_2;$$

R   S

(c)

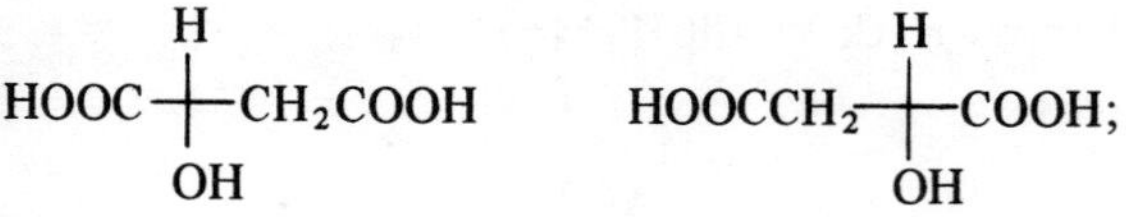

$$HOOC \overset{\text{H}}{\underset{\text{OH}}{\rule{1em}{0.4pt}}} CH_2COOH \qquad HOOCCH_2 \overset{\text{H}}{\underset{\text{OH}}{\rule{1em}{0.4pt}}} COOH;$$

R   S

(d)

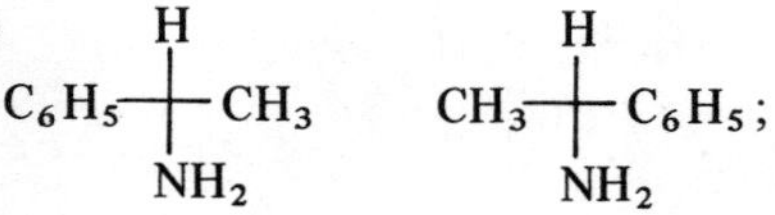

$$C_6H_5 \overset{\text{H}}{\underset{\text{NH}_2}{\rule{1em}{0.4pt}}} CH_3 \qquad CH_3 \overset{\text{H}}{\underset{\text{NH}_2}{\rule{1em}{0.4pt}}} C_6H_5;$$

R   S

(e)

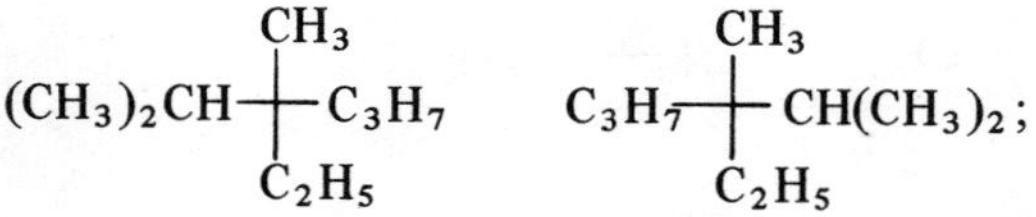

$$(CH_3)_2CH \overset{\text{CH}_3}{\underset{\text{C}_2\text{H}_5}{\rule{1em}{0.4pt}}} C_3H_7 \qquad C_3H_7 \overset{\text{CH}_3}{\underset{\text{C}_2\text{H}_5}{\rule{1em}{0.4pt}}} CH(CH_3)_2;$$

R   S

(f)

$$HOOC \overset{\text{H}}{\underset{\text{OH}}{\rule{1em}{0.4pt}}} C_6H_5 \qquad C_6H_5 \overset{\text{H}}{\underset{\text{OH}}{\rule{1em}{0.4pt}}} COOH;$$

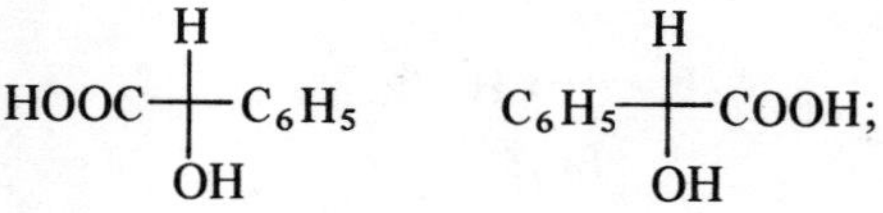

R   S

(g)

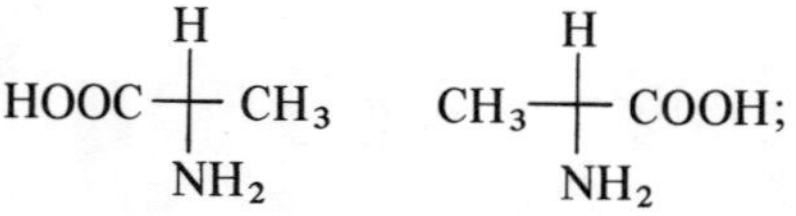

$$\text{HOOC} \overset{\displaystyle H}{\underset{\displaystyle NH_2}{\vert\!\!-\!\!\vert}} \text{CH}_3 \qquad \text{CH}_3 \overset{\displaystyle H}{\underset{\displaystyle NH_2}{\vert\!\!-\!\!\vert}} \text{COOH};$$

R   S

4.12 (a), (g): 2 enantiomers, both active. (b), (c), (e): 2 enantiomers, both active; 1 inactive *meso* compound. (f), (h): 2 pairs of enantiomers, all active. (d) 4 pairs of enantiomers, all active.

4.14 (a) For (a): 3 conformers, 2 enantiomers (B, C). For (b): 3 conformers, 2 enantiomers (D, F). For (c): 1 conformer. (b) For (a): enantiomers less abundant. For (b): enantiomers more abundant.

4.15 (a) Two: A, and B plus C. (b) Neither active: A is achiral, B plus C is a racemic modification.

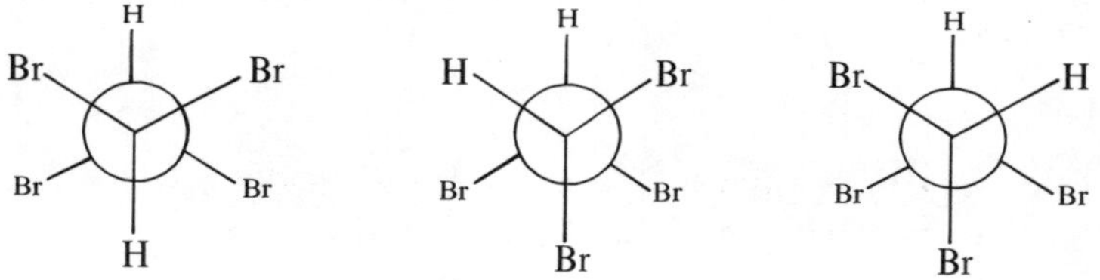

A   B   C

1. (a) Secs. 4.3 and 4.4; (b) Sec. 4.4; (c) Sec. 4.4; (d) Sec. 4.5; (e) Sec. 4.9; (f) Sec. 4.9; (g) Sec. 4.10; (h) Sec. 4.2; (i) Secs. 4.7 and 4.11; (j) Secs. 4.7 and 4.17; (k) Sec. 4.18; (l) Sec. 4.12; (m) Sec. 4.14; (n) Sec. 3.3; (o) Sec. 4.15; (p) Sec. 4.15; (q) Sec. 4.4; (r) Sec. 4.4; (s) Sec. 4.20; (t) 4.20.

2. (a) Chirality; (b) chirality; (c) usually an excess of one enantiomer that persists long enough to permit measurement; (d) mirror image not superimposable on original. (e) Restrictions on planar formulas are discussed in Sec. 4.10. In models, no bond to a chiral center should be broken. (f) Draw a picture or build a model of the molecule; then follow the steps in Sec. 4.15 and Sequence Rules in Sec. 4.16.

3. Equal but opposite specific rotations; opposite R/S specifications; all other properties the same.

4. (a) Screw, scissors, spool of thread; (b) glove, shoe, coat sweater, tied scarf; (c) helix, double helix; (d) football (laced), golf club, rifle barrel; (e) hand, foot, ear, nose, yourself.

5. (a) Sawing; (b) opening milk bottle; (c) throwing a ball.

6. (a)

$$n\text{-}C_3H_7 \overset{\displaystyle H}{\underset{\displaystyle Br}{\rule{0pt}{0pt}|\!\!-\!\!|}} C_2H_5 \qquad C_2H_5 \overset{\displaystyle H}{\underset{\displaystyle Br}{\rule{0pt}{0pt}|\!\!-\!\!|}} C_3H_7\text{-}n;$$

      R   S

(b) achiral;

(c)

$$BrCH_2 \overset{\displaystyle CH_3}{\underset{\displaystyle Br}{\rule{0pt}{0pt}|\!\!-\!\!|}} C_2H_5 \qquad C_2H_5 \overset{\displaystyle CH_3}{\underset{\displaystyle Br}{\rule{0pt}{0pt}|\!\!-\!\!|}} CH_2Br;$$

      R   S

(d)

$$ClCH_2CH_2 \overset{\displaystyle H}{\underset{\displaystyle Cl}{\rule{0pt}{0pt}|\!\!-\!\!|}} CH_2CH_3 \qquad CH_3CH_2 \overset{\displaystyle H}{\underset{\displaystyle Cl}{\rule{0pt}{0pt}|\!\!-\!\!|}} CH_2CH_2Cl$$

      R   S

(e)

$$t\text{-}C_4H_9 \overset{\displaystyle H}{\underset{\displaystyle Cl}{\rule{0pt}{0pt}|\!\!-\!\!|}} C_4H_9\text{-}iso \qquad iso\text{-}C_4H_9 \overset{\displaystyle H}{\underset{\displaystyle Cl}{\rule{0pt}{0pt}|\!\!-\!\!|}} C_4H_9\text{-}t;$$

      R   S

(f)

$$n\text{-}C_3H_7 \overset{\displaystyle H}{\underset{\displaystyle Cl}{\rule{0pt}{0pt}|\!\!-\!\!|}} D \qquad D \overset{\displaystyle H}{\underset{\displaystyle Cl}{\rule{0pt}{0pt}|\!\!-\!\!|}} C_3H_7\text{-}n.$$

      R   S

7. (a) 3-Methylhexane; (b) 2,3-Dimethylpentane.

8. 2 pairs enantiomers: a, b, e, k.
   1 pair enantiomers, 1 *meso*: c, d, h.
   4 pairs enantiomers: f.
   1 pair enantiomers, 2 *meso*: g.
   2 diastereomers: i.
   1 pair enantiomers: j.

9. A, $CH_3CCl_2CH_3$; B, $ClCH_2CH_2CH_2Cl$; C, $CH_3CHClCH_2Cl$;
   D, $CH_3CH_2CHCl_2$; E, $CH_3CHClCHCl_2$. Inactive products from active
   C: $CH_3CCl_2CH_2Cl$ and $ClCH_2CHClCH_2Cl$.

10. (a) None; (b) one pair of configurational enantiomers; (c) conforma-
    tional enantiomers: A, B; D, G; E, H; F, I.

Br—Cl—H top, with H (left down), H (right down), H (bottom)
A

Cl top, H (left), Br (right), H (left down), H (right down), H (bottom)
B

Cl top, H (left), H (right), H (left down), H (right down), Br (bottom)
C

CH₃ top, H (left), H (right), H (left down), Br (right down), Cl (bottom)
D

CH₃ top, Cl (left), H (right), H (left down), Br (right down), H (bottom)
E

CH₃ top, H (left), Cl (right), H (left down), Br (right down), H (bottom)
F

Cl top, H (left), Br (right), H (left down), H (right down), CH₃ (bottom)
G

H top, H (left), Br (right), Cl (left down), H (right down), CH₃ (bottom)
H

H top, H (left), Br (right), H (left down), Cl (right down), CH₃ (bottom)
I

11. Dipole—dipole attraction.

12. (a) Zero. (b) The *gauche* conformer is present. (c) 12% *gauche* (as non-resolvable racemic modification), 88% *anti*.

CHAPTER 5

5.1 (a) 1-Pentene, *cis*- and *trans*-2-pentene, 2-methyl-1-butene, 3-methyl-1-butene, 2-methyl-2-butene; (b) *cis*- and *trans*-1-chloropropene, 2-chloropropene, 3-chloropropene; (c) *cis*- and *trans*-1-chloro-1-butene, 2-chloro-1-butene, 3-chloro-1-butene, 4-chloro-1-butene, *cis*- and *trans*-1-chloro-2-butene, *cis*- and *trans*-2-chloro-2-butene, 1-chloro-2-methylpropene, 3-chloro-2-methylpropene.

Z isomers are:

19

H   CH$_3$ H   Cl   H   Cl
 \\ /   \\ /   \\ /
  C   C   C
  ‖   ‖   ‖
  C   C   C
 / \\   / \\   / \\
H   C$_2$H$_5$ H   CH$_3$ H   C$_2$H$_5$

H   CH$_2$Cl   CH$_3$ Cl
 \\ /   \\ /
  C   C
  ‖   ‖
  C   C
 / \\   / \\
H   CH$_3$ H   C$_2$H$_5$

5.2 (a) $(CH_3)_2C=C(CH_3)_2$; (b) $CH_2=C(CH_3)CH_2Br$;

(c) H   CH(CH$_3$)$_2$ (d) H   CH$_3$
     \\ /   \\ /
      C   C
      ‖   ‖
      C   C
     / \\   / \\
    H   CH$_2$CH$_2$CH$_3$ Cl   CH$_3$

5.3 Order of isomers as in Problem 5.1.

5.4 (a) *trans*-1,2-Dichloroethene is non-polar; in 1,1- and *cis*-1,2-dichloro-
ethene, dipole lies in plane of molecule along bisector of angle between
Cl atoms.   (b) The C_4 compound has the larger dipole moment because
of electron release by the two —CH$_3$ groups in the same direction as the
C—Cl dipole.   (c) Net dipole in direction of Cl atoms, but smaller because C—Br dipoles oppose the C—Cl dipoles.

5.5 (a) 1-Pentene; (b) 1-pentene, *cis*- and *trans*-2-pentene; (c) *cis*- and
trans-2-pentene; (d) 2-methyl-2-butene, 2-methyl-1-butene;
(e) 2-methyl-2-butene, 3-methyl-1-butene; (f) 2,3-dimethyl-2-butene,
2,3-dimethyl-1-butene; (g) none.

5.6 (a) *tert*-Butyl or isobutyl; (b) *n*-pentyl; (c) 3-pentyl;
(d) $CH_3CH_2CH(CH_3)CH_2X$; (e) none; (f) isopentyl.

5.7 (a) 1-Pentene; (b) 2-pentenes (predominately *trans*); (c) 2-pentenes
(predominately *trans*); (d) 2-methyl-2-butene; (e) 2-methyl-2-butene;
(f) 2,3-dimethyl-2-butene; (g) none.

5.8 See page 193.

5.9 (a) 2-Methyl-2-butene; (b) 2-methyl-2-butene; (c) 2,3-dimethyl-2-
butene.

1. (a) $CH_3CH_2CH(CH_3)CH_2CH_2CH(CH_3)CH=CH_2$; (b) $ClCH_2CH=CH_2$;
    (c) $(CH_3)_3CCH=C(CH_3)_2$; (d) *trans*-$C_2H_5C(CH_3)=C(CH_3)C_2H_5$;

    (e)
    $$\underset{CH_3 \quad C_2H_5}{\overset{C_2H_5 \qquad Cl}{\underset{\|}{C}{=}C}}$$

    (f)
    $$\underset{CH_3 \qquad Cl}{\overset{D \qquad H}{\underset{\|}{C}{=}C}}$$

    (g) $CH_2{=}CH{-}\underset{Br}{\overset{H}{\underset{|}{C}}}{-}CH_3$;

    (h) $CH_3CH_2{-}\underset{CH_3}{\overset{H \quad H}{\underset{|}{C}}}{-}\underset{\underset{H}{C}{-}CH_3}{\overset{|}{C}}$

2. (a) 2-Methylpropene; (b) *cis*-3-hexene; (c) 3,3-dimethyl-1-butene;
    (d) *trans*-2,5-dimethyl-3-hexene; (e) 2,5-dimethyl-2-hexene;
    (f) 2-ethyl-1-butene.

3. b, d, g, h, i, k (3 isomers).

4. (a) 1-Hexene, 2-hexene, 3-hexene, 2-methyl-1-pentene, 2-methyl-2-
    pentene, 4-methyl-2-pentene, 4-methyl-1-pentene, 3-methyl-1-pentene,
    3-methyl-2-pentene, 3,3-dimethyl-1-butene, 2,3-dimethyl-1-butene,
    2,3-dimethyl-2-butene, 2-ethyl-1-butene; (b) 2-hexene, 3-hexene,
    4-methyl-2-pentene, 3-methyl-2-pentene; (c) 3-methyl-1-pentene,

    $$CH_3CH_2{-}\underset{H}{\overset{CH_3}{\underset{|}{C}}}{-}CH=CH_2 \text{ is R.}$$

5. Differ in all except (h); (l) dipole moment would tell.

6. (a) $CH_3CH_2CH_2OH \xrightarrow{\text{H}^+, \text{ heat}} CH_3CH=CH_2 + H_2O$.
    (b) $CH_3CHOHCH_3 \xrightarrow{\text{H}^+, \text{ heat}} CH_3CH=CH_2 + H_2O$.
    (c) $CH_3CHClCH_3 + KOH \longrightarrow CH_3CH=CH_2 + KCl + H_2O$.
    (d) $CH_3C{\equiv}CH + H_2$, Lindlar or Brown cat. $\longrightarrow CH_2CH=CH_2$ (See Sec.
    8.9).
    (e) $CH_3CHBrCH_2Br + Zn \longrightarrow CH_3CH=CH_2 + ZnBr_2$.

7. (a) 1-Hexene; (b) 1-hexene, *cis*- and *trans*-2-hexene; (c) 2-methyl-1-
    pentene; (d) 2-methyl-2-pentene, 2-methyl-1-pentene; (e) 2-methyl-2-
    pentene, *cis*- and *trans*-4-methyl-2-pentene; (f) 4-methyl-1-pentene,
    cis- and *trans*-4-methyl-2-pentene; (g) 4-methyl-1-pentene;

(h) 2,3-dimethyl-2-pentene, *cis*- and *trans*-3,4-dimethyl-2-pentene, 2-ethyl-3-methyl-1-butene.

8. (b) 2-Hexenes (predominately *trans*);
(d) 2-methyl-2-pentene; (e) 2-methyl-2-pentene; (f) 4-methyl-2-pentenes (predominately *trans*); (h) 2,3-dimethyl-2-pentene.

9. (a) $CH_3CH_2CH_2CHOHCH_3$; (b) $(CH_3)_2C(OH)CH_2CH_3$;
(c) $(CH_3)_2CHC(OH)(CH_3)_2$.

10. (a) Br_2, heat, light; KOH(alc), heat. (b) Mixture of 1-butene and 2-butenes.

11. Isopropyl cation in both solutions; from *n*-PrF via rearrangement.

12. (a) $(CH_3)_2C=CHCH_3$ (major product) and $CH_2=C(CH_3)C_2H_5$, via rearrangement. (b) No. Slow ionization of halide to yield neopentyl cation, then the same alkenes as in (a). Acid catalysis not required because Br^- is a better leaving group than OH^-.

13. Rearrangement of a 2° cation into a 3° cation appears likely. See page 197 for equations.

CHAPTER 6

6.1 (a) $C_4H_8 + 6O_2 \longrightarrow 4CO_2 + 4H_2O$; (b) same as (a); (c) 1-butene 649.8, *cis*-2-butene 648.1, *trans*-2-butene 647.1. (d) 1-Pentene 806.9, *cis*-2-pentene 805.3, *trans*-2-pentene 804.3.

6.2 (a) H_3O^+; HBr; (b) HBr; (c) HBr.

6.3 If carbonium ions were formed reversibly and rapidly, some of them would lose H^+ rather than the newly acquired D^+, to form $(CH_3)_2C=CH(CH_3)$, which would be found in unconsumed alkene.

6.4 3-Chloro- and 2-chloro-2-methylbutane; the second product results from attachment of Cl^- to a 3° cation formed by hydride shift.

6.5 Protonation of alcohol, loss of water, alkyl shift to give 3° cation, attachment of Cl^-. (See page 197 for equations.)

6.6 $CH_2=CH_2 \overset{H^+}{\longrightarrow} CH_3CH_2{}^+ \overset{t\text{-BuH}}{\longrightarrow} CH_3CH_3 + t\text{-Bu}^+$

$$t\text{-Bu}^+ + CH_2=CH_2 \rightarrow CH_3\underset{\underset{CH_3}{|}}{\overset{\overset{CH_3}{|}}{C}}-CH_2-CH_2{}^+ \xrightarrow[\text{shift}]{\text{hydride}} CH_3\underset{\underset{CH_3}{|}}{\overset{\overset{CH_3}{|}}{C}}-\overset{+}{CH}-CH_3$$

           1° cation   2° cation

$$CH_3-\overset{\overset{\displaystyle CH_3}{|}}{\underset{\underset{\displaystyle CH_3}{|}}{C}}-\overset{+}{C}H-CH_3 \xrightarrow{\underset{shift}{alkyl}} CH_3-\overset{\overset{\displaystyle CH_3}{|}}{\underset{\underset{\displaystyle CH_3}{|}}{\overset{+}{C}}}-CH-CH_3 \xrightarrow{t\text{-}BuH}$$

3° cation

$$CH_3-\overset{\overset{\displaystyle CH_3}{|}}{\underset{\underset{\displaystyle H}{|}}{C}}-\overset{\overset{\displaystyle }{}}{\underset{\underset{\displaystyle CH_3}{|}}{C}}H-CH_3 + t\text{-}Bu^+$$

6.7 Same mechanism as on page 205, with radical in Steps (2) and (4) abstracting (a) H, (b) Br, (c) Br, (d) H from S, (e) H.

6.8 The radical produced in Step (3) of the CCl_4 sequence on page 205 adds to $RCH=CH_2$, and the new radical so formed then attacks CCl_4 in the manner of Step (4).

6.9 (a) No free radicals formed in the dark, and the ionic reaction is too slow with deactivated tetrachloroethylene.

 (b) (1) $Cl_2 \xrightarrow{h\nu} 2Cl\cdot$
   (2) $Cl\cdot + Cl_2C=CCl_2 \longrightarrow Cl_3C-\overset{\cdot}{C}Cl_2$
   (3) $Cl_3C-\overset{\cdot}{C}Cl_2 + Cl_2 \longrightarrow Cl_3C-CCl_3 + Cl\cdot$

 then (2), (3), (2), (3), etc.
 Oxygen stops the chain by reacting with the free radical or $Cl\cdot$.

6.10 Orlon, $CH_2=CH-CN$, acrylonitrile; Saran, $CH_2=CCl_2$, 1,1-dichloroethene; Teflon, $CF_2=CF_2$, tetrafluoroethylene.

6.11 If more stable radical is formed faster, orientation will always be the same.

6.12 React with HCl (minimum E_{act} 15 kcal).

6.13
$$\left[-\overset{+}{N}\overset{\displaystyle O}{\diagup\hspace{-0.3em}\diagdown}\underset{\displaystyle O^-}{} \quad -\overset{+}{N}\overset{\displaystyle O^-}{\diagup}\underset{\displaystyle O}{\diagdown} \right] \text{equivalent to} \left\{ -\overset{+}{N}\overset{\displaystyle O}{\diagup\hspace{-0.3em}\diagdown}\underset{\displaystyle O}{} \right\} -$$

6.14
$$\left[O=C\overset{\displaystyle O^-}{\diagup}\underset{\displaystyle O^-}{\diagdown} \quad {}^-O-C\overset{\displaystyle O}{\diagup\hspace{-0.3em}\diagdown}\underset{\displaystyle O^-}{} \quad {}^-O-C\overset{\displaystyle O^-}{\diagup}\underset{\displaystyle O}{\diagdown} \right] \text{equivalent to} \left[O\!=\!C\overset{\displaystyle O}{\diagup\hspace{-0.3em}\diagdown}\underset{\displaystyle O}{} \right]^=$$

6.15 (a) 24 kcal more stable than ethyl cation, about as stable as isopropyl cation.

(b) $\left[\underset{+}{CH_2}-CH=CH_2 \quad CH_2=CH-\underset{+}{CH_2} \right]$ equivalent to $\underbrace{CH_2{=\!=}CH{=\!=}CH_2}_{+}$.

Orbital picture as in Fig. 6.5 (p. 214), except only two π electrons instead of three.

6.16 (a) No.

(b)

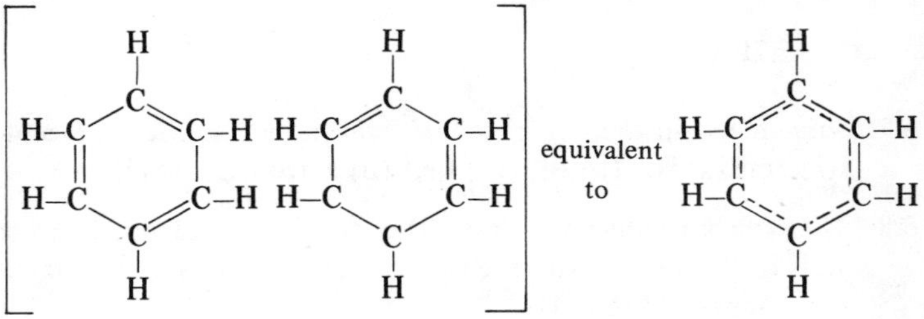

6.17 Hyperconjugation involving structures like I-IV on page 217 with + replacing odd electron; in orbital picture on page 217, p orbital contains "no e" instead of "1 e".

6.18 (a) $H-\overset{\overset{\displaystyle H}{|}}{C}=O$ and $(CH_3)_3CCH_2C=O$; $(CH_3)_2C=O$ and $(CH_3)_3C-\overset{\overset{\displaystyle H}{|}}{C}=O$;
$\overset{|}{CH_3}$

(b) CO_2 and $(CH_3)_3CCH_2C=O$; $(CH_3)_2C=O$ and $(CH_3)_3C-COOH$.
$\overset{|}{CH_3}$

6.19 (a) Br_2/CCl_4 or $KMnO_4$, or conc. H_2SO_4; (b) Br_2/CCl_4 or $KMnO_4$, or conc. H_2SO_4, or halogen test; (c) Br_2/CCl_4, or CrO_3/H_2SO_4; (d) only alkene gives positive Br_2/CCl_4 test; only alkyl halide gives halogen test; only 2° alcohol gives positive CrO_3/H_2SO_4 test.

6.20 A, alkane; B, 2° alcohol; C, alkyl halide; D, alkene; E, 3° alcohol.

1. (a) 1,2-Dibromoethane; (b) bromoethane; (c) bromoethene (vinyl bromide); (d) 1,2-ethanediol; (e) 1,2-propanediol; (f) 1-bromo-2-propanol; (g) bromoethene (bromoethylene); (h) 3-chloro-1-propene.

2. (a) Isobutane; (b) 1,2-dichloro-2-methylpropane; (c) 1,2-dibromo-2-methylpropane; (d) no reaction; (e) *tert*-butyl bromide; (f) isobutyl bromide; (g) *tert*-butyl iodide; (h) *tert*-butyl iodide; (i) *tert*-butyl hydrogen sulfate; (j) *tert*-butyl alcohol; (k) 1-bromo-2-methyl-2-

propanol; (l) 1-bromo-2-chloro-2-methylpropane and products (c) and (k); (m) 2,4,4-trimethyl-1-pentene and 2,4,4-trimethyl-2-pentene; (n) 2,2,4-trimethylpentane; (o) 2-methyl-1,2-propanediol (isobutylene glycol); (p) acetone and carbon dioxide; (q) same as (o); (r) acetone and formaldehyde.

3. (a) Propylene; (b) ethylene; (c) 2-butene; (d) isobutylene; (e) vinyl chloride; (f) 2-methyl-1-butene; (g) ethylene; (h) propylene.

4. (a) 2-Iodobutane; (b) 3-iodopentane and 2-iodopentane; (c) *tert*-pentyl iodide; (d) *tert*-pentyl iodide; (e) 3-iodo-2-methylbutane and 2-iodo-2-methylbutane; (f) 1-bromo-1-iodoethane; (g) 2-iodo-2,3-dimethyl-butane; (h) 4-iodo-2,2,4-trimethylpentane.

5.
$$\begin{array}{c} \quad\;\; H_3C\;\; H\;\; H\;\; H\;\; H \\ \quad\;\; |\quad |\quad |\quad |\quad | \\ CH_3-C-C-C-C=C-CH_3 \\ \quad\;\; |\quad |\quad | \\ \quad\;\; H\;\; H\;\; H \end{array}$$

     5   3 4 1 6 6   2   order of reactivity.

6. 3° radical more stable than 2° radical, forms faster.

7. Methyl alcohol (rather than water) adds to carbonium ion; subsequent loss of proton leads to an ether.

8. If alkene were formed, it should undergo reaction with D^+ as well as H^+, and the product (alcohol) should contain D attached to carbon.

9. (a) Less likely: formation of C–Br bond less exothermic than formation of C–H bond; (4a) would have minimum E_{act} of 19 kcal for addition to ethylene, even bigger for other alkenes. (b) Intermediate radical (Step

3, page 203) must be $-\overset{|}{\underset{\underset{Br}{|}}{C}}-\overset{|}{\underset{\cdot}{C}}-$ since otherwise (Step 3a, page 222) it

would be $-\overset{|}{\underset{\underset{H}{|}}{C}}-\overset{|}{\underset{\cdot}{C}}-$ or $-\overset{|}{\underset{\underset{D}{|}}{C}}-\overset{|}{\underset{\cdot}{C}}-$ depending on whether HBr or DBr was

used.

10. (c) Using 68 kcal for π bond and 95 kcal for 2° R–H, one calculates: for HBr, Step (3) −1 kcal, Step (4) −7; for HCl, Step (3) −14, Step (4) +8. (d) Steps (2) and (4) are too difficult with HCl, cannot compete with ionic addition.

11. (a) $Cl^{14}CH_2C(CH_3)=CH_2$; (b) ionic;

(c) $(CH_3)_2C=CH_2 + Cl_2 \longrightarrow (CH_3)_2\overset{+}{C}-CH_2Cl + Cl^-$

$$(CH_3)_2\overset{+}{C}-CH_2Cl \longrightarrow CH_2=\overset{\underset{|}{CH_3}}{C}-CH_2Cl + H^+$$

(d) Perhaps more stable $3°$ cation less reactive toward Cl^-, but more prone to lose one of six hydrogens to form branched alkene.

(e) $(CH_3)_3CCH=CH_2 + Cl_2 \longrightarrow (CH_3)_3CC\overset{+}{H}-CH_2Cl + Cl^-$

$$(CH_3)_3CC\overset{+}{H}-CH_2Cl \xrightarrow{\text{rearr.}} (CH_3)_2\overset{+}{C}-CH(CH_3)-CH_2Cl$$

$$(CH_3)_2\overset{+}{C}-CH(CH_2)-CH_2Cl \longrightarrow CH_2=\overset{\underset{|}{CH_3}}{C}-CH(CH_3)-CH_2Cl + H^+.$$

12. See pp. 597-598.

13. (a) Bromine can become attached to either C-1 or C-3 of intermediate radical, $C_5H_{11}CH\!\cdots\!CH\!\cdots\!CH_2$.

    (b) ^{14}C will be distributed equally between C-1 and C-3.

14. (a) 1-Pentene;   (b) 4-methyl-2-pentene;   (c) 2,3-dimethyl-2-butene;
    (d) 1,4-hexadiene;   (e) $CH_3CH_2CH_2COOH$ and CO_2^- from (a),
    $(CH_3)_2CHCOOH$ and $HOOCCH_3$ from (b), $(CH_3)_2CO$ from (c),
    CH_3COOH and $HOOCCH_2COOH$ and CO_2 from (d).

15. (a) $AgNO_3$;   (b) Br_2/CCl_4 or $KMnO_4$, or $AgNO_3$, or conc. H_2SO_4;
    (c) Br_2/CCl_4 or $KMnO_4$ or conc. H_2SO_4;   (d) $AgNO_3$;   (e) CrO_3/H_2SO_4,
    or conc. H_2SO_4 (actually, alcohol is soluble in water);   (f) Br_2/CCl_4,
    or CrO_3/H_2SO_4;   (g) conc. H_2SO_4 (actually, alcohol is soluble in
    water);   (h) Br_2/CCl_4.

16. 3-Hexene.

17. (a) Br_2, light; KOH(alc).   (b) Br_2, light; KOH(alc).   (c) Br_2, light;
    KOH(alc); HI.   (d) Br_2, light; KOH(alc); HBr.   (e) Br_2, light; KOH(alc);
    Br_2/CCl_4.   (f) KOH(alc); Br_2/CCl_4.   (g) KOH(alc); HI.   (h) HBr,
    peroxides $\longrightarrow$ *n*-PrBr. HBr; Li; CuI; *n*-PrBr.   (i) KOH(alc); HBr; Li; CuI;
    n-BuBr.   (j) Br_2, light; KOH(alc); Br_2/CCl_4.   (k) H_2SO_4, heat; HI.
    (l) KOH(alc); HBr, peroxides.   (m) KOH(alc); Cl_2, H_2O.   (n) H_2SO_4,
    heat; H_2, catalyst, pressure, heat.   (o) Mg, anhyd. ether; H_2O.

CHAPTER 7

7.1 (a) Abstraction of either 2° hydrogen equally likely, giving equal amounts of enantiomeric pyramidal radicals, each of which reacts equally readily with chlorine, thus giving equal amounts of enantiomeric *sec*-BuCl molecules (i.e., the racemic modification); also, a pyramidal radical would probably undergo rapid inversion and lose configuration; (b) displacement of either 2° hydrogen equally likely, giving equal amounts of enantiomeric *sec*-BuCl molecules (racemic modification).

7.2 (a) 4;   (b) 1-Cl-3-Me, 3-Cl-2-Me (2 enantiomers), 2-Cl-2-Me, 1-Cl-2-Me (2 enantiomers);   (c) none;   (d) replacement of either H on $-CH_2-$ equally likely, and replacement of any H on either $-CH_3$ equally likely, in each case giving rise to the racemic modification.

7.3 (a) (R) - $ClCH_2-\overset{\overset{\displaystyle H}{|}}{\underset{\underset{\displaystyle Cl}{|}}{C}}-CH_2CH_3$, $CH_3-CCl_2-CH_2CH_3$,

(S) - $CH_3-\overset{\overset{\displaystyle H}{|}}{\underset{\underset{\displaystyle Cl}{|}}{C}}-CH_2CH_2Cl$.   (b) 1,2- and 1,3-dichlorobutane will be

optically active, 2,2-dichlorobutane will be optically inactive.

7.4 c, d, e, g.

7.5 (a) C—O bond is broken; acid catalysis suggests that this happens by separation of H_2O from protonated alcohol. Clearly, C—O bond is re-formed; most probably this happens by attachment of H_2O to carbon: either *after* (carbonium ion mechanism) or *simultaneously with* (Sec. 14.9) loss of original H_2O. Whatever the mechanism, the new C—O bond most probably involves, not the original oxygen, but oxygen from the solvent.   (b) Same as in (a), with C—I bond and I⁻ involved. (c) Try the experiments with $H_2{}^{18}O$ and radioactive I⁻: expect to find ^{18}O and radioactive I in products.

7.6 $-0.89°$.

7.7 (a) V is mirror image of III, VI is mirror image of IV;   (b) V and VI are diastereomers;   (c) ratio is same;   (d) V $\longrightarrow$ *meso*, VI $\longrightarrow$ (R,R)-isomer;   (e) *meso*-product;   (f) R,R:*meso* = 29:71.

7.8 (a) 5 fractions, two inactive, others active;   (b) 5, all inactive; (c) 6, all inactive;   (d) 2, both active.

7.9 Rapidly inverting pyramid.

7.10 In each active fraction there is only one compound, each of which is chiral: (S)-1,1-dichloro-2-methylbutane, (2R,3R)-1,3-dichloro-2-methylbutane, (2R,3S)-1,3-dichloro-2-methylbutane, (S)-1,4-dichloro-2-methylbutane. In one of the inactive fractions there is only one compound, achiral $CH_3CH_2CH(CH_2Cl)CH_2Cl$ (only 3 different groups on C-2); the other inactive fraction is a racemic modification, 1,2-dichloro-2-methylbutane, C-2 having been attacked and the resultant planar free radical giving equal numbers of enantiomeric product molecules.

7.11 (a) M.p. 19°, racemic; m.p. 32°, *meso*; (b) hydroxylation with permanganate is *syn*; (c) hydroxylation with peroxy acids is *anti.*

7.12 Enantiomers: a, c, d. Same achiral structure, b.

7.13 (a) Attack by two paths not equally likely, but there are equal amounts of enantiomeric bromonium ions undergoing attack. Total product consists of equal amounts of the two possible enantiomers. (b) Similar to (a).

7.14 F is most electronegative halogen, has least tendency to share electrons and acquire positive charge.

1. (a) 3; (b) 5; (c) 7 (5 active); (d) 7 (6 active); (e) 1; (f) 3; (g) 5; (h) 2 (1 active); (i) 2.

2. See Sec. 17.12.

3. A, (S,S); B, (R,S); C, S; D, (S,S); E, (2R,3S)-4-bromo-1,2,3-butanetriol; F, (R,R); G, (R,S).

4. The three fractions are: the two diastereomeric esters (in unequal amounts); and unreacted chloroacid, which now contains an excess of one of the enantiomers.

5. *Anti.* Opposite-side attack by water on intermediate chloronium ion.

6. Reaction proceeds (partly, at least) via a bridged bromonium ion formed from (or perhaps instead of) the open carbonium ion resulting from addition of a proton; subsequent attack by water cleaves either C–Br bond.

7. (a) Intermediate iodonium ion undergoes opposite-side attack by N_3^- ion. (b) Polar solvents favor ionic reaction like that of IN_3. Light or peroxides cause free-radical addition:

$$Rad\cdot + BrN_3 \longrightarrow RadBr + N_3\cdot$$
$$N_3\cdot + RCH{=}CH_2 \longrightarrow R\overset{.}{C}HCH_2N_3 ; etc.$$

Oxygen breaks chain by combining with organic free radicals. In non-polar solvent, slow spontaneous free radical formation, $BrN_3 \longrightarrow Br\cdot + N_3\cdot$, makes itself evident; conceivably, there is concerted homolysis, $BrN_3 + RCH=CH_2 \longrightarrow R\dot{C}HCH_2Br + N_3\cdot$.

CHAPTER 8

8.1 CO_2: O=C=O, linear; C uses two sp orbitals, and two p orbitals at right angles (compare allene, Problem 15, page 280). H_2O: sp^3, tetrahedral.

8.2 (a) $CH_3CBr=CBrCH_3$, $CH_3CBr_2CBr_2CH_3$; (b) decrease (compare vinyl bromide); (c) the dibromo compound is made a poorer competitor; (d) excess butyne; (e) drip Br_2 into a solution of 2-butyne.

8.3 Br_2; KOH(alc); $NaNH_2$; H_2, Pd/C or Ni-B(P-2).

8.4 (a) Propane; (b) $C_4H_9C{\equiv}CH + C_3H_7MgBr \longrightarrow C_4H_9C{\equiv}CMgBr + C_3H_8$; (c) 1-alkynes more acidic than alkanes.

8.5 $Ca^{++}\ {}^-C{\equiv}C^-$; calcium acetylide; acid-base reaction.

8.6 H goes to terminal C.

8.7 1,3-Hexadiene.

8.8 (a) 56—60 kcal; (b) cumulated double bonds unstable relative to conjugated or isolated double bonds.

8.9 Hyperconjugation involving structures like I-IV on page 217 with + replacing odd electron; in orbital picture on page 217, p orbital contains "no e" instead of "1 e".

8.10 (a) Attachment of proton to C-1 end of conjugated system gives the more stable allylic cation; (b) attachment of Br^+ to C-1 end of conjugated system gives the more stable allylic cation.

8.11 (a) Yes; (b) 3,6-dibromo-1,4-hexadiene; (c) position of equilibrium, which favors more stable, conjugated dienes.

8.12 (a)

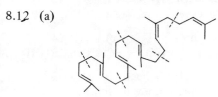

(b) At the center; molecule probably made by head-to-head combination of two identical C_{15} units. (c) 4 ring closures, methyl migration; loss of 3 methyl groups.

8.13 (a) $CH_3CH_2CH_2COOH$ and CO_2; (b) CH_3CH_2COOH and $HOOCCH_3$; (c) $(CH_3)_2CHCOOH$ and CO_2; (d) CH_3CHO and $OHC-CHO$ and $HCHO$; (e) $HCHO$ and $OHCCH_2CHO$ and $HCHO$; (f) $HCHO$ and CH_3COCHO and $HCHO$.

8.14 (a) $(-CH_2-\underset{\underset{CHO}{|}}{CH}-)_n$ and $nHCHO$; (b) $OHCCH_2CH_2CHO$.

8.15 Head-to-tail polymer of isoprene.

1. (b) 1-Hexyne, *n*-butylacetylene; 2-hexyne, *n*-propylmethylacetylene; 3-hexyne, diethylacetylene; 4-methyl-2-pentyne, isopropylmethylacetylene; 4-methyl-1-pentyne, isobutylacetylene; 3-methyl-1-pentyne, *sec*-butylacetylene; 3,3-dimethyl-1-butyne, *tert*-butylacetylene. (c) 1-Hexyne, 4-methyl-1-pentyne, 3-methyl-1-pentyne, 3,3-dimethyl-1-butyne. (d) $CH_3(CH_2)_3COOH$, $HCOOH$; $CH_3(CH_2)_2COOH$, CH_3COOH; $2CH_3CH_2COOH$; CH_3COOH, $(CH_3)_2CHCOOH$; $HCOOH$, $(CH_3)_2CHCH_2COOH$; $C_2H_5CH(CH_3)COOH$, $HCOOH$; $HCOOH$, $(CH_3)_3CCOOH$.

2. 1,3-Hexadiene, conjugated, geom. isom.; 1,4-hexadiene, geom. isom.; 1,5-hexadiene; 2,4-hexadiene, conjugated, geom. isom. (3 isomers); 2-methyl-1,3-pentadiene, conjugated, geom. isom.; 2-methyl-1,4-pentadiene; 4-methyl-1,3-pentadiene, conjugated; 3-methyl-1,3-pentadiene, conjugated, geom. isom.; 3-methyl-1,4-pentadiene; 2,3-dimethyl-1,3-butadiene, conjugated; 2-ethyl-1,3-butadiene, conjugated. (e) CH_3CH_2CHO, $OHC-CHO$, $HCHO$; CH_3CHO, $OHCCH_2CHO$, $HCHO$; $HCHO$, $OHC(CH_2)_2CHO$, $HCHO$; CH_3CHO, $OHC-CHO$, CH_3CHO; CH_3CHO, CH_3COCHO, $HCHO$; $HCHO$, CH_3COCH_2CHO, $HCHO$; $HCHO$, $OHC-CHO$, $(CH_3)_2CO$; CH_3CHO, CH_3COCHO, $HCHO$; $HCHO$, $CH_3CH(CHO)_2$, $HCHO$; $HCHO$, $CH_3COCOCH_3$, $HCHO$; $HCHO$, $OHCCOC_2H_5$, $HCHO$. (f) 2-Methyl-1,3-pentadiene and 3-methyl-1,3-pentadiene.

3. $CaCO_3$ + heat $\longrightarrow CaO + CO_2$; coal + heat $\longrightarrow$ C (coke); $CaO + 3C$ + heat $\longrightarrow CaC_2 + CO$; $CaC_2 + 2H_2O \longrightarrow HC\equiv CH + Ca(OH)_2$.

4. (a) KOH(alc), heat. (b) Br_2/CCl_4; KOH(alc), heat. (c) KOH(alc), heat; then as in (b). (d) Br_2, heat, light; mixture of isomers, KOH(alc), heat; then as in (b). (e) Acid, heat; then as in (b).

(f) KOH(alc), heat; or KOH(alc), heat, followed by $NaNH_2$. (g) $NaNH_2$; CH_3I. (h) Zn, heat.

5. (a) $1H_2$, Ni, heat, pressure. (b) As in (a); then excess H_2, Ni, heat, pressure. (c) 1HBr; then HBr, no peroxides. (d) HCl, CuCl. (e) As in (a); then Cl_2. (f) H_2O, H^+, Hg^{++}. (g) $NaNH_2$; CH_3I. (h) $NaNH_2$; C_2H_5Br. (i) As in (g); then additional $NaNH_2$; CH_3I. (j) Product (i), H_2, Lindlar's or Brown's catalyst. (k) Product (i), Na, NH_3(liq). (l) $NaNH_2$; n-C_3H_7Br. (m) As in (h); then additional $NaNH_2$; CH_3I. (n) As in (h); then additional $NaNH_2$; C_2H_5Br.

6. (a) 1-Butene; (b) n-butane; (c) 1,2-dibromo-1-butene; (d) 1,1,2,2-tetrabromobutane; (e) 2-chloro-1-butene; (f) 2,2-dichlorobutane; (g) methyl ethyl ketone (2-butanone); (h) $AgC{\equiv}CC_2H_5$; (i) 1-butyne; (j) $NaC{\equiv}CC_2H_5$; (k) 3-hexyne; (l) 1-butyne and isobutylene; (m) $C_2H_5C{\equiv}CMgBr$ and ethane; (n) 1-butyne; (o) CH_3CH_2COOH, HCOOH; (p) CH_3CH_2COOH, CO_2.

7. (a) 1- and 2-butene; (b) n-butane; (c) 1,4-dibromo-2-butene, 3,4-dibromo-1-butene; (d) 1,2,3,4-tetrabromobutane; (e) 1-chloro-2-butene, 3-chloro-1-butene; (f) 1,3- and 2,3-dichlorobutane; (o) HCHO, OHC–CHO, HCHO; (p) $4CO_2$. No reaction in (g) through (n).

8. (a) 1-Pentene; (b) n-pentane; (c) 4,5-dibromo-1-pentene; (d) 1,2,4,5-tetrabromopentane; (e) 4-chloro-1-pentene; (f) 2,4-dichloropentane; (o) HCHO, $OHCCH_2CHO$, HCHO; (p) CO_2, $HOOCCH_2COOH$, CO_2. No reaction in (g) through (n).

9. First-named alkene of each set is major product. (a) 1-Butene; *trans*- and *cis*-2-butene, 1-butene. (b) 1-Butene; 1,3-butadiene. (c) 2-Methyl-2-butene, 2-methyl-1-butene; 2-methyl-2-butene, 3-methyl-1-butene. (d) 2-Methyl-1-butene; 3-methyl-1-butene. (e) 2,3-Dimethyl-1-butene; 2,3-dimethyl-2-butene, 2,3-dimethyl-1-butene. (f) 1,3-Butadiene; 1,4-pentadiene.

10. (a) 2-Chlorobutane; (b) 4-chloro-1-butene; (c) 2-bromo-2-methyl-butane; (d) 1-bromo-2-methylbutane; (e) 2-chloro-2,3-dimethylbutane; (f) 4-chloro-1-butene.

11. 1,3-Butadiene gives 1-chloro-2-butene and 3-chloro-1-butene. The other products are: (a) 2-chlorobutane; (b) 4-chloro-1-pentene; (c) 3-chloro-3-methyl-1-butene and 1-chloro-3-methyl-2-butene; (d) 4-chloro-2-pentene.

12. 1,3-Butadiene gives 1-bromo-5,5,5-trichloro-2-pentene and

3-bromo-5,5,5-trichloro-1-pentene. The other products are:
(a) 3-bromo-1,1,1-trichloropentane;   (b) 4-bromo-6,6,6-trichloro-
1-hexene;   (c) 3-bromo-5,5,5-trichloro-3-methyl-1-pentene and
1-bromo-5,5,5-trichloro-3-methyl-2-pentene;   (d) 4-bromo-6,6,6-
trichloro-2-hexene and 5-bromo-1,1,1-trichloro-3-hexene.

13. (a) 1,3-Butadiene;   (b) 1,3-butadiene;   (c) 2-methyl-1,3-butadiene;
(d) 1,3-pentadiene.

14. (a) -42.2 kcal;   (b) alkyne less stable relative to alkene than alkene
relative to alkane;   (c) more reactive;   (d) $CH_3CH=CH\cdot$ less stable than
$CH_3CH_2CH_2\cdot$, expect slower addition to acetylene;   (e) radical stability.

15. (a) CH_2 planes perpendicular to each other.   (b) Yes; even though no
chiral carbon is present, the molecules are chiral.   (c) Central carbon *sp,*
linear; terminal carbons sp^2, trigonal; planes of 2 double bonds perpendicular. Yes.

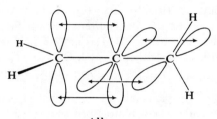

Allene

16. (a) *n*-Hexane, 1,2-dibromohexane, 1,2,5,6-tetrabromohexane;   (b) heat
middle fraction with Zn (or NaI in acetone), collect 1-hexene (b.p.
63.5°).   (c) Br_2; fractionate mixture; heat bromo compound with Zn
(or NaI in acetone).

17. (a) *n*-BuOH, PBr_3; KOH(alc); Br_2; KOH(alc); $NaNH_2$; C_2H_5Br (from
C_2H_5OH); then Br_2.   (b) As in (a), except start with *n*-PrOH or *i*-PrOH,
and use *n*-BuBr (from *n*-BuOH); then $KMnO_4$. Or reduce with H_2,
Lindlar's catalyst or Brown's catalyst, rather than with Li/NH_3; then
HCO_2OH.

18. Attack by H^+ to give 3° cation; intramolecular attack on other double
bond by electron-deficient carbon to give new 3° cation with
5-membered ring; loss of H^+.

19. Gutta percha is *trans*-isomer.

20. (a) $KMnO_4$ or Br_2/CCl_4;   (b) $Ag(NH_3)_2OH$;   (c) $Ag(NH_3)_2OH$;
(d) $KMnO_4$ or Br_2/CCl_4;   (e) $Ag(NH_3)_2OH$;   (f) Br_2/CCl_4, or
CrO_3/H_2SO_4;   (g) $AgNO_3$.

21. (a) Quantitative hydrogenation;   (b) same as (a);   (c) ozonolysis, followed by identification of products;   (d) same as (c).

22. Only *n*-pentane and methylene chloride give negative $KMnO_4$ test; distinguish by elemental analysis. Of the unsaturated compounds, only 1-chloropropene gives a positive halide test, and only 1-pentyne gives a precipitate with $Ag(NH_3)_2OH$. Distinguish the others by ozonolysis and identification of the cleavage products; or by infrared and nmr spectra.

23. Cyclohexene.

24. 1,3,5-hexatriene.

25. (a) $(CH_3)_2C=CHCH_2CH_2C(=CH_2)CH=CH_2$,
    $(CH_3)_2C=CHC(=CH_2)CH_2CH_2CH=CH_2$,
    $(CH_3)_2C=C(CH=CH_2)CH_2CH_2CH=CH_2$;
    (b) myrcene, $(CH_3)_2C=CHCH_2CH_2C(=CH_2)CH=CH_2$.

26. (a) Dihydromyrcene, $(CH_3)_2C=CHCH_2CH_2C(CH_3)=CHCH_3$;
    (b) no; 1,4-addition.

27. (a) Loss of OPP^- to form dimethylallyl cation, which attacks terminal unsaturated carbon of isopentenyl pyrophosphate to form a $3°$ cation, which in turn loses a proton to yield geranyl pyrophosphate.
    (b) $(CH_3)_2C=CHCH_2CH_2C(CH_3)=CHCH_2CH_2C(CH_3)=CHCH_2OPP$, farnesyl pyrophosphate.   (c) Two farnesyl units, head-to-head, form the squalene skeleton.   (d) Continuation of the sequence started in (a) and (b).

CHAPTER 9

9.1   (a) H^+, heat;   (b) as in (a), then N-bromosuccinimide;   (c) as in (b), then KOH(alc).

9.2   Mg, anhyd. Et_2O; H_2O.

9.3   No matter how the *tert*-butyl group is rotated, a large methyl group interferes with the axial H's on C-3 and C-5.

9.4   *Trans* isomer is resolvable; *cis* is not.

9.5   (a) H_2SO_4, heat; $KMnO_4$.   (b) H_2SO_4, heat; HCO_2OH.

9.6   All the *cis* compounds, and *trans*-1,3-cyclobutanecarboxylic acid.

9.7   (a) Axial-equatorial = equatorial-axial;   (b) equatorial-equatorial $>$ axial-axial;   (c) equatorial-equatorial $>$ axial-axial;

(d) axial-equatorial = equatorial-axial; (e) axial-equatorial =
equatorial-axial; (f) equatorial-equatorial > axial-axial; (g) 0 kcal;
2.7 kcal; 1.8 kcal + methyl—methyl interaction (Problem 9.8); 0 kcal;
0 kcal; 3.6 kcal.

9.8 (a) 1,3-Diaxial interaction of two —CH_3 groups; (b) 3.6 kcal. (c) The
trans-isomer exists as either of two equivalent chair conformations,
with two methyl—hydrogen interactions and one methyl—methyl interaction. The *cis*-isomer exists (almost) exclusively in the chair conformation with only one axial methyl group and hence two methyl—hydrogen
interactions. Thus the difference in stability between the two isomers
(3.7 kcal) is due to one methyl—methyl diaxial interaction, in excellent
agreement with Pitzer's calculation.

9.9 (a) *cis* > *trans*; (b) *trans* > *cis*; (c) 1.8 kcal/mole in each case.

9.10 More than: (a) 3.2 kcal; (b) 6.8 kcal; (c) 2.3 kcal.

9.11 Resolvable: b, d. *Meso:* c. (Neither e nor f contains chiral carbons.)

9.12 (a) e; (b) a; (c) c, f; (d) d; (e) b; (f) none.

9.13 Pairs of enantiomers: a, b, c, d. No *meso* compounds. None are non-
resolvable racemic modifications.

9.14 Oxygen reacts with triplet, or with diradical intermediate, leaves only
addition of singlet.

9.15 (a)   (b)

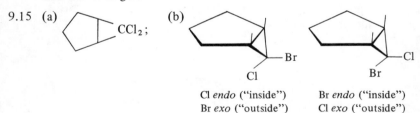

Cl *endo* ("inside")   Br *endo* ("inside")
Br *exo* ("outside")   Cl *exo* ("outside")

9.16 (a) $CHCl_3$ has no β-carbon; (b) electron-withdrawal by chlorines stabilizes anion, speeds up its formation and/or shifts equilibrium (1) (on
page 311) to right.

9.17 (a) C_6H_{14}, C_6H_{12}; (b) C_5H_{12}, C_5H_{10}; (c) C_6H_{12}, C_6H_{10};
(d) $C_{12}H_{26}, C_{12}H_{24}, C_{12}H_{22}$; (e) for the same degree of unsatura-
tion, there are two fewer hydrogens for each ring.

9.18 All are C_6H_{12}; no information about ring size.

9.19 α-Carotene, 2 rings, 11 double bonds; β-carotene, 2 rings, 11 double
bonds; γ-carotene, 1 ring, 12 double bonds; lycopene, no ring, 13
double bonds.

9.20 (a) OHC(CH$_2$)$_4$CHO; (b) CH$_3$CO(CH$_2$)$_3$CHO;
(c) OHCCH(CH$_3$)CH$_2$CH$_2$CHO; (d) OHCCH$_2$CH$_2$CHO and
OHC–CHO; (e) OHCCH$_2$CHO (2 moles).

9.21 Diene takes up two moles H$_2$, cyclohexene only one.

1. (d) Two Cl atoms *trans* to each other, on opposite sides of plane of
   molecule; (f) two puckered rings joined equatorially (consider either
   ring as an equatorial substituent on the other).

   (i)   (j)

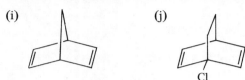

2. (a) 1,3-Dibromopropane; (b) cyclopropyl chloride; (c) *n*-propyl
   alcohol; (d) no reaction; (e) cyclopentyl chloride; (f) no reaction;
   (g) *trans*-1,2-dibromocyclopentane; (h) 3-bromocyclopentene;
   (i) 1-chloro-1-methylcyclohexane; (j) 2-bromo-1-methylcyclohexanol
   (Br *trans* to OH) and 1,2-dibromo-1-methylcyclohexane (*trans*-
   dibromide); (k) 2-bromo-1-methylcyclohexane (actually, *cis*);
   (l) 3-chlorocyclohexene; (m) cyclopentene; (n) cyclohexene;
   (o) *cis*-1,2-cyclopentanediol; (p) *trans*-1,2-cyclopentanediol;
   (q) HOOC(CH$_2$)$_3$COOH, glutaric acid; (r) ethylcyclopentane;
   (s) 1-methyl-1-cyclopentyl hydrogen sulfate;
   (t) OHCCH(CH$_3$)CH$_2$CH$_2$CHO, α-methylglutaraldehyde;
   (u) 1-cyclohexylcyclohexene; (v) see Problem 9.15(a);
   (w) bicyclo[1.3]hexane.

3. (a) H$_2$SO$_4$, heat. (b) As in (a); H$_2$, Ni, heat, pressure. (c) As in (a);
   Br$_2$, cold. (d) As in (a); KMnO$_4$, cold. (e) As in (a); HCO$_2$OH.
   (f) As in (a); O$_3$; H$_2$O, Zn. (g) As in (a); KMnO$_4$, hot. (h) As in (a);
   HBr. (i) As in (a); Cl$_2$, H$_2$O. (j) As in (a); Br$_2$, 300°. (k) As in (j);
   KOH(alc). (l) As in (h); Na, heat. Or as in (a); dimerization; H$_2$, Ni,
   heat, pressure. (m) As in (a); CH$_2$I$_2$, Zn(Cu).

4. (a) 4; (b) 6; (c) 7; (d) 9; (e) 5; (f) 2; (g) all-equatorial.

5. A, *cis*-dimethyl; B, racemic *trans*-dimethyl.

6. (a) No chiral carbons; chiral centers are double ring system and ring-
   plus-double bond.

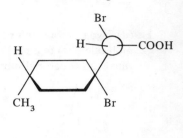

and mirror image   and mirror image

(b) Assuming above configuration, gives

7. (a) Dipole–dipole repulsions between C–Br bonds. (c) *cis*-3-*trans*-4-dibromo isomer; balance between dipole–dipole repulsions in diequatorial and 1,3-diaxial interactions in diaxial. (c) *trans*-3-*trans*-4-dibromo and *cis*-3-*cis*-4-dibromo; no relief of dipole–dipole repulsions, together with presence of 1,3-diaxial interactions.

8. (a) See formulas in Sec. 30.6; (b) 3 for each isomer; (c) see Sec. 30.6; (d) in the *trans*-isomer, both large substituents (the other ring) are diequatorial; (e) high energy barrier (E_{act}) between decalins since bond must be broken.

9. *cis*-Isomer exists in chair conformation with both *tert*-butyl groups equatorial. *trans*-Isomer exists in twist-boat conformation that accommodates both *tert*-butyl groups in quasi-equatorial positions.

10. (a) Essentially equatorial $-CH_3$; (b) very much like corresponding cyclohexane isomers with regard to equatorial-axial relationships, as well as diaxial interactions; (c) "folded" ring puts both substituents in *cis*-isomer in quasi-equatorial positions.

Methylcyclopentane   *trans*-1,2-Dimethylcyclopentane

cis-1,3-Dimethylcyclopentane   *cis*-1,3-Dimethylcyclobutane

11. (a), (b), (c) 2 (1 active); (d) 2.

12. (a) CaC_2, H_2O; $NaNH_2 \longrightarrow HC\equiv CNa$; *n*-PrOH, $PBr_3 \longrightarrow$ *n*-PrBr; $HC\equiv CNa$, *n*-PrBr; $NaNH_2$; *n*-PrBr; H_2, Lindlar's or Brown's cat.; CH_2I_2, Zn(Cu). (b) *n*-BuOH, PBr_3; KOH(alc); Br_2; KOH(alc); $NaNH_2$; CH_3Br (from CH_3OH); Li, NH_3; $CHCl_3$, *t*-BuOK.

13. (a) Br_2/CCl_4; (b) $KMnO_4$; (c) Br_2/CCl_4; (d) $KMnO_4$, or Br_2/CCl_4; (e) $KMnO_4$, or Br_2/CCl_4; (f) $KMnO_4$, or Br_2/CCl_4; (g) CrO_3/H_2SO_4; (h) Br_2/CCl_4, or CrO_3/H_2SO_4; (i) Br_2/CCl_4 detects cyclohexene; CrO_3/H_2SO_4 detects cyclohexanol; sodium fusion, then $AgNO_3$ detects bromocyclohexane; cyclohexane is unaffected by any of these tests.

14. (a) 2; (b) 4; (c) 1; (d) 3; (e) 4.

15. (a) 1; (b) 2; (c) 1; (d) 3; (e) 3; (f) 5; (g) 4.

16. (a) 2; (b)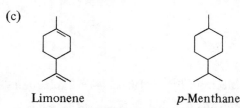

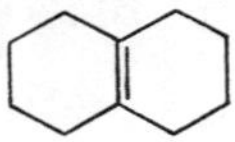

17. (a) 1; (b) see (c), or 4-allyl-1,2-dimethyl-1-cyclopentene;

(c)

Limonene   *p*-Menthane

(d) α-terpineol, Problem 19 (p. 317), or the 3° alcohol resulting from hydration of the other double bond of limonene; (e) terpin hydrate, ditertiary alcohol from limonene.

18. (a) 1; (b)

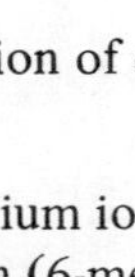

α-Terpinene

(c) hydroxylation of diene by $KMnO_4$, then cleavage between middle two.

19. Nerol $\longrightarrow$ oxonium ion $\longrightarrow$ open-chain allylic cation $\longrightarrow$ cyclic 3° cation (6-membered ring) $\longrightarrow$ α-terpineol.

CHAPTER 10

10.1   (a) +5.6 kcal;   (b) −26.8 kcal.

10.2   (a) 824.1 kcal;   (b) 35.0 kcal greater.

10.3   The sp^2-s character of the C—H bond in benzene. It should be (and is) shorter, and thus stronger, than the sp^3-s C—H bond in cyclohexane.

10.4   (a) No;   (b) see Sec. 32.6.

10.5   (a)

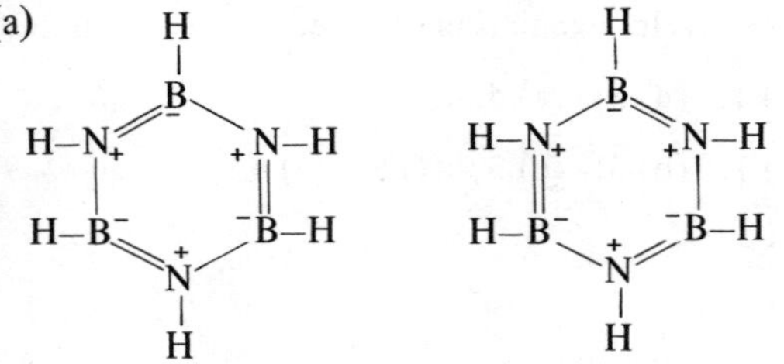

;

(b) similar to Figs. 10.2 and 10.3;   (c) 6, "from" N.

10.6   (a) Cyclopropenium hexachloroborate,

     $SbCl_6^-$

(b) The number of π electrons fits the Hückel $4n + 2$ role for $n = 0$.

10.7   (a) Cyclic structure with alternating double and single bonds.
(b) No "aromatic sextet;" does not follow Hückel rule.
(c) The number of π electrons in the anion is 10, fitting the $4n + 2$ Hückel rule for $n = 2$. Evidently stabilization due to aromaticity is enough to outweigh double negative charge and angle strain (ring must be flat for π overlap, and hence must have C—C—C angles of 135°).
(d) Cyclooctatetraene: puckered rings maintaining geometry of carbon—carbon double bonds (X-ray diffraction shows it to be a "tub"). $C_8H_8^{--}$: flat, regular octagon.

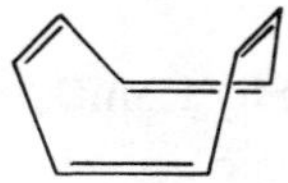

Cyclooctatetraene

10.8   *ortho,* +6°; *meta,* −7°; *para,* +87°.

10.9 KOH takes out CO_2 and H_2O; the other liquids would not do this.

10.10 26.0%.

10.11 22.8%.

10.12 18.5%.

10.13 25.9%, 22.9%, 18.6%.

1. (h) $-SO_3H$ on C-1; (i) $-CH_3$ on C-1; (j) $-COOH$ on C-1; (l) $-OH$ on C-1.

2. (a) 3; (b) 3; (c) 3; (d) 6; (e) 10; (f) 6.

3. (a) 2, 3, 3, 1, 2; (b) 5, 5, 5, 2, 4 (neglecting stereoisomers); (c) none.

4. (a) 2; (b) 3; (c) 1; (d) 4; (e) 4; (f) 2; (g) 4; (h) 4; (i) 2; (j) 1; (k) 3; (l) 2.

5. (a) *p*-Xylene; (b) *o*-xylene; (c) *m*-xylene, ethylbenzene; (d) $1,3,5\text{-}C_6H_3(CH_3)_3$ (mesitylene); (e) 1,2,3-trimethylbenzene, *p*-ethyltoluene; (f) *n*- or isopropylbenzene, 1,2,4-trimethylbenzene; (g) *o*- or *m*-ethyltoluene.

6. Yes. Each isomer has a different number of mononitro compounds that can be related to it; 1,2,3-, two; 1,2,4-, three; 1,3,5-, one.

7. (a) Two substituents attached to VI: one above other on any vertical edge; at opposite corners of any square; at two corners of one triangle. (b) *para; ortho; meta.* (c) No, the *ortho* isomer is chiral; enantiomeric structures are possible:

Enantiomers

8. *ortho,* 104°; *meta,* 63°; *para,* 142°.

9. (a) [6]Annulene (benzene); [10]annulene, [14]annulene, [18]annulene. (Actually, for [10] and [14]annulenes, geometry is unfavorable: crowding of hydrogens inside ring prevents planarity and hence π overlap.) (b) $C_9H_9^-$.

10. Six π electrons (see Sec. 31.2), 4 from carbons, 2 from nitrogen.

11. (a) $C_6H_6Cl_6$; (b) 1,2,3,4,5,6-hexachlorocyclohexane; (c) addition; (d) no; (e) differ in stereochemistry; (f) there are more than six stereoisomers.

12. Since the electron pair of acetylene anion is in an *sp* orbital, it has more *s* character and is therefore held more tightly than the electron pair (sp^2 orbital) of the benzene anion, and this in turn more tightly than the electron pair (sp^3 orbital) of the *n*-pentane anion. The acetylene anion is thus the weakest base, acetylene the strongest acid. (Compare page 259.)

CHAPTER 11

11.1 $HONO_2 + HONO_2 \rightleftarrows H_2\overset{+}{O}NO_2 + ONO_2^-$

$H_2\overset{+}{O}NO_2 \rightleftarrows H_2O + {}^+NO_2$

$H_2O + HONO_2 \rightleftarrows H_3O^+ + ONO_2^-$

$\overline{3HONO_2 \rightleftarrows {}^+NO_2 + 2NO_3^- + H_3O^+}$

11.2 (a) $2H_2SO_4 \rightleftarrows H_3SO_4^+ + HSO_4^-$
(b) as in (a), then $H_3SO_4^+ \rightleftarrows H_2O + HSO_3^+$
(c) as on page 347, then $H_2SO_4 + SO_3 \rightleftarrows H_2S_2O_7$

11.3 (a) $n\text{-}Pr^+ \longrightarrow iso\text{-}Pr^+$; (b) $iso\text{-}Bu^+ \longrightarrow tert\text{-}Bu^+$;
(c) $(CH_3)_3CCH_2^+ \longrightarrow tert$-pentyl cation; (d) carbonium ion mechanism.

11.4 (a) $t\text{-}BuOH \longrightarrow t\text{-}BuOH_2^+ \longrightarrow t\text{-}Bu^+$;
(b) $CH_3CH{=}CH_2 + H^+ \longrightarrow CH_3\overset{+}{C}HCH_3$.

11.5 $HOCl + H^+ \rightleftarrows H_2\overset{+}{O}{-}Cl \rightleftarrows H_2O + Cl^+$

11.6 Large size of complex.

11.7 (a) *o*- and *p*-Bromotoluene. (b) *o*-Bromotoluene. (c) C_6H_6, Br_2, Fe; SO_3, H_2SO_4, warm; Br_2, Fe, heat; H_2SO_4, steam-distill. As previous synthesis, except start C_6H_6, Cl_2, Fe.

11.8 (a) $R{-}C{\equiv}\overset{..}{O}{}^+$; (b) $Ar'{-}N{\equiv}N{:}^+$; (c) NO^+.

11.9 (a) Intermediate ion is $(ArHD)^+$, which can lose either H or D.
(b) Hydrogen ion is displaced from ring by another hydrogen (deuterium ion) in typical electrophilic aromatic substitution that is fast with phenol, slow with benzene, and negligible with benzenesulfonic acid.

11.10 (a) 2.05; (b) 1.02 moles HCl:1 mole DCl.

11.11

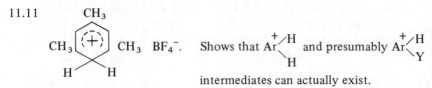

CH_3 $\overset{CH_3}{\underset{\underset{H}{\overset{}{\bigcirc}}}{\underset{H}{\bigcirc}}}$ CH_3 BF_4^-. Shows that $Ar\overset{+}{\underset{H}{\diagdown}}{}^{\diagup H}$ and presumably $Ar\overset{+}{\underset{Y}{\diagdown}}{}^{\diagup H}$ intermediates can actually exist.

11.12 (a) 6.77; (b) yes; (c) no; (d) yes.

11.13 (a) CH_3CHCl^+; (b) $CH_3CH_2^+$; (c) $CH_3CH_2^+$; (d) electron-withdrawing Cl intensifies positive charge, destabilizes carbonium ion; (e) $^+CH_2CH_2Cl$; (f) CH_3CHCl^+; (g) resonance stabilization through contribution by $CH_3CH=Cl^+$; (h) inductive effect; (i) resonance effect.

1. (a) *p*-Bromoacetanilide (very little *o*-isomer); (b) *p*- and *o*-bromo-iodobenzene; (c) *p*- and *o*-bromo-*sec*-butylbenzene; (d) *p*-bromo-N-methylaniline (very little *o*-isomer); (e) ethyl *m*-bromobenzoate; (f) *m*-bromoacetophenone; (g) *p*- and *o*-bromophenetole; (h) *p*- and *o*-bromodiphenylmethane; (i) *m*-bromobenzonitrile; (j) *m*-bromo-benzotrifluoride; (k) *p*- and *o*-bromobiphenyl. Faster: a, c, d, g, h, k. Slower: b, e, f, i, j.

2. (a) 2,4- and 2,6-dinitrotoluene; (b) 2,4-dibromonitrobenzene; (c) 2,4-dinitroacetanilide; (d) 1,3,5-trinitrobenzene; (e) 4- and 6-nitro-3-methylphenol; (f) 4- and 6-nitro-2-methylphenol; (g) 2-nitro-4-methylphenol; (h) 3,4-dinitrotoluene; (i) 2-nitro-1,4-dimethylbenzene; (j) 2-nitro-1,4-benzenedicarboxylic acid; (k) *m*-nitroaniline (actually, much *p*- is also formed, pages 759-760).

3. (a) *p*- (and *o*-) Cyclohexylbenzenesulfonic acid; (b) *m*-nitrobenzene-sulfonic acid; (c) *p*- (and *o*-) methoxybenzenesulfonic acid; (d) *m*-benzenedisulfonic acid; (e) 4- (and 2-) hydroxy-3-formyl-benzenesulfonic acid; (f) 4-hydroxy-2-nitrobenzenesulfonic acid and 2-hydroxy-4-nitrobenzenesulfonic acid; (g) 3-fluoro-4- (and 2-) methoxybenzenesulfonic acid; (h) 4- (and 2-) acetamido-3-nitro-benzenesulfonic acid; (i) 3,4- (and some 2,3-) dimethylbenzenesulfonic acid; (j) 2,4-dimethylbenzenesulfonic acid; (k) 2,5-dimethylbenzene-sulfonic acid.

4. (a) Mesitylene $>$ *m*-xylene $>$ *p*-xylene $>$ toluene $>$ benzene; (b) toluene $>$ benzene $>$ bromobenzene $>$ nitrobenzene; (c) aniline $>$ acetanilide $>$ benzene $>$ acetophenone;

    (d) p-xylene $>$ toluene $> p$-toluic acid $>$ terephthalic acid;

    (e) $C_6H_5Cl > p\text{-}O_2NC_6H_4Cl > 2,4\text{-}(O_2N)_2C_6H_3Cl$;

    (f) 2,4-dinitrophenol $>$ 2,4-dinitrochlorobenzene;

    (g) 2,4-dinitrotoluene $> m$-dinitrobenzene.

5. Toluene more easily nitrated — and *poly*nitrated — than benzene.

6. (a) 4,4′- and 2,4′-dinitrobiphenyl; (b) 2,3′- and 3,4′-dinitrodiphenyl-methane; (c) *o*- and *p*-nitrophenyl benzoate.

7. (a) $PhCH_2CH_2CH_2NMe_3^+ > PhCH_2CH_2NMe_3^+ > PhCH_2NMe_3^+ > PhNMe_3^+$; (b) $PhCH_2CH_2NO_2 > PhCH_2NO_2 > PhNO_2$; (c) $PhCH_3 > PhCH_2COOEt > PhCH(COOEt)_2 > PhC(COOEt)_3$. The most active compound in each set gives the lowest percentage of *m*-isomer, the least active the highest percentage.

8. Positive charge of intermediate can be dispersed (3 extra structures) by second phenyl group when attack is *ortho* or when it is *para,* but not when it is *meta.*

9. (a) Complexing with O of side chain; (b) equilibrium control; (c) complexing with C=O of side chain, must separate to attack ring.

10. $HONO_2 + H_2SO_4 \rightleftharpoons H_2\overset{+}{O}NO_2 + HSO_4^-$

     $H_2\overset{+}{O}NO_2 \longrightarrow H_2O + {}^+NO_2$ *(slow)*

     $H_2O + H_2SO_4 \rightleftharpoons H_3O^+ + HSO_4^-$

11. Instead of —H the —SO_3H group is displaced from ring by an electrophilic reagent (Br^+ or ${}^+NO_2$) in a typical electrophilic aromatic substitution in which —NH_2 and —OH activate the ring and are *ortho,para*-directing.

12. $AlBr_3 + Br_2 \rightleftharpoons Br^+ + AlBr_4^-$

    $C_6H_5C(CH_3)_3 + Br^+ \longrightarrow C_6\overset{+}{H}_5\diagup\diagdown\begin{smallmatrix}Br\\C(CH_3)_3\end{smallmatrix}$

    $C_6\overset{+}{H}_5\diagup\diagdown\begin{smallmatrix}Br\\C(CH_3)_3\end{smallmatrix} \longrightarrow C_6H_5Br + (CH_3)_3C^+$

    $(CH_3)_3C^+ + AlBr_4^- \longrightarrow (CH_3)_2C{=}CH_2 + HBr + AlBr_3$

13. (a) $(CH_3)_3\overset{+}{N}CH_2CH_2I$; (b) $BrCH_2CH_2CF_3$; (c) to provide the stronger acid ($HAlBr_4$) needed to attack the alkene, which is deactivated (toward electrophiles) by powerfully electron-withdrawing —CF_3.

14. (a) Measure relative rates of reaction; expect lower rate with C_6D_6.
    (b) Measure relative amounts of C_6H_5Y and C_6D_5Y by mass spec-
    trometry; expect more C_6H_5Y. (c) Measure *o/p* ratio from the two
    starting materials; expect higher ratio from anisole-4-d. (d) Measure
    ratio of $C_6H_2D_3Y$ to $C_6H_3D_2Y$; expect value greater than 1.

15. (a) Toluene, HNO_3, H_2SO_4. (b) Br_2, Fe; HNO_3, H_2SO_4. (c) Cl_2, Fe;
    Cl_2, Fe. (d) SO_3, H_2SO_4; Br_2, Fe. (e) Br_2, Fe; SO_3, H_2SO_4.
    (f) Toluene, Br_2, Fe; $KMnO_4$, heat. (g) Toluene, $KMnO_4$, heat; Br_2,
    Fe. (h) Toluene, $KMnO_4$, heat; $Tl(OOCCF_3)_3$; KI. (i) HNO_3,
    H_2SO_4; HNO_3, H_2SO_4, heat; HNO_3, H_2SO_4, high heat. (j) Toluene,
    HNO_3, H_2SO_4; Br_2, Fe. (k) As in (j); then $KMnO_4$, heat. (l) As in
    (f); then HNO_3, H_2SO_4. (m) Toluene, $KMnO_4$, heat; HNO_3, H_2SO_4;
    HNO_3, H_2SO_4, heat. (n) As in (b); then Br_2, Fe. (o) As in (c);
    then HNO_3, H_2SO_4. (p) Toluene, $Tl(OOCCF_3)_3$, 73°; KI.

16. (a) HNO_3, H_2SO_4; Br_2, Fe. (b) Br_2, Fe; $KMnO_4$, heat. (c) Br_2(aq).
    (d) HNO_3, H_2SO_4; HNO_3, H_2SO_4. (e) $KMnO_4$, heat; HNO_3, H_2SO_4.
    (f) HNO_3, H_2SO_4; $KMnO_4$, heat. (g) HNO_3, H_2SO_4; $KMnO_4$, heat.
    (g, 2nd way) $KMnO_4$, heat; HNO_3, H_2SO_4. (h) First way is preferable,
    since this uses the activating effect of the two $-CH_3$ groups. Nitration
    of ring deactivated by two $-COOH$ groups would be very difficult.

CHAPTER 12

12.1 (a) H_2SO_4, heat. (b) Zn(Hg), HCl. (c) H_2, Pt, heat, pressure.
      (d) H_2SO_4, heat; then as in (c). (e) KOH(alc); then as in (c). Or
      Mg, anhyd. ether; H_2O.

12.2 PBr_3; Na.

12.3 Formation of *tert*-pentyl cation, in each case from the original car-
      bonium ion by: (a) hydride shift; (b) hydride shift; (c) two hydride
      shifts; (d) alkyl shift.

12.4 Because of positive charge, group should be strongly deactivating,
      comparable to $-NR_3^+$.

12.5 Formation of *o*- and *p*-xylene rapid but reversible; formation of
      m-xylene slow, but favored by final equilibrium.

12.6 Alkylation introduces activating group, which promotes further sub-
      stitution; other reactions introduce deactivating groups.

12.7 To permit overlap of π cloud and *p* orbital.

12.8 Hyperconjugation stabilizes *o*- or *p*-$CH_3C_6H_4CH_2\cdot$ but not *meta* radical.

12.9 (a) Similar to Fig. 2.2, p. 53, with E_{act} = 19 kcal, and ΔH = +11 kcal; (b) 8 kcal; (c) steric hindrance to combination.

12.10 Apparent mol. wt. of 300 compared with expected mol. wt. of 542 indicates considerable dissociation into free radicals.

12.11 (a)

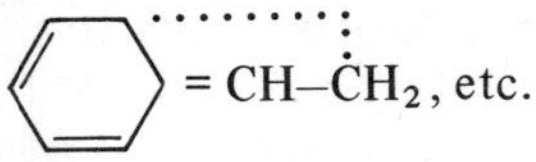

= CH–$\overset{\cdot}{C}H_2$, etc.

(b) Same argument as for conjugated dienes (Sec. 8.19).

12.12 (a) Ph_3C^+ ion stabilized by dispersal of positive charge over 3 rings, and ionization promoted by polar solvents; (b) formation of same ion as in (a).

12.13 Ph_3C^+ too stable to react with C_6H_6 in final stage.

12.14 In Fig. 8.9 (p. 275), replace diene by alkenylbenzene, allyl free radical by benzylic cation, and alkyl free radical by alkyl cation.

12.15 Because of conjugation of each ring with double bond, and perhaps between rings through the double bond, reactant may be stabilized more than transition state.

12.16 (a) Br_2, heat, light; KOH(alc); Br_2/CCl_4; KOH(alc); $NaNH_2$.
(b) Br_2/CCl_4; KOH(alc); $NaNH_2$; H_2, Brown's or Lindlar's catalyst.

12.17 (a) Elemental analysis; (b) $KMnO_4$; (c) $KMnO_4$; (d) fuming sulfuric acid; (e) Br_2/CCl_4 or $KMnO_4$; (f) CrO_3/H_2SO_4.

12.18 Upon oxidation by $KMnO_4$, *n*-butylbenzene gives C_6H_5COOH (m.p. 122°), and *m*-diethylbenzene gives *m*-$C_6H_4(COOH)_2$ (m.p. 348°).

12.19 (a) Soluble (or polymerizes); (b) discharge of color; (c) discharge of color, forms brown MnO_2; (d) orange-red color; (e) negative test.

12.20 (a) Br_2/CCl_4 or $KMnO_4$; (b) $Ag(NH_3)_2OH$ or $Cu(NH_3)_2OH$; (c) oxidation of allylbenzene gives C_6H_5COOH (m.p. 122°); 1-nonene gives $C_7H_{15}COOH$ (m.p. 16°, b.p. 239°); (d) CrO_3/H_2SO_4.

1. (e) Phenyl group in equatorial position; (h) *trans*-PhCH=CHPh; (i) *cis–trans* isomerism possible.

2. (a) Ethylene, HF. (b) H_2, Pt or Ni, heat, pressure. (c) $2H_2$, Pt. (d) H_2SO_4, heat; H_2, Pt. (e) H_2SO_4, heat; H_2, Pt. Or PBr_3; Mg, anhyd.

ether; H_2O.   (f) Mg, anhyd. ether; H_2O. Or KOH(alc); H_2, Pt.
(g) KOH(alc); H_2, Pt. Or Mg, anhyd. ether; H_2O.   (h) Mg, anhyd. ether;
H_2O.   (i) Zn(Hg), HCl.

3. (b) *n*-Propylcyclohexane;   (d) benzoic acid (or salt);   (e) benzoic acid;
(h) *o*- and *p*-nitro-*n*-propylbenzene;   (i) *o*- and *p*-*n*-propylbenzene-
sulfonic acid;   (j) *p*-tolylthallium ditrifluoroacetate;   (k) *o*- and
p-chloro-*n*-propylbenzene;   (l) *o*- and *p*-bromo-*n*-propylbenzene;
(n) 1-bromo-1-phenylpropane;   (o) *o*- and *p*-*n*-propyltoluene;   (p) *o*-
and *p*-*n*-propyldiphenylmethane;   (r) *p*-*tert*-butyl-*n*-propylbenzene;
(s) *p*-*tert*-butyl-*n*-propylbenzene;   (t) *p*-cyclohexyl-*n*-propylbenzene.
No reaction: a, c, f, g, m, q.

4. (a) *n*-Propylbenzene;   (b) *n*-propylcyclohexane;   (c) 1,2-dibromo-1-
phenylpropane. (For stereochemistry, wait for Problem 21, page 403.)
(d) 1,2-Dibromo-1-(*p*-bromophenyl)propane;   (e) 1-chloro-1-phenyl-
propane;   (f) 1-bromo-1-phenylpropane;   (g) 2-bromo-1-phenylpropane;
(h) 1-phenyl-1-propyl hydrogen sulfate;   (i) 2-bromo-1-phenyl-1-
propanol;   (j) racemic (R,R; S,S)-1-phenyl-1,2-propanediol;   (k) benzoic
acid;   (l) racemic (1R,2S; 1S,2R)-1-phenyl-1,2-propanediol;   (m) benzaldehyde and acetaldehyde;   (n) 3-bromo-1-phenyl-1-propene;
(o) 1,1-dibromo-*trans*-2-phenyl-3-methylcyclopropane;   (p) 1-phenyl-
propyne.

5. (a) Cyclohexylbenzene;   (b) silver phenylacetylide;   (c) *m*-nitro-
benzoic acid;   (d) 2-chloro-1-phenylpropane;   (e) *p*-chlorobenzoic acid;
(f) see structures in Sec. 24.4;   (g) benzylmagnesium chloride;
(h) toluene;   (i) 2-bromo-1,4-dimethylbenzene;   (j) 1-phenyl-1-butene
(only product reported; suggests reaction is equilibrium-controlled);
(k) benzaldehyde;   (l) *cis*-1,3-diphenylpropene;   (m) *trans*-1,3-diphenyl-
propene;   (n) *p*-$CH_3OC_6H_4CHBrCH_2C_6H_5$.

6. ∼∼∼ $CH_2C_6H_4CH_2C_6H_4CH_2C_6H_4$ ∼∼∼ .

7. (a) Ph–C–C=C–C–C–CH$_3$; with H substituents, numbered 1 5 5 2 3 4

(b) $CH_3-C_6H_4-CH_2-C_6H_4-CH_2-CH_2-CH_3$
        3   1   2   4   5

(c) H–1 > H–2, H–4.   (d) (1) 1-bromo-1-phenyl-2-hexene and 3-bromo-
1-phenyl-1-hexene;   (2) 4-bromo-1-phenyl-2-hexene and 2-bromo-1-
phenyl-3-hexene;   (3) 5-bromo-1-phenyl-2-hexene;   (4) 6-bromo-1-

phenyl-2-hexene;   (5) 2-bromo-1-phenyl-2-hexene or 3-bromo-1-phenyl-2-hexene.

8. (a) *trans-* (major) and *cis-*1-phenyl-1-butene;   (b) 2-phenyl-1-butene;   (c) 2-phenyl-2-butene (major), and 2-phenyl-1-butene;   (d) 1-phenyl-1-butene (major), and 1-phenyl-2-butene;   (e) 2-phenyl-2-butene (major), and 3-phenyl-1-butene.

9. (a) *trans-* (major) and *cis-*1-phenyl-1-butene;   (b) 2-phenyl-2-butene (major) and 2-phenyl-1-butene;   (c) 2-phenyl-2-butene (major) and 2-phenyl-1-butene;   (d) 1-phenyl-1-butene;   (e) 2-phenyl-2-butene (major) and 2-phenyl-1-butene.

10. (a) $c > a > e$, $d > b$;   (b) $Ph_2C(OH)CH_3 > PhCHOHCH_3 > PhCH_2CH_2OH$.

11. (a) *p*-Methylstyrene $>$ styrene $>$ *p*-chlorostyrene;   (b) α-(*p*-aminophenyl)-ethyl alcohol $>$ α-phenylethyl alcohol $>$ α-(*p*-nitrophenyl)ethyl alcohol.

12. (a) $C_6H_5CHBrCH=CHCH_2Br$, $C_6H_5CHBrCHBrCH=CH_2$, $C_6H_5CH=CHCHBrCH_2Br$;   (b) first and third;   (c) most stable product, suggests equilibrium control.

13. (a) *trans.*   (b) Bromine atom; $C_6H_5CHBr\dot{C}HC_6H_5$ undergoes rotation, after which Br· is lost before second step of addition (reaction with scarce Br_2 or HBr) can occur.   (c) Equilibration favors more stable *trans.*

14. $Ph_3COH + 2H_2SO_4 \rightleftarrows Ph_3C^+ + H_3O^+ + 2HSO_4^-$.

15. Resonance stabilization of anion with dispersal of negative charge is greatest for Ph_3C^-, least for $C_5H_{11}^-$.

16. (a) (1) $CBrCl_3 \overset{h\nu}{\longrightarrow} Br\cdot + \cdot CCl_3$
     (2) $C_6H_5CH_3 + \cdot CCl_3 \longrightarrow C_6H_5CH_2\cdot + HCCl_3$
     (3) $C_6H_5CH_2\cdot + CBrCl_3 \longrightarrow C_6H_5CH_2Br + \cdot CCl_3$
     then (2), (3), (2), (3), etc.

     (b) (4) $C_6H_5CH_3 + \cdot Br \longrightarrow C_6H_5CH_2\cdot + HBr$
     (5) $Cl_3C\cdot + \cdot CCl_3 \longrightarrow C_2Cl_6$
     Chain-length is 20: i.e., (2), (3) occur 20 times for each time (1) and (4) occur.

17. 2-, 3-, 4-, 5-, and 6-phenyldodecane, from rearrangement of initial secondary cation having charge on C-2 to other secondary cations with charge on C-3, C-4, C-5, or C-6.

18. Bent bonds in cyclopropyl rings have π character (see Sec. 9.9); overlap with p orbital of free radical stabilizes, much as for benzyl radical.

19. (a) Transition state reached either earlier or later in chlorination than in bromination; (b) reached earlier in chlorination.

20. (a) *m*-Xylene sulfonated fastest, since methyl groups reinforce each other's activation. (Unreacted *o*- and *p*-xylenes then separated by distillation.) (b) Sulfonic acid of *m*-xylene; see (a). (c) *m*-Xylene most basic, forms salt as in Problem 11.11 (p. 358).
    (d) $C_6H_5C(CH_3)_2^-Na^+ + m\text{-}CH_3C_6H_4CH_3 \rightleftarrows$
    $$C_6H_5CH(CH_3)_2 + m\text{-}CH_3C_6H_4CH_2^-Na^+$$
    Carbanion from $C_6H_5CH(CH_3)_2$ less stable than carbanion from a xylene, since electron release by side-chain methyls intensifies negative charge. Carbanion from *m*-xylene most stable since negative charge dispersed by resonance to ring carbons that do not carry methyl groups.

21. Addition is predominantly, but *not* exclusively, *anti*. Formation of resonance-stabilized open cation competes with formation of cyclic bromonium ion. *p*-Methoxy further stabilizes open cation through contribution from structures like that on page 365.

22. (a) Benzene, ethylene, HF. (b) Product (a), heat $(- H_2)$. (c) Product (b), Br_2; KOH(alc); $NaNH_2$. (d) Benzene, propylene, HF. (e) As in (d); then Br_2, heat; KOH(alc). (f) Benzene, allyl chloride, HF. (g) Product (c), $NaNH_2$; CH_3I. And product (f), KOH(alc), heat ($\longrightarrow$ 1-phenylpropene); Br_2; KOH(alc); $NaNH_2$. (h) Product (g), Li, NH_3. (i) Product (g), H_2, Pd. (j) Toluene, isobutylene, HF. (k) Product (a), HNO_3, H_2SO_4; Br_2, light, heat; KOH(alc). (l) Toluene, Br_2, Fe; separate *p*-isomer; Br_2, heat. (m) Toluene, HNO_3, H_2SO_4; separate *p*-isomer; $2Br_2$, heat. (n) Toluene, Br_2, Fe; $KMnO_4$ or $K_2Cr_2O_7/H_2SO_4$, heat. (o) Toluene, $KMnO_4$, NaOH, heat; H^+; HNO_3 (fuming). (p) Toluene, Br_2, heat; Na. (q) Toluene, HNO_3, H_2SO_4; Cl_2, heat; benzene, $AlCl_3$.

23. (a) Fuming sulfuric acid, or $CHCl_3/AlCl_3$; (b) Br_2/CCl_4, or $KMnO_4$; (c) same as (a); (d) Br_2/CCl_4; (e) CrO_3/H_2SO_4; (f) Br_2/CCl_4; (g) $AgNO_3$ after sodium fusion; (h) nitrogen or bromine test after sodium fusion.

24. (a) Ozonolysis and identification of the products. (c), (d), (e): Oxidation and determination of m.p.'s of the resulting acids. (b) As in (c) for the isomeric trimethylbenzenes and ethyltoluenes; side-chain chlorination followed by dehydrohalogenation and then ozonolysis of the resulting alkenes will distinguish between *n*- and isopropylbenzene.

25. Bromobenzene is the only one that will give a Br test; the three that give a Cl test can be distinguished from each other by oxidation to the

acids and determination of m.p.'s. The two unsaturated compounds (positive $KMnO_4$ test) can be distinguished by ozonolysis and identification of the products. The five arenes can be oxidized to carboxylic acids, which can be distinguished by their m.p.'s. The very high melting acids from mesitylene and *m*-ethyltoluene can be further distinguished by their neutralization equivalents (Sec. 18.21).

26.

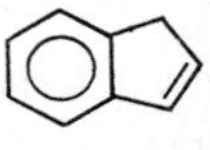

Indene 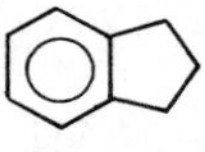   Indane

27. X and Y, racemic and *meso*-$C_6H_5CH(CH_3)-CH(CH_3)C_6H_5$; Z, $C_6H_5C(CH_3)_2-C(CH_3)_2C_6H_5$. Dimerization of radicals formed by

$$Ar-\overset{|}{\underset{|}{C}}-H + t\text{-BuO}\cdot \longrightarrow Ar-\overset{|}{\underset{|}{C}}\cdot + t\text{-BuOH}.$$

CHAPTER 13

13.1 (a) $(CH_3)_3C^+$; $CH_2=CH-CH_2^+$; $CH_3CH_2^+$; $CH_2=CH^+$.
(b) $C_5H_{12}^+\cdot \longrightarrow C_4H_9^+ + CH_3$.

13.2

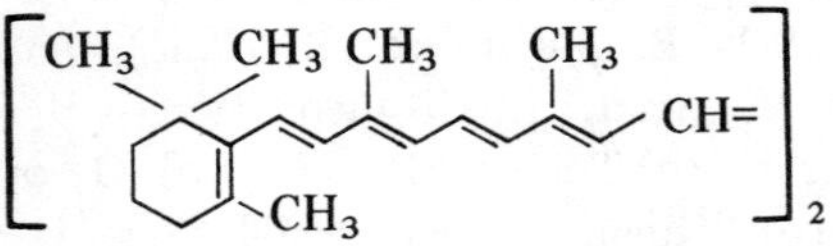

β-Carotene

13.3 (a) A, 1,4-pentadiene; B and C, *cis*- and *trans*-1,3-pentadiene;
(b) heats of hydrogenation, infrared spectra.

13.4 (a) CH_3CHCl_2, 2 signals; CH_2ClCH_2Cl, 1 signal.
    a *b*   *a*   *a*
(b) $CH_3CBr_2CH_3$, 1 signal; $CH_2BrCH_2CH_2Br$, 2 signals;
    a   *a*   *b*   *a* *b*

$$CH_3CH_2CHBr_2, \text{3 signals}; \quad CH_3CHBr-\overset{H^{b(\text{or }c)}}{\underset{H_{c(\text{or }b)}}{C}}-Br, \text{4 signals}.$$
    a   *b*   *c*   *a*   *b*

(c) $C_6H_5CH_2CH_3$, 3 signals; *p*-$CH_3C_6H_4CH_3$, 2 signals.
    c   *b*   *a*   *a*   *b*   *a*

(d) 1,3,5-$C_6H_3(CH_3)_3$, 2 signals; p-$CH_3C_6H_4CH_2CH_3$, 4 signals;
        b   *a*   *b*   *d*   *c*   *a*

   $C_6H_5CH(CH_3)_2$, 3 signals.
     c   *b*   *a*

(e) CH_3CH_2OH, 3 signals; CH_3OCH_3, 1 signal.
     a   *b*   *c*   *a*   *a*

(f) $CH_3CH_2OCH_2CH_3$, 2 signals; $CH_3OCH_2CH_2CH_3$, 4 signals;
     a   *b*   *b*   *a*   *c*   *d*   *b*   *a*

   $CH_3OCH(CH_3)_2$, 3 signals; $CH_3CH_2CH_2CH_2OH$, 5 signals.
     b   *c*   *a*   *a*   *b*   *c*   *d*   *e*

(g) $^{a}H_2C$–$CH_2{}^{b}$, 2 signals; CH_3–CH–C with $H^{b(or\ c)}$ and O, $H_{c(or\ b)}$, *d*, *a*, 4 signals.
     H_2C–O
      b

(h) CH_3CH_2CHO, 3 signals; CH_3COCH_3, 1 signal;
     a   *b*   *c*   *a*   *a*

$$^{c}H \qquad H^{e}$$
$$\underset{d}{}C=C$$
$$_{d}H \qquad CH_2OH$$
$$\qquad\qquad a\ \ b$$

     5 signals.

13.5   1,1-Dimethylcyclopropane, two; *trans*-1,2-dimethylcyclopropane, three; *cis*-1,2-dimethylcyclopropane, four.

13.6   1; rapid interconversion of equatorial and axial protons.

13.7   Electron release by methyl groups lowers deshielding of ring protons.

13.8   Relative positions of protons indicated by sequence of letters in answer to Problem 13.4 (Shift of −OH varies, Sec. 16.13.)
   (a) *a* 3H, *b* 1H; *a*;   (b) *a*; *a* 2H, *b* 4H; *a* 3H, *b* 2H, *c* 1H; *a* 3H, *b* 1H, *c* 1H, *d* 1H;   (c) *a* 3H, *b* 2H, *c* 5H; *a* 6H, *b* 4H;   (d) *a* 9H, *b* 3H; *a* 3H, *b* 3H, *c* 2H, *d* 4H; *a* 6H, *b* 1H, *c* 5H;   (e) *a* 3H, *b* 2H, *c* 1H; *a*;
   (f) *a* 6H, *b* 4H; *a* 3H, *b* 2H, *c* 3H, *d* 2H; *a* 6H, *b* 3H, *c* 1H; *a* 3H, *b* 2H, *c* 2H, *d* 2H, *e* 1H;   (g) *a* 2H, *b* 4H; *a* 3H, *b* 1H, *c* 1H, *d* 1H;
   (h) *a* 3H, *b* 2H, *c* 1H; *a*; *a* 2H, *b* 1H, *c d e* 1H each.

13.9   (a) Neopentylbenzene;   (b) isobutylene bromide, $(CH_3)_2CBrCH_2Br$;   (c) benzyl alcohol, $C_6H_5CH_2OH$.

13.10   Order of compounds same as in answer to Problem 13.4:
     (a) *a*, doublet, 3H
        b, quartet, 1H;
        a, singlet.

(b) *a,* singlet;

    a, quintet, 2H
    b, triplet, 4H;

    a, triplet, 3H
    b, multiplet, 2H
    c, triplet, 1H;

    a, doublet, 3H
    b, pair of doublets, 1H
    c, pair of doublets, 1H
    d, complex, 1H.

(c) *a,* triplet, 3H
    b, quartet, 2H
    c, complex, 5H;

    a, singlet, 6H
    b, singlet, 4H.

(d) *a,* singlet, 9H
    b, singlet, 3H;

    a, triplet, 3H
    b, singlet, 3H
    c, quartet, 2H
    d, complex, 4H;

    a, doublet, 6H
    b, heptet, 1H
    c, complex, 5H.

(e) *a,* triplet, 3H
    b, quartet, 2H
    c, singlet, 1H;

    a, singlet.

(f) *a,* triplet, 6H
    b, quartet, 4H;

    a, triplet, 3H
    b, multiplet, 2H
    c, singlet, 3H
    d, triplet, 2H;

    a, doublet, 6H
    b, singlet, 3H
    c, heptet, 1H;

a, triplet, 3H
b, multiplet, 2H
c, multiplet, 2H
d, triplet, 2H
e, singlet, 1H.

(g) *a,* quintet, 2H
b, triplet, 4H;

a, doublet, 3H
b, pair of doublets, 1H
c, pair of doublets, 1H
d, complex, 1H.

(h) *a,* triplet, 3H
b, multiplet, 2H
c, triplet, 1H;

a, singlet;

a, multiplet, 2H
b, singlet, 1H
c, d, and *e,* multiplets, 1H each.

13.11 No; same compounds as in answer to Problem 13.9.

13.12 (a) Ethylbenzene; (b) 1,3-dibromopropane; (c) *n*-propyl bromide.

13.13 At room temperature, interconversion of the three possible conformers is so rapid that a single average signal is given; at −120°, interconversion is so slow that separate signals are given by the achiral (I) and (racemic) chiral structures (II and III). Unequal peak areas indicate different amounts of the two components; no splitting because in any conformation fluorines are equivalent.

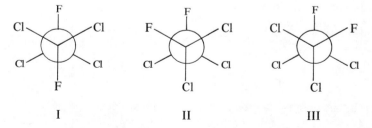

I   II   III

13.14 At room temperature, interconversion of the three possible conformers is so rapid that a single average signal is given; at −98°, interconversion is so slow that separate signals are given by the achiral (IV) and (racemic) chiral structures (V and VI). The pair of doublets is given by V and VI: in each, the fluorines are not equivalent — one is "between" two —Br, the other "between" —Br and —CN. Relative peak areas indicate that V and VI are favored: less crowding of Br atoms than in IV.

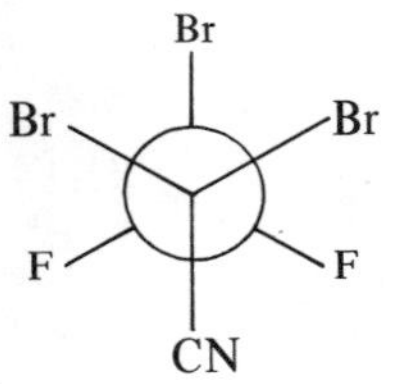

IV 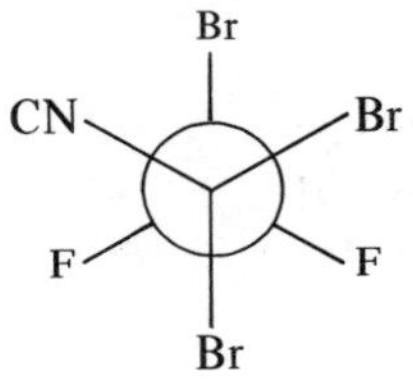   V 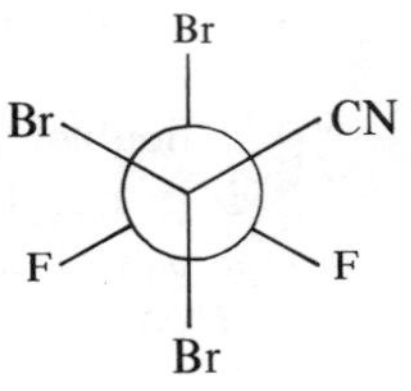   VI

13.15   (a) Impossible to reverse spin of only one of a pair: violation of Pauli principle.   (b) If both spins of a pair are reversed, no net change in energy, no signal.

13.16   (a) $CH_3\cdot$;   (b) $CH_3\dot{C}HCH_3$, $CH_3CH_2\dot{C}HCH_3$;   (c) $Ph_3C\cdot$.

13.17   Cyclohexane.

1.   (a) $CHCl_2CHClCHCl_2$;   (b) $CH_2ClCCl_2CH_3$;   (c) $(CH_3)_2CHCH_2Br$;
     (d) $C_6H_5C(CH_3)_3$;   (e) $C_6H_5CH_2CH(CH_3)_2$;   (f) indane (see answer to Prob. 26, Ch. 12);   (g) $C_6H_5CH_2CCl(CH_3)_2$;   (h) 1-phenyl-1-methylcyclopropane;   (i) $C_6H_5CH_2CH_2CH_2Br$;   (j) $CH_2ClCF_2CH_3$.

2.   X, *trans*-1,3-dibromo-*trans*-1,3-dimethylcyclobutane;
     Y, the *cis,cis*-isomer.

3.   See answer to Prob. 11.11.

4.   (a)

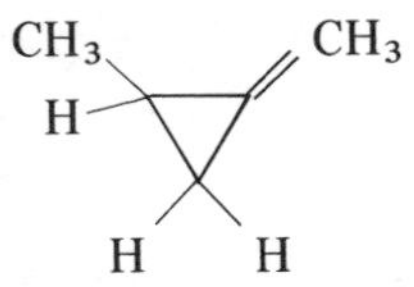

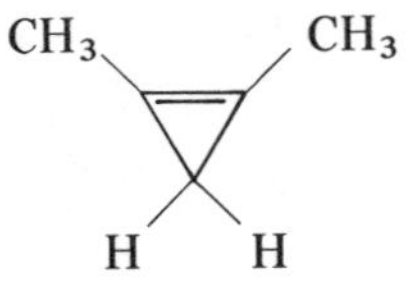

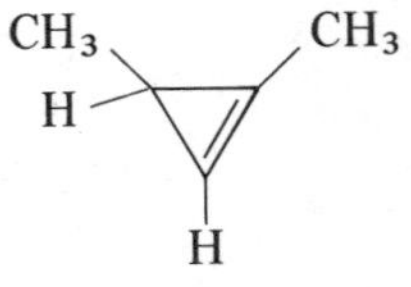

(b) one with $=CH_2$ group;   (c) A, 1,2-dimethylcyclopropene;
(d) aromatic cyclopropenyl cation formed by loss of ring proton from A (compare Problem 10.6, page 330);   (e) $CH_3C\equiv CCH_3 + CH_2N_2$ + light.

5.   (a) Yes. Planarity and nmr spectrum just what one would expect: 12H

outside ring deshielded, absorb downfield; 6H inside ring *shielded* (see Figure 13.4, page 419), absorb upfield. See page 935.

6. (a) 2 rings; (b) 2 rings, 2 double bonds; (c) B,

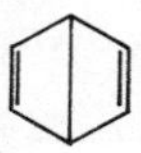

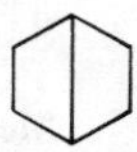

    (B is "Dewar benzene," pages 319, 321.)
    (d) 3° H split by all the vinylic protons; in turn, these are split by both 3° H.

7. (a) eeeee, eeeaaa; (b) eeeeea; (c) eeeeaa, eeaeea; (d) eeeeee, no change; eeeaaa, split into two peaks, of equal area.

8. (a) H on carbon carrying Br. (b) *Trans* isomer has equatorial *t*-Bu and equatorial Br, hence axial H at C-1 (upfield signal). *Cis* isomer has equatorial *t*-Bu and axial Br, hence equatorial H at C-1 (downfield signal). Other things being equal, an equatorial proton absorbs farther downfield than an axial proton.

9. At $-75°$, interconversion of chair conformers becomes so slow that signals for both axial and equatorial H are seen. Conformation with equatorial Br (axial H, upfield signal) predominates, accounting for

    $$(\frac{4.6}{4.6 + 1.0} \times 100 =) \ 82\% \text{ of the molecules.}$$

10. (a) Isopropylbenzene; (b) isobutylene; (c) phenylacetylene.

11. (a) Isobutylbenzene; (b) *tert*-butylbenzene; (c) *p*-isopropyltoluene.

12. (a) α-Phenylethyl bromide, $C_6H_5CHBrCH_3$; (b) *tert*-pentylbenzene; (c) *sec*-butyl bromide.

13. D, α-methylstyrene, $C_6H_5C(CH_3)=CH_2$.

CHAPTER 14

14.1 (a) *trans*-1,4-Cyclohexanediol; (b) *cis*-1,4-cyclohexanediol; (c) not if stereoisomerism can be detected by other physical properties.

14.2 (a) G is Me, Et, *i*-Pr, *t*-Bu; (b) the larger G, the lower the rate, and effect of size parallels effect of number of groups.

14.3 The slow step — the one being measured in both reactions — is the dissociation of the dimer; subsequent steps are fast.

14.4 (a) 1.9%; (b) 16.4%; (c) 66.2%; (d) 95.1%; (e) 99.0%.

14.5 (a) Optical purity: bromide, 60%; alcohol, 40%. (b) 33% racemization, 67% inversion; (c) 17% front-side attack, 83% back-side attack.

14.6 $S_N 1$ slow because 1° RX; $S_N 2$ slow because of steric factor.

14.7 Me, 300; Et, 24; *i*-Pr, 1; *t*-Bu, 1410.

14.8 (a) Formic acid, more polar solvent, favors $S_N 1$;
(b) ethoxide ion, more nucleophilic reagent, favors $S_N 2$;
(e) electron release by —CH₃ favors $S_N 1$, has little effect on $S_N 2$.

14.9 Ethanol less nucleophilic than ethoxide ion, "waits to be invited in" after $S_N 1$ ionization; hybrid carbonium ion, $CH_3 CH{=\!=\!=}CH{=\!=\!=}CH_2$, yields two products (compare page 271).

14.10 (a) Speeds up, transition state more polar than reactants; (b) slows down slightly, since charge more dispersed in transition state.

14.11 (a) Dehydrohalogenation favors formation of alkene with fewer hydrogens on doubly-bonded carbons; that is, more highly substituted alkene. (b) Both 1-phenyl-1-butene and 1-phenyl-2-butene.
(c) 1-Phenyl-1-butene.

14.12 Some carbanion character to transition state; partial negative charge on C-2 dispersed by phenyl group, through resonance and inductive effect.

14.13 *Anti* conformation.

14.14 All Cl atoms equatorial; no Cl *anti* to H.

14.15 Transition state leading to *cis*-alkene has crowding between methyl groups, is less stable. This interpretation is based on the fact that dehydrohalogenation is a relatively difficult reaction (E_{act} 20–25 kcal), and hence much slower than interconversion of conformations of reactant (see page 235). However, we would expect same general results if product ratio were determined by conformational populations, since the conformation with CH₃ groups *anti* to each other would be more abundant.

14.16 E1 elimination to yield both 2- and 3-menthene via carbonium ion becomes more important than E2 in absence of added base.

14.17 (a) Both isomers yield the more stable alkene: the *cis* isomer by *anti* elimination, which requires twisting of the ring; and the *trans* isomer by *syn* elimination. The significant thing is that *syn* elimination occurs as fast as it does; it requires eclipsing of groups, but in cyclopentane compounds, groups are already badly eclipsed. (The corresponding cyclohexane compounds give analogous results, but there the *cis* isomer reacts over 10,000 times as fast as the *trans*.)

(b) VII must react by *anti* elimination, and VIII by *syn* elimination. Here, *syn* elimination is actually faster. In this rigid bicyclic system, the twisting of VII required for *anti*-periplanar elimination is more difficult than in a simple cyclopentane derivative, whereas in VIII the leaving groups are already held *syn*-periplanar. (In addition, in VII both Cl's are tucked in a fold of the molecule, making solvation of a leaving Cl$^-$ difficult.)

14.18   (a) EtBr;   (b) PhCH$_2$CH$_2$Br;   (c) *n*-BuBr;   (d) iso-BuBr.

14.19   (a) *t*-BuO$^-$ in DMSO is not solvated via hydrogen bonding, is much stronger base than strongly solvated OH$^-$ in alcohol;   (b) F$^-$ in DMSO is not solvated via hydrogen bonding, is strong base, favors E2.

14.20   (a) CrO$_3$/H$_2$SO$_4$;   (b) Br$_2$/CCl$_4$, or KMnO$_4$;   (c) AgNO$_3$(alc), or fuming sulfuric acid;   (d) solubility in conc. H$_2$SO$_4$.

1.   (a) Br$_2$, heat or light;   (b) HBr(g);   (c) conc. HBr (used in laboratory).

2.   (a) b or c;   (b) none;   (c) c;   (d) c;   (e) b or c;   (f) a or c;   (g) c;   (h) a or c.

3.   (a) HBr, heat.   (b) Acid, heat; Cl$_2$, 600°.   (c) Acid, heat; Cl$_2$, H$_2$O.   (d) Acid, heat; Br$_2$/CCl$_4$.   (e) As in (d); then KOH(alc), heat; NaNH$_2$, heat; 2HBr.   (f) As in (e); then KOH(alc), heat.   (g) As in (d); then KOH(alc), heat.   (h) Product (b), Cl$_2$, H$_2$O.   (i) Product (b), OH$^-$(aq); Br$_2$/CCl$_4$.   (j) H$_2$SO$_4$, heat; CHCl$_3$, *t*-BuOK.

4.   (a) HBr, heat.   (b) HI (or P, I$_2$), heat.   (c) Acid, heat; Br$_2$/CCl$_4$.   (d) Acid, heat; N-bromosuccinimide.   (e) Acid, heat; Cl$_2$, H$_2$O.   (f) H$_2$SO$_4$, heat; CHCl$_3$, *t*-BuOK; Na, CH$_3$OH.

5.   (a) Toluene, Br$_2$, Fe; Cl$_2$, heat.   (b) Benzene, CCl$_4$, AlCl$_3$ (compare Problem 12.13, page 398).   (c) Allyl alcohol, HI.   (d) Toluene, 2Br$_2$, heat.   (e) Toluene, 3Cl$_2$, heat; HNO$_3$, H$_2$SO$_4$, heat.   (f) Benzene, C$_2$H$_4$, HF; heat, catalyst ($-$ H$_2$); Cl$_2$.   (g) Product (f), KOH(alc); NaNH$_2$/NH$_3$.   (h) Benzene, C$_2$H$_4$, HF; heat, catalyst ($-$ H$_2$); CHCl$_3$, *t*-BuOK; Na, CH$_3$OH.

6.   (a) 1-Butanol;   (b) 1-butene;   (c) no reaction;   (d) *n*-butane;   (e) *n*-hexane;   (f) *n*-butylmagnesium bromide;   (g) CH$_3$CH$_2$CH$_2$CH$_2$D;   (h) *n*-butane;   (i) no reaction;   (j) 1-iodobutane;   (k) *sec*-butylbenzene (major) and *n*-butylbenzene;   (l) 2-heptyne;   (m) 1-fluorobutane;   (n) no reaction.

7. (a) n-BuNH$_3$$^+$ (or n-BuNH$_2$); (b) n-BuNH$_2$Ph (or n-BuNHPh);
   (c) n-BuCN; (d) n-BuOEt; (e) n-BuOOCCH$_3$; (f) n-BuSCH$_3$.

8. (a) 1-Butene; (b) 1-butene; (c) 1-butanol and n-BuOEt; (d) 1-butene.
   With *tert*-BuBr, (a), (b), and (d) are more important, (c) is less important.

9. (a) 1-Bromopentane > 2-bromopentane > 2-bromo-2-methylbutane;
   (b) 1-bromo-3-methylbutane > 3-bromo-2-methylbutane > 2-bromo-2-
   methylbutane; (c) 1-bromobutane > 1-bromo-3-methylbutane >
   1-bromo-2-methylbutane > 1-bromo-2,2-dimethylpropane.

10. (a) 2-Bromo-2-methylbutane > 2-bromopentane > 1-bromopentane;
    (b) 2-bromo-2-methylbutane > 3-bromo-2-methylbutane > 1-bromo-3-
    methylbutane; (c) p-MeOC$_6$H$_4$CH$_2$Cl > p-MeC$_6$H$_4$CH$_2$Cl >
    C$_6$H$_5$CH$_2$Cl > p-ClC$_6$H$_4$CH$_2$Cl > p-O$_2$NC$_6$H$_4$CH$_2$Cl; (d) α-phenyl-
    ethyl bromide > benzyl bromide > β-phenylethyl bromide.

11. (a) 2-Bromo-2-methylbutane > 2-bromopentane > 1-bromopentane;
    (b) 2-bromo-2-methylbutane > 3-bromo-2-methylbutane > 1-bromo-
    3-methylbutane; (c) 2-bromo-1-phenylpropane > 3-bromo-1-phenyl-
    propane; (d) 5-bromo-1,3-cyclohexadiene > 3-bromocyclohexene >
    bromocyclohexane; (e) *cis* > *trans*.

12. S$_N$2: inversion; 2nd order; no rearrangement; Me > Et > i-Pr > t-Bu;
    RI > RBr > RCl; faster at higher temp.; rate doubled; rate doubled;
    little affected by solvent changes. S$_N$1: racemization; 1st order; re-
    arrangement; t-Bu > i-Pr > Et > Me; RI > RBr > RCl; faster at higher
    temp.; rate doubled; rate unaffected; faster with increased water
    content (more polar solvent).

13. Protonated alcohol ionizes to a planar carbonium ion, hydration of
    which can occur in two ways to give racemic alcohol; or, protonated
    alcohol suffers S$_N$2 attack by water, with inversion and loss of optical
    activity (see answer to Problem 14). (Actually, studies with H$_2$^{18}O gave
    results similar to those in Problem 14: racemization was twice as fast as
    isotopic exchange, indicating inversion with every attack.)

14. When *one* molecule of halide suffers exchange and inversion, optical
    activity of *two* molecules is lost, since rotation of inverted molecule
    cancels rotation of one unreacted molecule.

15. In transition state for elimination from menthyl chloride, for —Cl to be
    in required axial position, bulky methyl and isopropyl groups must also
    be axial; in either transition state for elimination from neomenthyl
    chloride, alkyl groups are equatorial.

16. A, (1R,2S; 1S,2R)-1,2-dichloro-1-phenylpropane;

B, (1R,2R; 1S,2S)-1,2-dichloro-1-phenylpropane; not stereospecific. (Addition of chlorine to this alkene has been found *not* to be stereospecific, and this has been attributed to the unimportance of a bridged chloronium structure (Sec. 7.12) for the resonance-stabilized benzylic cation. Compare answer to Problem 20, Chapter 12.

17. The *cis* isomer reacts via E2 *anti* elimination, with leaving groups axial and *tert*-butyl equatorial. The *trans* isomer undergoes E1 elimination since formation of carbonium ion is easier than either (a) *anti*-periplanar elimination with *tert*-butyl axial, or (b) *syn*-periplanar elimination with ring in boat conformation.

18. (a) (i) *anti*-Elimination, with I⁻ as base.

$$-\underset{\underset{Br}{|}}{\overset{\overset{Br}{|}}{C}}-\underset{|}{\overset{|}{C}}- \longrightarrow -\overset{|}{C}=\overset{|}{C}- + IBr + Br^-$$

(ii) Intermolecular nucleophilic attack, with inversion; intramolecular attack, with inversion; elimination, which is necessarily *syn*. Net result: over-all *syn*-elimination.

$$-\overset{\overset{Br}{|}}{C}-\overset{\overset{Br}{|}}{C}- \longrightarrow -\overset{\overset{Br}{|}}{C}-\overset{|}{\underset{I}{C}}- \xrightarrow{I^-} -\overset{|}{\underset{I}{C}}-\overset{|}{\underset{I}{C}}- \longrightarrow -\overset{|}{C}=\overset{|}{C}-$$

(b) Mechanism (ii) for *meso*-1,2-dibromo-1,2-dideuterioethane. Mechanism (i) for 2,3-dibromobutanes: more hindrance to nucleophilic attack in first step of (i); greater stabilization of incipient double bond in (ii). (c) Elimination (like addition) is *anti*, and removes same (radioactive) Br's that were added.

19. (a) Racemic dibromide undergoes usual *anti* dehydrohalogenation, with pyridine attacking H. *Meso* dibromide undergoes *anti* elimination by mechanism (i) of preceding problem, with pyridine (instead of iodide ion) attacking Br. (b) Each reaction proceeds via transition state in which leaving groups are *anti*-periplanar and bulky phenyl groups are *trans*.

20. 1,1-Dimethylcyclopropane; 1,1-dimethylcyclopropane-2-d. Formed by intramolecular insertion of a methylene produced by α-elimination.

21. (a) t-BuF: splitting of CH_3 signal by F ($J = 20$). i-PrF: splitting of CH_3 signal by H ($J = 4$) and by F ($J = 23$); and splitting of H signal by CH_3 ($J = 4$) and by F ($J = 48$). (b) t-BuF $\longrightarrow$ t-Bu$^+$SbF$_6^-$; i-PrF $\longrightarrow$ i-Pr$^+$SbF$_6^-$. Deshielding by positive charge produces large downfield shift. Shows existence of carbonium ions.

22. (a) 1-Methylcyclopropene; formed by intramolecular insertion of a methylene produced by α-elimination. (b) Cyclopropene.

23. (a) C, ; (b) by Wurtz reaction; by intramolecular addition of a methylene.

24. (a) Br_2/CCl_4, or $KMnO_4$; (b) Br_2/CCl_4; (c) glycol and chlorohydrin give tests with CrO_3/H_2SO_4, only chlorohydrin gives test for Cl; (d) alkene detected by Br_2/CCl_4, alcohol detected by CrO_3/H_2SO_4; (e) chloride gives test for Cl, alkene detected by Br_2/CCl_4; (f) $AgNO_3$.

25. (a) CH_3I, CH_2Cl_2, (C_2H_5Br?); (b) CH_3I; (c) $Br^- \longrightarrow Br_2$, which is red-brown in CCl_4; Cl^- unaffected.

26. (a) Bromo and chloro compounds by elemental analysis; n-decane and p-cymene by insolubility in cold conc. H_2SO_4, but only p-cymene is soluble in fuming sulfuric acid; limonene gives Br_2/CCl_4 test, the alcohol does not. (b) Chloro and iodo compounds by elemental analysis; only propenylbenzene gives Br_2/CCl_4 test; only 2-octanol gives iodoform. (c) n-Octyl chloride by elemental analysis; only the alcohol is oxidized by CrO_3/H_2SO_4; of the hydrocarbons, *trans*-decalin is insoluble in fuming sulfuric acid; oxidation to acids and determination of m.p.'s identifies the arenes.

CHAPTER 15

15.1 Intramolecular hydrogen bond in *cis*-isomer (see Sec. 24.2).

15.2 Yes: carbon (a) carrying three —Cl's or (b) sp-hybridized (Sec. 8.10) is, in effect, a more electronegative element.

15.3 Contains many —OH groups per molecule.

15.4 See answer to Problem 8, Chapter 1.

15.5 (a) Leucine $\longrightarrow$ isopentyl alcohol; isoleucine $\longrightarrow$ active amyl alcohol; (b) chirality about one of the two original chiral carbons of isoleucine is retained.

15.6 First fraction: 18.5 g ethanol, 7.5 g water, 74 g benzene. Second fraction: 124 g pure ethanol.

15.7 A, $ClCH_2CH=CH_2$; B, $HOCH_2CH=CH_2$; C, $HOCH_2CHClCH_2OH$; D, $HOCH_2CHOHCH_2OH$.

15.8 $C_6H_5CH(OCH_3)CH_3$.

15.9 (a)

```
      CH3            CH3              (b)    CH3            CH3
HO ───┼── H     H ──┼── OH                H ──┼── OH   HO ──┼── H
   H ─┼── Ph  + Ph ─┼── H     ;        H ──┼── Ph  + Ph ──┼── H    ;
      CH3            CH3                     CH3            CH3
```

(c) *trans*-2-methylcyclohexanol.

15.10 *syn*-Addition, retention; or *anti*-addition, inversion.

15.11

	(a)	(b)	(c)	(d)
Acid:	H_2O	Et_3B	$(BH_3)_2$	$(BH_3)_2$
Base:	H^-	NH_3	Me_3N	H^-

15.12 *syn*-Addition, retention.

1. (a) $CH_3CH_2CH_2CH_2CH_2OH$; $CH_3CH_2CH_2CHOHCH_3$; $CH_3CH_2CHOHCH_2CH_3$; $CH_3CH_2CH(CH_3)CH_2OH$; $CH_3CH_2C(OH)(CH_3)_2$; $CH_3CHOHCH(CH_3)_2$; $(CH_3)_2CHCH_2CH_2OH$; $(CH_3)_3CCH_2OH$. (b) 1-Pentanol, *n*-butylcarbinol; 2-pentanol, methyl-*n*-propylcarbinol; 3-pentanol, diethylcarbinol; 2-methyl-1-butanol, *sec*-butylcarbinol; 2-methyl-2-butanol, dimethylethylcarbinol; 3-methyl-2-butanol, methylisopropylcarbinol; 3-methyl-1-butanol, isobutylcarbinol; 2,2-dimethylpropanol, *tert*-butylcarbinol. (c) 1°; 2°; 2°; 1°; 3°; 2°; 1°; 1°. (d) Isopentyl alcohol, $(CH_3)_2CHCH_2CH_2OH$; *n*-pentyl alcohol, $CH_3CH_2CH_2CH_2CH_2OH$; *tert*-pentyl alcohol, $CH_3CH_2C(OH)(CH_3)_2$.

2. d, e, a, c, b.

3. (a) Alcohols, acids, amides, sulfonic acids, amines, phenols, glycols, dicarboxylic acids, hydroxy acids, carbohydrates, $-N-H$ heterocyclic compounds, amino acids, proteins. (b) All, except hydrocarbons and halides.

4. (a) *p*-Cresol; (b) propionic acid; (c) ethylene glycol.

5. (a) Acid-catalyzed hydration of propylene. (b) Hydrolysis of isopropyl chloride by alkali. (c) Acetaldehyde, MeMgBr; H_2O. (d) Method a: cheapest; alkene available; excellent orientation; ease of handling.

6. (a) n-BuMgX + HCHO; (b) n-PrMgX + CH_3CHO, or $CH_3CH_2CH_2CHO$ + MeMgX; (c) EtMgX + CH_3CH_2CHO; (d) sec-BuMgX + HCHO; (e) EtMgX + $(CH_3)_2CO$, or $CH_3CH_2COCH_3$ + MeMgX; (f) MeMgX + $(CH_3)_2CHCHO$, or CH_3CHO + i-PrMgX; (g) iso-BuMgX + HCHO; (h) t-BuMgX + HCHO; (i) PhMgBr + CH_3CH_2CHO, or PhCHO + EtMgX; (j) PhMgBr + $(CH_3)_2CO$, or PhCOCH$_3$ + MeMgX; (k) PhCH$_2$CHO + MeMgX (PhCH$_2$MgX reacts abnormally with CH_3CHO and many other aldehydes to give *ortho* substitution); (l) PhCH$_2$CH$_2$MgX + HCHO; (m) cyclohexanone + MeMgX; (n) $cyclo$-C_6H_{11}MgX + HCHO; (o) $cyclo$-C_6H_{11}MgX + CH_3CHO, or $cyclo$-C_6H_{11}CHO + MeMgX; (p) i-PrMgX + $(CH_3)_2CHCHO$; (q) p-CH$_3$C$_6$H$_4$MgBr + CH_3CHO, or p-CH$_3$C$_6$H$_4$CHO + MeMgX; (r) PhMgBr + Ph$_2$CO.

7. Intramolecular H-bond between $-OH$ and $-G$.

8. (a) Coprostane-3β, 6β-diol, by *syn*-hydration at more hindered "top" face of molecule. (b) *syn*-Hydration from beneath gives *alpha* $-OH$ at C-11.

9. (a) Both $-OH$'s axial, or both equatorial; (b) diequatorial; (c) both $-OH$'s axial, stabilized by H-bonding between them.

10. Twist-boat; both *tert*-Bu groups "equatorial," $-OH$ groups "flagpole" with intramol. H-bonding.

11. (a) 5α,6β- and 5β,6α-; 2β,3α- and 2α,3β-. (b) Preferred formation of bromonium ion by less hindered attack from beneath. Bromonium ion opens via an *anti* transition state to yield diaxial dibromide.

12. *Anti* elimination.

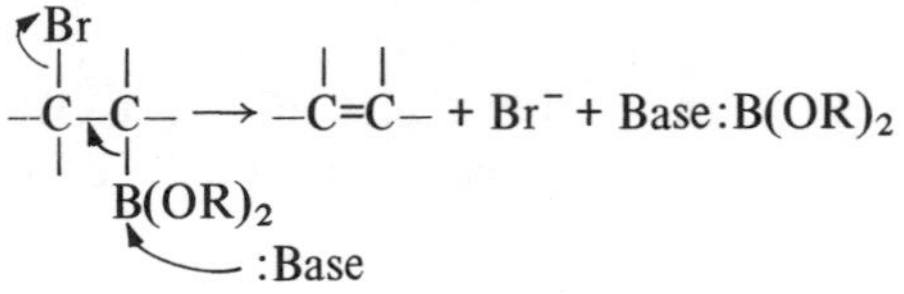

$$-\overset{\overset{\displaystyle Br}{|}}{\underset{\underset{\displaystyle \overset{B(OR)_2}{\underset{:Base}{}}}{|}}{C}}-\overset{|}{C}- \longrightarrow -\overset{|}{C}=\overset{|}{C}- + Br^- + Base:B(OR)_2$$

CHAPTER 16

16.1 Zinc chloride increases the acidity of the medium, possibly by $2HCl + ZnCl_2 \longrightarrow 2H^+ + ZnCl_4^=$.

16.2 Free radical chlorination of neopentane.

16.3   (a) *p*-Methylbenzyl alcohol > benzyl alcohol > *p*-nitrobenzyl alcohol;
(b) α-phenylethyl alcohol > benzyl alcohol > β-phenylethyl alcohol.

16.4   (a) Allylic alcohol yields allylic cation, which in turn yields 3-bromo-1-butene and 1-bromo-2-butene;   (b) 3-bromo-1-butene and 1-bromo-2-butene;   (c) no change in carbon skeleton or in position of hydrogen atoms.

16.5   (a) $ROH + HCl \rightleftarrows ROH_2^+ + Cl^-$
$ROH_2^+ \rightleftarrows R^+ + H_2O$
$R^+ + Cl^- \longrightarrow RCl$

(b) formation of R^+;   (c) ROH_2^+;   (d) ROH and HCl;   (e) on acid concentration also.

16.6   (a) β-Chloroethyl alcohol;   (b) *p*-nitrobenzyl alcohol;   (c) glycerol.

16.7   (a) $t\text{-BuOH} + Na \longrightarrow 1/2 \ H_2 + t\text{-BuO}^-Na^+ \xrightarrow{EtBr} t\text{-BuOEt} + NaBr$;
$EtOH + Na \longrightarrow 1/2 \ H_2 + EtO^-Na^+ \xrightarrow{t\text{-BuBr}} (CH_3)_2C{=}CH_2 + EtOH + NaBr$.

(b) Nucleophilic substitution in first case, elimination in second case.
(c) Substitution fast with 1° halide, elimination predominates with 3° halide.

16.8 $C_6H_5CH_3$, H_2SO_4, SO_3; PCl_5; *sec*-BuOH.

16.9   Complete inversion.

16.10   (a) Insoluble in cold conc. H_2SO_4: alkanes, cycloalkanes, alkylbenzenes (unless many alkyl sidechains present), alkyl halides.   (b) Negative to $KMnO_4$: alkanes, cycloalkanes, alkylbenzenes, alkyl halides, alcohols.   (c) Positive to Br_2/CCl_4: alkenes, alkynes, dienes.   (d) Positive to CrO_3/H_2SO_4: 1° and 2° alcohols.   (e) Insoluble in fuming sulfuric acid: alkanes, cycloalkanes, alkyl halides.   (f) Positive to $CHCl_3/AlCl_3$: alkylbenzenes.   (g) Reaction with Na: 1-alkynes, alcohols.

16.11   1 HIO_4: a, b, c, e; 4 HIO_4: f, g; no reaction, d.   (a) CH_3CHO, HCHO;   (b) CH_3CHO, HCOOH;   (c) HCHO, $OHCCH_2OCH_3$;   (e) $OHC(CH_2)_3CHO$;   (f) HCHO, 4HCOOH;   (g) HCHO, 3HCOOH, HCHO.

16.12   A, $(CH_3)_2C(OH)CH_2OH$;   B, 1,2-cyclohexanediol;
C, 2-hydroxycyclohexanone;   D, HOOCCHOHCHOHCOOH;
E, $HOCH_2CHOHCHOHCH_2OH$;   F, $HOCH_2CHOHCOCHO$;
G, $HOCH_2(CHOH)_4CHO$.

16.13   Change concentration.

16.14   (a) 1°, triplet; 2°, doublet; 3°, singlet.

(b) Acid: R*OH* + H:B $\rightleftarrows$ $\begin{bmatrix} R*\overset{|}{\underset{|}{O}}H* \\ H \end{bmatrix}^+$ + :B⁻

$\begin{bmatrix} R*\overset{|}{\underset{|}{O}}H* \\ H \end{bmatrix}^+$ + ROH $\rightleftarrows$ R*OH + $\begin{bmatrix} R\overset{|}{\underset{|}{O}}H \\ H* \end{bmatrix}^+$

$\begin{bmatrix} R\overset{|}{\underset{|}{O}}H \\ H* \end{bmatrix}^+$ + :B⁻ $\rightleftarrows$ ROH* + H:B

Base: R*OH* + :B $\rightleftarrows$ R*O⁻ + [H*:B]⁺
R*O⁻ + ROH $\rightleftarrows$ R*OH + RO⁻
RO⁻ + [H*:B]⁺ $\rightleftarrows$ ROH* + :B

1.   (a) 2-Pentanol and 3-methyl-2-butanol give iodoform; all others negative.
(b) 2-Methyl-2-butanol reacts rapidly; 2-pentanol, 3-pentanol, and
3-methyl-2-butanol react slowly; the others do not respond.
(c) 2-Methyl-2-butanol gives a negative test; all the others give a positive
test.   (d) 1-Pentanol: *n*-BuMgBr (from *n*-BuOH) and HCHO (from
MeOH). 2-Pentanol: *n*-PrMgBr (from *n*-PrOH) and CH₃CHO (from
EtOH); or MeMgBr (from MeOH) and CH₃CH₂CH₂CHO (from
n-BuOH). 3-Pentanol: EtMgBr (from EtOH) and CH₃CH₂CHO (from
n-PrOH). 2-Methyl-1-butanol: *sec*-BuMgBr (from *sec*-BuOH) and HCHO
(from MeOH). 2-Methyl-2-butanol: MeMgBr (from MeOH) and
CH₃CH₂COCH₃ (from *sec*-BuOH); or EtMgBr (from EtOH) and acetone
(from *i*-PrOH). 3-Methyl-2-butanol: MeMgBr (from MeOH) and
(CH₃)₂CHCHO (from iso-BuOH); or *i*-PrMgBr (from *i*-PrOH) and
CH₃CHO (from EtOH). 3-Methyl-1-butanol: iso-BuMgBr (from
iso-BuOH) and HCHO (from MeOH). 2,2-Dimethyl-1-propanol:
t-BuMgBr (from *t*-BuOH) and HCHO (from MeOH).

2.   (a) Cyclohexyl hydrogen sulfate;   (b) cyclohexene;   (c) no reaction
(cyclohexanone if heated);   (d) cyclohexanone;   (e) no reaction;
(f) cyclohexyl bromide;   (g) cyclohexyl iodide;   (h) *cyclo*-C₆H₁₁ONa;
(i) cyclohexyl acetate;   (j) no reaction;   (k) *cyclo*-C₆H₁₁OMgBr + CH₄;
(l) no reaction;   (m) cyclohexylmagnesium bromide;   (n) 1-cyclohexyl-
cyclohexanol;   (o) *cis*-1,2-cyclohexanediol;   (p) *trans*-1,2-dibromo-
cyclohexane;   (q) cyclohexylbenzene;   (r) cyclohexane;   (s) *o*- and
p-nitrocyclohexylbenzene;   (t) 3-bromocyclohexene;   (u) 7,7-dichloro-
norcarane;   (v) 1-phenylcyclohexanol.   (w) cyclohexyl tosylate;
(x) cyclohexene.

3. (a) HBr, heat. (b) HBr, heat; KOH(alc), heat. (c) Cold conc. H_2SO_4.
(d) K(metal). (e) $K_2Cr_2O_7$, H^+, heat. (f) $K_2Cr_2O_7$, H_2SO_4, heat.
(g) As in (b); then cat. H_2. (h) As in (b); then Br_2/CCl_4. (i) As in (b);
then Cl_2, H_2O. (j) As in (h); then KOH(alc), heat; $NaNH_2$, heat.
(k) Product (b), $CHCl_3$, *t*-BuOK; Na, CH_3OH. (l) Product (b),
HCO_2OH or cold $KMnO_4$. (m) As in (a); then Na, heat. (n) 1-Butyne
(from j), $NaNH_2$; combine this sodium salt with *n*-BuBr (from a).
(o) Product (n), H_2, Lindlar cat. (p) Product (n), Na/NH_3. (q) *n*-BuBr
(from a), Mg, anhyd. ether; combine this Grignard reagent with
$CH_3CH_2CH_2CHO$ (from e); H_2O. (r) As in (q); then CrO_3/H_2SO_4.
(s) Combine Grignard reagent from (q) with ketone from (r); H_2O.
(t) As in (f); then *n*-BuOH, H^+, heat.

4. (a) $(C_6H_5CH_2O)_2Mg$; (b) $C_6H_5COOCH_2CH(CH_3)_2$, isobutyl benzoate;
(c) $HOCH_2CH_2OH$, ethylene glycol; (d) no reaction;
(e) $CH_3CHOHCHBrCH_2OH$, 2-bromo-1,3-butanediol; (f) C_2H_6 and
$Mg(OCH_3)Br$; (g) *p*-$BrC_6H_4CH_2OH$, *p*-bromobenzyl alcohol;
(h) $C_6H_5C(CH_3)_3$, *tert*-butylbenzene.

5. Yellow dichromate reduced to green Cr(III) by ethyl alcohol; motorist
reduced to tears or rage and, often, to walking.

6. (a) 2-Methyl-2-butanol > (3-methyl-2-butanol, 3-pentanol, 2-pentanol) >
(2-methyl-1-butanol, 3-methyl-1-butanol, 1-pentanol) > 2,2-dimethyl-1-
propanol; (b) 1-phenyl-1-propanol > 1-phenyl-2-propanol > 3-phenyl-
1-propanol; (c) *p*-$HOC_6H_4CH_2OH$ > $C_6H_5CH_2OH$ > *p*-$NCC_6H_4CH_2OH$;
(d) 2-buten-1-ol > 3-buten-1-ol; (e) 1-methylcyclopentanol > *trans*-2-
methylcyclopentanol > cyclopentylcarbinol; (f) Ph_3COH > Ph_2CHOH >
$PhCH_2OH$ > CH_3OH.

7. (a) Hydride shift in carbonium ion. (b) Hydride shift in carbonium ion.
(c) First product formed without rearrangement; 2nd product after
hydride shift; 3rd product after methyl shift; 4th product after methyl
shift and loss of different proton; 5th product after methyl shift and
subsequent hydride shift; 6th product after an additional methyl shift.
(d) Dimethylcyclohexene from methyl shift; isopropylcyclopentene
from ring contraction followed by hydride shift. (e) Ring expansion,
followed by ethyl shift. (f) Ring expansion.

8. (a) $K_2Cr_2O_7$, H^+, heat. (b) HBr or PBr_3, heat. (c) As in (a); then
MeMgBr (from MeOH); H_2O. (d) Product (c), H_2SO_4, heat.
(e) Product (d), $(BH_3)_2$; H_2O_2, OH^-. (f) As in (b); then Mg, anhyd.
ether; CH_3CHO (from EtOH); H_2O. (g) H_2SO_4, heat; Br_2/CCl_4.
(h) As in (b); then Mg, anhyd. ether; HCHO (from MeOH); H_2O.
(i) Product (a), PhMgBr (from benzene); H_2O, H^+; HBr. (j) As in (b);

then Mg, anhyd. ether; CO_2; acidify. (k) HNO_3, heat. (l) H_2SO_4, heat; $CHCl_3$, *t*-BuOK; Na, MeOH.

9. (a) *i*-PrMgBr (from *i*-PrOH) and acetone (from *i*-PrOH); H_2O.
   (b) PhMgBr (from benzene) and acetone (from *i*-PrOH). (c) As in (b); then acid, heat. (d) *sec*-BuMgBr (from *sec*-BuOH) and HCHO (from MeOH); acidify; PBr_3, heat; KOH(alc), heat. (e) As in (d); then cat. H_2.
   (f) As in (d); then Br_2/CCl_4. (g) *n*-PrMgBr (from *n*-PrOH) and CH_3CH_2CHO (from *n*-PrOH); H_2O. (h) As in (g); then $K_2Cr_2O_7$, H^+, heat. (i) As in (h); then *n*-PrMgBr (from *n*-PrOH); H_2O. (j) *n*-BuMgBr (from *n*-BuOH) and acetone (from *i*-PrOH); acidify; conc. HBr.
   (k) *i*-PrOH, acid, heat; Br_2/CCl_4; KOH(alc), heat; $NaNH_2$, heat.
   (l) Product (k), $NaNH_2/NH_3$; CH_3I (from MeOH); Na, NH_3; $CHCl_3$, *t*-BuOK; Na, MeOH. (m) PhMgBr (from benzene) and CH_3CHO (from EtOH); H_2O; HCl. (n) *sec*-BuBr (from *sec*-BuOH), C_6H_6, $AlCl_3$.
   (o) *i*-PrMgBr (from *i*-PrOH) and CH_3CHO (from EtOH); acidify; $K_2Cr_2O_7$, H^+, heat. (p) *n*-BuMgBr (from *n*-BuOH) and acetone (from *i*-PrOH); acidify; acid, heat; cat. H_2. (q) PhMgBr (from benzene) + ethylene oxide (from EtOH via ethylene, Sec. 17.10); acidify; $K_2Cr_2O_7$, H^+, heat. (See comment about reaction of $PhCH_2MgX$ with aldehydes in answer to Problem 6(k), page 516.) (r) As in (m); then Na, heat.
   (s) $PhCH_2CHOHCH_3$ (made in q), PBr_3. (t) *n*-BuOH, HBr, heat; KOH(alc), heat; Br_2/CCl_4; KOH(alc), heat; $NaNH_2$, heat; Na, NH_3; *n*-PrBr (from *n*-PrOH). (u) CH_3CH_2COOH (from *n*-PrOH), EtOH, acid, heat.

10. (a) $^{14}CH_3OH$, $K_2Cr_2O_7$, H^+, heat; *i*-PrMgBr; acidify. (b) $^{14}CH_3OH$, $K_2Cr_2O_7$, H^+, heat; MeMgBr; acidify; CrO_3/H_2SO_4; MeMgBr; acidify; HBr, heat; Mg, anhyd. ether; HCHO; acidify. (c) $^{14}CH_3OH$, HBr, heat; Mg, anhyd. ether; CH_3CHO; acidify; HBr, heat; Mg, anhyd. ether; HCHO; acidify. (d) $^{14}CH_3OH$, $K_2Cr_2O_7$, H^+, heat; EtMgBr; acidify; PBr_3; KOH(alc), heat. (e) $(CH_3)_2{}^{14}CHOH$ (made in b), acid, heat.
    (f) $^{14}CH_3OH$, HBr, heat; Mg, anhyd. ether; ethylene oxide (Sec. 17.10); acidify; PBr_3; KOH(alc), heat. (g) PhMgBr, D_2O. (h) $PhCH_2MgCl$, D_2O. (i) *p*-$CH_3C_6H_4Br$, Mg, anhyd. ether; D_2O. (j) $^{14}CH_3OH$, HBr, heat; Mg, anhyd. ether; CH_3CH_2CHO; acidify; PBr_3; Mg, anhyd. ether; D_2O.

11. (a) Almost certainly *anti* elimination. (Note contrast to behavior of *trans*-2-phenylcyclopentyl tosylate, Problem 14.17 (p. 484). There, greater stabilizing effect of phenyl group forced Saytzeff orientation even though it had to be *syn*.) (b) RMgX; acid, warm; $(BH_3)_2$; H_2O_2, OH^-; tosyl chloride, base; *t*-BuOK. (c) Inversion at C-2 during replacement of $-OH$ by $-X$ would give *cis*-2-halo-1-alkylcyclopentane, which

would undergo *anti*-elimination to yield chiefly 1-alkylcyclopentene, the more stable alkene.

12. (a) $(BH_3)_2$; H_2O_2, OH^-; CrO_3/H_2SO_4. (b) $(BH_3)_2$; H_2O_2, OH^-; CrO_3/H_2SO_4. (c) IsopentylMgBr; H_2O, H^+; I_2, heat $(-H_2O)$; cat. H_2; OH^-, heat; CrO_3/H_2SO_4.

13. A, $HOCH_2CH_2Cl$; B, $HOCH_2CH_2OH$; C, $ClCH_2COOH$;
    D, $HOCH_2COOH$; E, *cyclo*-$C_6H_6(OH)_6$;
    F, $CH_3(CH_2)_7CH=CH(CH_2)_7COOH$;
    G, $CH_3(CH_2)_7CHOHCHOH(CH_2)_7COOH$; H, $BrCH_2CHBrCH_2OH$;
    I, $BrCH_2CHBrCOOH$; J, $CH_2=CHCOOH$; K, $BrCH_2CH=CHBr$;
    L, $HOCH_2CH=CHBr$; M, $HOCH_2C\equiv CH$; N, $CH_3C(OH)_2CH_3$;
    O, CH_3COCH_3; P, $CH_3C(OH)_2CHCl_2$; Q, $CH_3COCHCl_2$;
    R, CH_3COCCl_3; S, CH_3COONa; T, *cis*-1,2-cyclohexanediol;
    U, diacetate of T; V, $HOCH_2CHOHCH_2OH$; W, triacetate of V;
    X, cyclohexanone; Y, 1-(*m*-tolyl)cyclohexanol; Z, 1-(*m*-tolyl)cyclo-
    hexene; AA, 3-methylbiphenyl, *m*-$CH_3C_6H_4C_6H_5$; BB, active
    (R)-$(CH_3)_2CHCH_2CH(CH_3)CH_2MgBr$; CC, mixture of two di-
    astereomers of 2,6,8-trimethyl-4-nonanol (4R,6R and 4S,6R);
    DD, active 2,6,8-trimethyl-4-nonanone (6R); EE, mixture of two
    diastereomers of 2,4,6,8-tetramethyl-4-nonanol (4R,6R and 4S,6R);
    FF, mixture of 2,4,6,8-tetramethyl-3-nonene and 2,4,6,8-tetramethyl-
    4-nonene (both R); GG, active 2,4,6,8-tetramethylnonane (R,R);
    HH, *meso*-2,4,6,8-tetramethylnonane (R,S).

14. See Sec. 28.10.

15. (a) $CH_3OH_2^+$; $\underset{a\quad b}{CH_3}-\overset{\overset{a}{\overset{CH_3}{|}}}{\underset{\underset{b}{\overset{|}{H}}}{C}}-\underset{c}{CH_2}-\underset{d}{OH_2^+}$

(b) Isobutyl alcohol slowly transformed into *t*-Bu cation, the same cation that in (c) is given immediately, even at $-60°$, by *tert*-butyl alcohol.

16. (a) R_3C^+. (i) $R_3COH + 2H_2SO_4 \rightarrow R_3C^+ + H_3O^+ + 2HSO_4^-$;
    (ii) conjugation; (iii) downfield shift due to deshielding by positive
    charge. Stabilized by overlap of empty p orbital with π clouds of cyclo-
    propyl rings. (b) Methyls not equivalent, located unsymmetrically;
    plane of methyls and trigonal carbon perpendicular to, and bisecting,
    ring. Ring is *cis* to one methyl and *trans* to the other.

Chapter 16

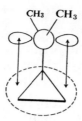

CH₃   CH₃

2-Cyclopropyl-2-propyl cation

17. II, 3-pentanol. JJ, 2-methyl-1-butanol or 3-methyl-1-butanol; distinguish by α-naphthylurethane. KK, ethylene chlorohydrin or 4-methyl-2-pentanol; distinguish by elemental analysis or by 3,5-dinitrobenzoate. LL, *n*-butyl alcohol or 2-pentanol; distinguish by iodoform test. MM, 3-pentanol or *n*-butyl alcohol; distinguish by 3,5-dinitrobenzoate.

18. (a) CrO_3/H_2SO_4; (b) Br_2/CCl_4, or CrO_3/H_2SO_4; (c) CrO_3/H_2SO_4; (d) Br_2/CCl_4; (e) Lucas reagent gives immediate reaction with allylic alcohol; (f) Lucas reagent; (g) iodoform test; (h) Br_2/CCl_4; (i) HIO_4; then $AgNO_3$; (j) Lucas reagent, or CrO_3/H_2SO_4; (k) elemental analysis for Br; (l) iodoform test.

19. Electron-withdrawing chlorine decreases stability, rate of formation of carbonium ion.

20. NN, $C_6H_5CH_2CHOHCH_3$; OO, $C_6H_5CH(CH_3)CH_2OH$.

21. PP, 1,2,2-triphenylethanol; QQ, 1,1,2-triphenylethanol; distinguish by CrO_3/H_2SO_4 test.

22. (a) *sec*-Butyl alcohol; (b) isobutyl alcohol; (c) ethyl ether.

23. (a) α-Phenylethyl alcohol; (b) β-phenylethyl alcohol; (c) benzyl methyl ether.

24. RR, 2-methyl-2-propen-1-ol; SS, isobutyl alcohol.

25. TT, 3,3-dimethyl-2-butanol.

26. (a) Aliphatic; 1° alcohol; C=C; yes; (b) 9 (methyl, allylic?), 4 (methylene, allylic?), 1 (−OH), 2 (−CH₂OH), 2 (vinylic); (c) 3 CH₃−, 2 −CH₂−, 2 olefinic H, one −CH₂OH; (d) and (e), $(CH_3)_2C=CHCH_2CH_2C(CH_3)=CHCH_2OH$, geraniol; fits isoprene rule.

27. (a) Same as Problem 26; (b) geometric isomers; (c) in geraniol, −H and −CH₃ are *trans*.

28. Both alcohols give same allylic cation, and hence same bromide.

CHAPTER 17

17.1 (a) $ROH + H^+ \rightleftarrows ROH_2^+$

$ROH_2^+ \rightarrow R^+ + H_2O$ *(slow)*

$$R^+ + ROH \rightarrow R\overset{\overset{\displaystyle H}{|}}{O}R^+$$

$$R\overset{\overset{\displaystyle H}{|}}{O}R^+ \rightleftarrows ROR + H^+$$

(b) $ROH + ROH_2^+ \rightarrow R\overset{\overset{\displaystyle H}{|}}{O}R^+ + H_2O$ *(slow)*

$$R\overset{\overset{\displaystyle H}{|}}{O}R^+ \rightleftarrows ROR + H^+$$

(c) Mechanism (b).

17.2 Alcohol $\rightarrow$ alkene, most important for $3°$ alcohols.

17.3 (a) Ethyl ether, ethyl *n*-propyl ether, *n*-propyl ether; (b) *tert*-butyl ethyl ether in good yield, because *t*-BuOH gives a carbonium ion so much faster than EtOH.

17.4 (a) The anions, $CH_3OSO_3^-$ and $SO_4^=$, are very weakly basic and hence very good leaving groups. (b) Alkyl sulfonates.

17.5 (a) EtBr and *t*-BuONa; (b) *n*-PrBr and PhONa; (c) *iso*-BuBr and Na 2-butoxide; (d) MeBr and Na salt of cyclohexanol.

17.6 PhOH, NaOH $\rightarrow$ PhONa. Toluene, HNO_3, H_2SO_4; Cl_2, heat; PhONa.

17.7 (a) Configuration of (−)-ether same as (−)-alcohol; (b) maximum rotation is $-18.3°$.

17.8 (a) Practically complete inversion; (b) S_N2; (c) yes, solvent of low polarity, reagent of high basicity; (d) S_N2 also; (e) in one there is attack (with inversion) on the chiral carbon, in the other there is retention of configuration since there is no attack on chiral carbon.

17.9 Alkene + Hg^{++} gives cyclic mercurinium ion (page 504); nucleophilic attack by alcohol to form alkylmercuric trifluoroacetate.

17.10 Acetate ion competes with alcohol in attack on cyclic mercurinium ion; less basic, less nucleophilic trifluoroacetate ion cannot.

17.11 (a) *n*-HexOH, PBr$_3$ $\longrightarrow$ *n*-HexBr. *iso*-PrOH, Na; *n*-HexBr. (b) *n*-HexBr, KOH(alc); Hg(OOCCF$_3$)$_2$, *iso*-PrOH; (c) *cyclo*-HexOH, H$_2$SO$_4$, heat ($\longrightarrow$ alkene); Hg(OOCCF$_3$)$_2$, *t*-BuOH. (d) *cyclo*-HexOH, H$_2$SO$_4$, heat ($\longrightarrow$ ether).

17.12 Reaction of protonated ether with bromide ion would be expected to take either of two alternative courses: (a) if S$_N$2, attack at least hindered group, methyl, to yield MeBr and *sec*-BuOH, or (b) if S$_N$1, formation of more stable cation, *sec*-butyl, to yield *sec*-BuBr and MeOH. Evidence indicates reaction is actually S$_N$2. (Since *sec*-Bu–O bond is not broken, must observe retention of configuration and optical purity.)

17.13 (a) 2-Bromo-4-methylanisole; (b) 3,4- and 2,5-dinitroanisole; (c) benzyl *p*- and *o*-nitrophenyl ether.

17.14 Ethylene glycol (1,2-ethanediol).

17.15 (a) Furan, cat. H$_2$; (b) product (a), excess HCl, heat.

17.16 (a) EtOH and ethylene oxide; additional ethylene oxide. (b) As in (a), replacing EtOH by PhOH. (c) As in (a), replacing EtOH by H$_2$O. (d) Product (c) and ethylene oxide.

17.17 S$_N$1 via HOCH$_2$CH$_2$$^+$, S$_N$2 as shown on page 569.

17.18 (a)-(e) As in Figures 7.6 and 7.7 (pages 244-245), with O in place of Br$^+$, and H$_2$O in place of Br$^-$. (f) None.

17.19 (a) CH$_3$OCH$_2$CH$_2$OH; (b) CH$_3$OCH$_2$CH$_2$OH; (c) C$_6$H$_5$NHCH$_2$CH$_2$OH.

17.20 Phenoxide ion is more basic than ethylene oxide, and would gain the proton.

17.21 CH$_3$CHOHCH$_2$OH + OH$^-$ $\rightleftharpoons$ CH$_3$CHOHCH$_2$O$^-$ + H$_2$O

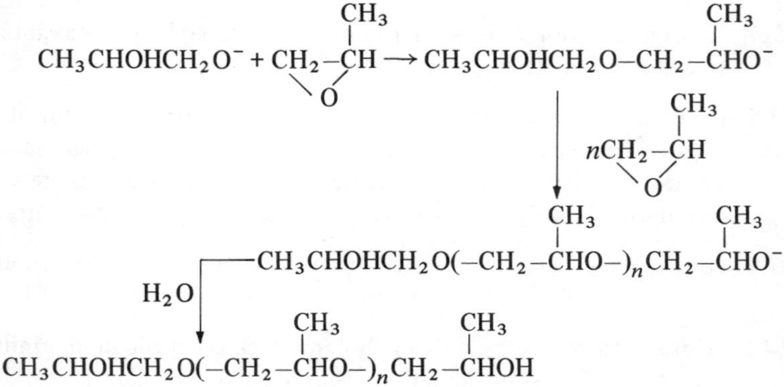

17.22 (a) $PhCHClCH_2OH$; (b) $PhCHOHCH_2OCH_3$;
(c) $CH_3CHOHCH_2NHPh$; (d) $(CH_3)_2CClCHOHCH_3$.

17.23 Formation of HBr as a product of a substitution reaction.

17.24 Ethers: soluble in cold conc. H_2SO_4; negative to $KMnO_4$; negative to Br_2/CCl_4; negative to CrO_3/H_2SO_4; soluble in fuming sulfuric acid; $CHCl_3/AlCl_3$ test not applicable; no reaction with Na.

17.25 (a) Solubility of ether in cold conc. H_2SO_4; (b) Br_2/CCl_4 or $KMnO_4$;
(c) same as (b); (d) same as (a); (e) CrO_3/H_2SO_4; (f) warm acid followed by $KMnO_4$; (g) Br_2, accompanied by test for HBr.

17.26 4.

1. (a) CH_3OCH_3; (b) $(CH_3)_2CHOCH(CH_3)_2$; (c) $n\text{-}C_4H_9OCH_3$;
(d) $(CH_3)_2CHCH_2OC(CH_3)_3$; (e) $n\text{-}C_3H_7CH(OCH_3)C_2H_5$;
(f) $H_2C{=}CH{-}O{-}CH{=}CH_2$; (g) $H_2C{=}CH{-}CH_2{-}O{-}CH_2{-}CH{=}CH_2$;
(h) $ClCH_2CH_2OCH_2CH_2Cl$; (i) $C_6H_5OCH_3$; (j) $C_6H_5OC_2H_5$;
(k) $C_6H_5OC_6H_5$; (l) see page 562; (m) $p\text{-}O_2NC_6H_4CH_2OC_3H_7\text{-}n$;
(n) $n\text{-}BuCH{-}CH_2$
$\qquad\quad \diagdown \diagup$
$\qquad\qquad O$

2. (a) Isobutyl ether; (b) methyl isopropyl ether; (c) ethyl *tert*-butyl ether; (d) 4-methoxyheptane; (e) *p*-bromophenetole; (f) *o*-nitrobenzyl phenyl ether; (g) 2,4-dibromoanisole.

3. (a) *t*-BuOH, Na; MeBr. (b) PhOH, NaOH; EtI. (c) Cyclohexanol, Na; *n*-BuBr. (d) *p*-Cresol, NaOH; PhCH$_2$Cl. (e) *i*-PrOH, Na; *iso*-BuBr.
(f) *t*-BuOH, H_2SO_4, heat; $Hg(OOCCF_3)_2$, *iso*-PrOH. (g) Resorcinol, 2NaOH; 2MeI, or 2Me$_2$SO$_4$.

4. (a) $PhOH > PhOCH_3 > C_6H_6 > PhCl > PhNO_2$; (b) $m\text{-}HOC_6H_4OMe > m\text{-}MeC_6H_4OMe > o\text{-}MeC_6H_4OMe > C_6H_5OMe$; (c) $p\text{-}C_6H_4(OH)_2 > p\text{-}MeOC_6H_4OH > p\text{-}C_6H_4(OMe)_2$.

5. (a) *t*-BuOEt; (b) isobutylene; (c) Et_2O; (d) no reaction; (e) MeI and EtI; (f) no reaction; (g) $Et_2OH^+HSO_4^-$; (h) 2EtOH; (i) PhOH and EtBr; (j) *p*- and $o\text{-}O_2NC_6H_4OEt$; (k) $p\text{-}KOOCC_6H_4OMe$;
(l) *p*- and $o\text{-}BrC_6H_4OCH_2C_6H_5$.

6. Polyisobutylene.

7. (a) CrO_3/H_2SO_4; (b) $AgNO_3$; (c) Br_2/CCl_4 or $KMnO_4$; (d) Br_2/CCl_4 or $KMnO_4$; (e) cold conc. H_2SO_4; (f) Br_2/CCl_4 or $KMnO_4$; (g) cold conc. H_2SO_4.

8. (a) Ether soluble in conc. H_2SO_4; (b) allylic ether oxidized by $KMnO_4$; (c) oxidation to acid and detn. of m.p.; (d) MeOH reacts with CrO_3/H_2SO_4, 1-hexene reacts with $KMnO_4$; (e) alcohol and ether are soluble in cold conc. H_2SO_4, alcohol reacts with CrO_3/H_2SO_4, and determine others by elemental analysis; (f) isoprene reacts with Br_2/CCl_4, or with $KMnO_4$, pentane insoluble in H_2SO_4; (g) oxidize methyl *o*-tolyl ether to acid, cleave phenetole to phenol or test for ease of substitution by bromine.

9. A, 3-bromo-4-methoxytoluene; B, *o*-methoxybenzyl bromide; C, *o*-bromophenetole; D, 3-bromo-4-methoxybenzoic acid; E, *o*-methoxybenzoic acid; F, 2-bromo-4-methylphenol; G, *o*-hydroxybenzyl bromide; H, *o*-bromophenol; I, *o*-hydroxybenzoic acid (salicylic acid); J, *p*-methoxybenzoic acid (anisic acid).

10. A: CH_3 singlet, OCH_3 singlet, 3 aromatic protons;
    B: OCH_3 singlet, CH_2 singlet, 4 aromatic protons;
    C: CH_3 triplet, CH_2 quartet, 4 aromatic protons.

11. (a) $HOCH_2CH_2OH$, ethylene glycol; (b) same as a;
    (c) $HOCH_2CH_2OEt$, 2-ethoxyethanol; (d) $HOCH_2CH_2OCH_2CH_2OEt$, ethyl ether of diethylene glycol; (e) $HOCH_2CH_2OCH_2CH_2OH$, diethylene glycol; (f) $HO(CH_2CH_2O)_3H$, triethylene glycol;
    (g) $BrCH_2CH_2OH$, 2-bromoethanol; (h) $NCCH_2CH_2OH$, 2-cyano-ethanol; (i) $HCOOCH_2CH_2OH$, ethylene glycol monoformate;
    (j) $PhCH_2CH_2OH$, 2-phenylethanol (β-phenylethyl alcohol);
    (k) $H_2NCH_2CH_2OH$, 2-aminoethanol (ethanolamine);
    (l) $Et_2NCH_2CH_2OH$, 2-(N,N-diethylamino)ethanol;
    (m) $PhOCH_2CH_2OH$, 2-phenoxyethanol; (n) same as m;
    (o) $HOCH_2CH_2C{\equiv}CH$, 3-butyn-1-ol.

12. Alkaline hydrolysis proceeds with retention of configuration because attack by OH^- occurs on the 1° carbon. Acidic hydrolysis proceeds with inversion of configuration because attack by H_2O on the protonated epoxide occurs at the 2° (in this case, chiral) carbon atom.

13. (a) Nucleophilic substitution; (b) inversion. (c) In the *cis*-isomer, it is not possible for both —Cl and —O⁻ to be axial and thus permit backside displacement.

(d)

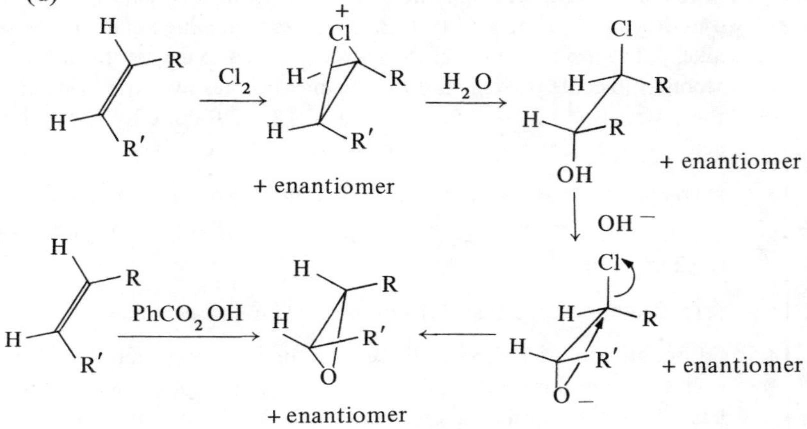

+ enantiomer

+ enantiomer

+ enantiomer

+ enantiomer

14. (a) 2-diastereomers (*cis* and *trans*); (b) neither is optically active;
    (c) isomer in which –OH and sidechain containing other –OH are *cis*.
    The ether is a cyclic ether involving oxygen in a bridge across a boat
    conformation of the cyclohexane ring.

15. K, CH_2ClCH_2OH; L, $(CH_2ClCH_2)_2O$; M, $(CH_2=CH)_2O$;
    N, $ClCH_2CHOHCH_2OCH_3$, retention; O, CH_3OCH_2COOH;
    P, $CH_3OCH_2CH-CH_2$; Q, CH_2-CH_2 ; R, $C_6H_5CH_2CH_2OH$;

    $\quad\quad\quad\quad\quad\quad\quad\quad$ O $\quad\quad\quad\quad$ CH$_2$–O

    S, 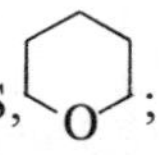 ; T, CH_3CHO; U, racemic *trans*-2-chlorocyclohexanol,

    inversion; V, racemic *trans*-2-methyl-1,2-cyclohexanediol, inversion;
    W, racemic and *meso*-$HOCH_2CHOHCHOHCH_2OH$; X, racemic
    2,3-butanediol; Y, *meso*-2,3-butanediol.

16. *m*-Methylanisole.

17. Z, *p*-methoxybenzyl alcohol, *p*-$CH_3OC_6H_4CH_2OH$.

18. (a) *tert*-Butyl ethyl ether; (b) *n*-propyl ether; (c) isopropyl ether.

19. AA, *p*-methylphenetole; BB, benzyl ethyl ether; CC, 3-phenyl-
    1-propanol.

CHAPTER 18

18.1 91 at 110°, 71 at 156°; association occurs even in vapor phase, de-
    creasing as temperature increases.

18.2 (a) Radical from decomposition of the peroxide abstracts an α-hydrogen from the acid to form a new radical which adds to the alkene; the resulting radical then abstracts an α-hydrogen from a second molecule of acid; and the chain continues by repetitions of these steps. (b) 2-Methyldecanoic acid; (c) 2,2-dimethyldodecanoic acid; (d) ethyl *n*-octylmalonate, n-$C_8H_{17}CH(COOEt)_2$.

18.3 (a) *tert*-Pentyl cation combines with carbon monoxide to yield an acylium ion, t-$C_5H_{11}-\overset{+}{C}\equiv O:$, which, upon hydration, yields the acid; (b) 2-methylbutanoic acid.

18.4 (a) *p*-Bromobenzoic acid; (b) *p*-bromophenylacetic acid.

18.5 Carbonate ion is a hybrid of three structures of equal stability, and each C—O bond is double in one structure and single in two, hence has less double bond character than the bonds in formate ion.

18.6 See Sec. 21.1.

18.7 (a) $F > Cl > Br > I$; (b) electron-withdrawing.

18.8 $^+OCH_3$ For anion, such a structure would involve separation of positive and *double* negative charges.

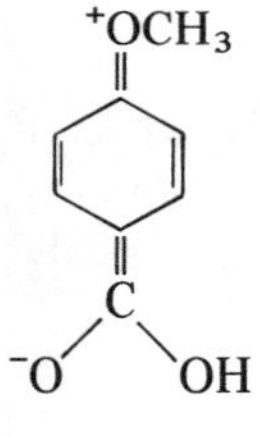

18.9 (a) C—OH bond; (b) C—OH bond of acid, CO—H bond of alcohol.

18.10 (a) $LiAlH_4$; PBr_3. (b) Product (a), Mg, anhyd. Et_2O; CO_2; acidify. (c) Product (a), Mg, anhyd. Et_2O; ethylene oxide; acidify. (d) Product (a), KOH(alc), heat. (e) Product (d), H_2, Ni, heat, pressure. (f) Product (d), Br_2/CCl_4; KOH(alc), heat; $NaNH_2$, heat. (g) Product (f), H_2O, H_2SO_4, $HgSO_4$. (h) Product (g), H_2, Ni, heat, pressure. (i) Product (g), NaOI; acidify. (j) Product (a), Mg, anhyd. Et_2O; CH_3CHO; acidify. (k) n-$C_{11}H_{23}CH_2MgBr$ (made in j), CH_3COCH_3; acidify.

18.11 (a) CH_3CH_2COOH; (b) *erythro*-2,3-dibromobutanoic acid (*erythro:* see page 247); (c) $C_6H_5CH=CHCOOH$; (d) γ-lactone (inner 5-ring ester); see page 674.

18.12 To prevent generation of HCN by action of strong acid on sodium cyanide.

18.13 (a) conc. HBr (excess); 2NaCN; H_2O, H^+, heat.   (b) $KMnO_4$, heat;
      (c) $2H_2$, Ni; $KMnO_4$, heat.

18.14 (a) Diester, $EtOOC(CH_2)_4COOEt$;   (b) monoester,
      $EtOOC(CH_2)_4COOH$;   (c) $HOCH_2CH_2CH_2CH_2OH$;
      (d) $HOOCCH_2CH_2CHBrCOOH$;   (e) p-$ClCOC_6H_4COCl$;
      (f) *racemic* HOOCCHBrCHBrCOOH.

18.15 —COOH is electron-withdrawing, acid-strengthening compared with
      —H or —CH_3.

18.16 Oxalic > malonic > succinic > glutaric. Decrease in inductive effect
      of one —COOH on the other with increase in distance between them.

18.17 (a) Cyclic diester (six-membered ring containing two oxygen atoms);
      (b) succinic anhydride (a cyclic anhydride);   (c) see page 1142.

18.18 Acids: soluble in cold conc. H_2SO_4; negative to $KMnO_4$, Br_2/CCl_4,
      and CrO_3/H_2SO_4; soluble in fuming sulfuric acid; $CHCl_3/AlCl_3$ test
      not applicable; explosive evolution of H_2 with Na metal.

18.19 *o*-Chlorobenzoic acid.

18.20 (a) 103;   (b) ethoxyacetic acid.

18.21 (a) Two, 83;   (b) N.E. = mol.wt./number acidic H per molecule;
      (c) 70, 57.

18.22 Sodium carbonate.

1. Formic, methanoic; acetic, ethanoic; propionic, propanoic; *n*-butyric,
    butanoic; *n*-valeric, pentanoic; *n*-caproic, hexanoic; *n*-caprylic, octanoic;
    n-capric, decanoic; lauric, dodecanoic; palmitic, hexadecanoic; stearic,
    octadecanoic.

2. (a) 3-Methylbutanoic acid;   (b) 2,2-dimethylpropanoic acid;
    (b) 2,3-dimethylhexanoic acid;   (d) α-methyl-γ-ethylcaprylic acid;
    (e) phenylethanoic acid;   (f) 4-phenylbutanoic acid;
    (g) hexanedioic acid;   (h) 4-methylbenzoic acid;
    (i) 1,2-benzenedicarboxylic acid;   (j) 1,3-benzenedicarboxylic acid;
    (k) 1,4-benzenedicarboxylic acid;   (l) 4-hydroxybenzoic acid;
    (m) potassium 2-methylbutanoate;   (n) magnesium α-chloropropionate;
    (o) *cis*-butenedioic acid;   (p) 2,3-dibromobutanedioic acid;
    (q) 2-methylpropanenitrile;   (r) 2,4-$(O_2N)_2C_6H_3CN$.

3. (a) $KMnO_4$, OH^-, heat; acidify.   (b) Mg, anhyd. ether; CO_2; acidify.

(c) H_2O, H^+, heat. (d) $KMnO_4$, H^+, heat. (e) H_2O, OH^-; acidify.
(f) NaOI; acidify.

4. (a) $KMnO_4$, H^+, heat. (b) HBr, heat; NaCN, warm; H_2O, H^+, heat.
(Cannot be used to prepare trimethylacetic acid.) (c) HBr, heat; Mg,
anhyd. ether; CO_2; acidify. (d) NaOI; acidify.

5. (a) H_2O, H^+, heat; $KMnO_4$, heat; acidify. (b) HCl, heat (to form
monohalide); NaCN; H_2O, H^+, heat; $KMnO_4$, heat; acidify. (c) HCl,
heat (to form dihalide); 2NaCN; H_2O, H^+, heat.

6. (a) PhCOOK; (b) $(PhCOO)_3Al$; (c) $(PhCOO)_2Ca$; (d) PhCOONa;
(e) $PhCOONH_4$; (g) $PhCH_2OH$; (i) PhCOCl; (j) PhCOCl; (k) PhCOCl;
(l) *m*-bromobenzoic acid; (n) *m*-nitrobenzoic acid; (o) *m*-carboxy-
benzenesulfonic acid; (q) *o*-carboxyphenylthallium ditrifluoroacetate;
(r) $PhCOOC_3H_7$. No reaction: f, h, m, p.

7. (a) C_4H_9COOK; (b) $(C_4H_9COO)_3Al$; (c) $(C_4H_9COO)_2Ca$;
(d) C_4H_9COONa; (e) $C_4H_9COONH_4$; (g) $C_4H_9CH_2OH$;
(i) C_4H_9COCl; (j) C_4H_9COCl; (k) C_4H_9COCl;
(m) $C_3H_7CHBrCOOH$; (r) $C_4H_9COOC_3H_7$. No reaction: f, h, l, n, o, p.

8. (a) EtOH, H^+, warm. (b) Thionyl chloride, heat. (c) Product (b),
$2NH_3$. (d) Mg metal. (e) $LiAlH_4$; acidify.

9. (a) NaOH. (b) PCl_5, heat. (c) Product (b), $2NH_3$. (d) NaOH; soda
lime, strong heat. (e) *n*-PrOH, H^+, warm. (f) Product (b), *p*-cresol,
OH^-. (g) Product (b), *m*-bromophenol, OH^-. (h) $LiAlH_4$; acidify.

10. (a) NaOH. (b) EtOH, H^+, warm. (c) $SOCl_2$, heat. (d) Product (c),
$2NH_3$. (e) Br_2, Fe. (f) HNO_3, H_2SO_4, warm. (g) $LiAlH_4$; acidify.
(h) Br_2, P, heat. (i) Product (h), excess NH_3. (j) Product (h), OH^-,
warm; acidify. (k) Product (h), CN^-, warm; H_2O, H^+, heat.

11. (a) Potassium benzoate; (b) 3-nitro-4-methylbenzoic acid;
(c) 1,4-butanediol; (d) benzyl benzoate, $C_6H_5COOCH_2C_6H_5$;
(e) *p*- and *o*-nitrobenzyl benzoate; (f) *o*-$HOOCCH_2C_6H_4Tl(OOCCF_3)_2$;
(g) cyclohexanecarboxylic acid; (h) ethyl cyclohexanecarboxylate;
(i) cyclohexanecarbonyl chloride; (j) *m*-methoxybenzoic acid;
(k) 1,3,5-benzenetricarboxylic acid; (l) isobutyl isobutyrate;
(m) 5- and 3-bromo-2-hydroxybenzoic acid; (n) *p*-nitrobenzyl acetate;
(o) stearic acid; (p) nonanoic acid and azelaic acid (1,9-nonanedioic
acid); (q) $C_5H_{11}CHO$, $OHCCH_2CHO$, $OHC(CH_2)_7COOH$;
(r) cyclohexanecarboxylic acid; (s) ethylene glycol dibenzoate,
$C_6H_5COOCH_2CH_2OOCC_6H_5$; (t) ethyl phthalate, *o*-$C_6H_4(COOEt)_2$;
(u) racemic *threo*-9,10-dibromooctadecanoic acid; (v) 9-octadecynoic

acid, $C_8H_{17}C\equiv C(CH_2)_7COOH$; (w) racemic *threo*-9,10-dihydroxyoc-
tadecanoic acid (*threo:* see page 247).

12. (a) *n*-PrMgBr, $^{14}CO_2$; acidify. (b) EtMgBr, $^{14}CO_2$; acidify; $LiAlH_4$;
acidify; PBr_3, heat; Mg, anhyd. ether; CO_2; acidify. (c) MeMgBr,
$^{14}CO_2$; acidify; $LiAlH_4$; acidify; PBr_3, heat; Mg, anhyd. ether; ethylene
oxide; acidify; $KMnO_4$, heat. (d) $^{14}CH_3OH$, HBr, heat; Mg, anhyd.
ether; HCHO; acidify; PBr_3, heat; Mg, anhyd. ether; ethylene oxide;
acidify; $KMnO_4$, heat.

13. $KMnO_4$, heat; acidify. (b) Cl_2, heat; CN^-; H_2O, H^+, heat. (c) Br_2, Fe;
Mg, anhyd. ether; CO_2; acidify. (d) Product (a), Cl_2, Fe, heat. (e) Cl_2,
Fe; $KMnO_4$, heat; acidify. (f) Br_2, Fe; Cl_2, heat; CN^-; H_2O, H^+, heat.
(g) Product (b), Cl_2, P.

14. (a) 2-Butanol, HBr, warm; Mg, anhyd. ether; CO_2; acidify; EtOH, acid,
warm. (b) Toluene, $KMnO_4$, heat; acidify; HNO_3, H_2SO_4, heat; HNO_3,
H_2SO_4, heat; PCl_5, heat. (c) As in 13(f); then Br_2, P; excess NH_3;
acidify. (d) *n*-PrOH, $K_2Cr_2O_7$, acid, heat; Br_2, P; OH^-; acidify.
(e) Toluene, fuming sulfuric acid; $KMnO_4$, heat; acidify. (f) *n*-BuOH,
HBr, heat; CN^-; H_2O, H^+, heat; Br_2, P; KOH, heat; acidify. (g) As in
13(c); then $SOCl_2$, heat; excess NH_3. (h) *n*-BuOH, HBr, heat; Mg,
anhyd. ether; ethylene oxide (from ethanol via ethylene); acidify;
benzoic acid (from toluene), H^+, warm. (i) As in 13(c); then Br_2, Fe,
heat. (j) Benzene, Br_2, Fe; Mg, anhyd. ether; CH_3CHO; acidify; HCl;
Mg, anhyd. ether; CO_2; acidify. (k) Toluene, HNO_3, H_2SO_4; Br_2, Fe;
$KMnO_4$, heat; acidify. (l) Toluene, CH_3Cl, $AlCl_3$; CH_3Cl, $AlCl_3$;
$KMnO_4$, heat; acidify.

15. (a) 2-Bromobutanoic acid > 3-bromobutanoic acid > 4-bromobutanoic
acid > butanoic acid; (b) 2,4,6-trichlorobenzoic acid > 2,4-dichloro-
benzoic acid > *p*-chlorobenzoic acid > benzoic acid; (c) *p*-nitrobenzoic
acid > benzoic acid > *p*-toluic acid; (d) α-chlorophenylacetic acid >
p-chlorophenylacetic acid > phenylacetic acid > α-phenylpropionic acid;
(e) *p*-nitrobenzoic acid > *p*-nitrophenylacetic acid > β-(*p*-nitrophenyl)-
propionic acid; (f) H_2SO_4 > CH_3COOH > H_2O > EtOH > $HC\equiv CH$ >
NH_3 > C_2H_6.

16. NaC_2H_5 > $NaNH_2$ > $NaC\equiv CH$ > NaOEt > NaOH > $NaOOCCH_3$ >
$NaHSO_4$.

17. *o*-Chlorobenzoic acid ($K_a = 120 \times 10^{-5}$) reacts with formate ion (a base)
to displace a weaker acid, formic acid ($K_a = 17.7 \times 10^{-5}$).

18. (a) MeOH > *n*-PrOH > *sec*-BuOH > *tert*-pentyl alcohol; (b) benzoic
acid > *o*-toluic acid > 2,6-dimethylbenzoic acid; (c) formic acid >

acetic acid > propionic acid > isobutyric acid > trimethylacetic acid.

19. A and B, *erythro* and *threo* α,β-dibromobutyric acid (*erythro* and *threo*:
see page 247); C, *meso*-tartaric acid, HOOCCHOHCHOHCOOH;

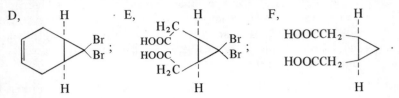

20. G, HC≡CMgBr; H, HC≡CCOOMgBr; I, HC≡CCOOH;
J, OHCCH₂COOH.

21. (a) NaHCO₃(aq); (b) NaHCO₃(aq); (c) NaHCO₃(aq); (d) AgNO₃;
(e) NaHCO₃(aq); (f) NaHCO₃(aq).

22. (a) Acid > salt; (b) salt > acid; (c) salt > acid; (d) acid > salt;
(e) salt > acid; (f) salt > acid; (g) basicity, salt > acid; acidity,
acid > salt. Same comparisons generally hold for acids and their salts.

23. (a) NaHCO₃(aq); separate layers; acidify aqueous layer, extract with
ether, dry, distill; dry and distill organic layer. (b) NaHCO₃(aq); separate layers; evaporate aqueous layer to dryness, add conc. H₂SO₄ to
residue, distill; dry and distill organic layer. (c) As in (b). (d) Ether;
filter; sodium benzoate remains on filter; evaporate filtrate, collect
residue.

24. (a) KMnO₄. (b) CrO₃/H₂SO₄. (c) Mesotartaric acid reacts with hot
KMnO₄; elemental analysis for other three acids. (d) Valeric acid gives
negative halogen test; use neutralization equivalents for others.
(e) Neutralization equivalents; or 3-nitrophthalic acid gives an anhydride
(m.p. 162°, neutral compound) when heated. (f) Cinnamic acid reacts
with KMnO₄; elemental analysis for the others. (g) *o*-Toluidine only
compound that contains nitrogen; α-phenylethyl chloride only compound that reacts with AgNO₃ to ppt. AgCl; 4-methylpentanoic acid
reacts with NaHCO₃(aq) with evolution of CO₂, and goes into solution;
two of the remaining compounds react with KMnO₄, and of these only
linalool reacts with CrO₃/H₂SO₄ and only β-chlorostyrene contains Cl;
of the remaining compounds, two contain Cl, and of these only
o-chloroanisole is soluble in cold conc. H₂SO₄; of the remaining compounds, only *cis*-decalin is insoluble in conc. H₂SO₄; of the remaining
two compounds, only the ether will give a positive Zeisel test
(page 570).

25. K, *m*-chlorobenzoic acid; confirm by amide (m.p. 134°). L, adipic acid or 2,4,6-trimethylbenzoic acid; distinguish by neutralization equivalent or *p*-nitrobenzyl ester. M, 2,5-dichlorobenzoic acid or *p*-chlorophenoxy-acetic acid; distinguish by amide. N, *trans*-crotonic acid or phenylacetic acid; distinguish by action of $KMnO_4$, or by oxidation of phenylacetic acid to benzoic acid (m.p. 122°). O, α-hydroxyisobutyric acid or β-iodopropionic acid; distinguish by elemental analysis. P, glycolic acid; confirm by amide or *p*-nitrobenzyl ester.

26. N.E. 165; *o*-nitrobenzoic acid.

27. Q, *m*-ethylbenzoic acid; R, isophthalic acid; S, ethylbenzene; T, benzoic acid; U, 3,5-dimethylbenzoic acid; V, 1,3,5-$C_6H_3(COOH)_3$.

28. Tropic acid, $C_6H_5CH(CH_2OH)COOH$; atropic acid, $C_6H_5C(=CH_2)COOH$; hydratropic acid, $C_6H_5CH(CH_3)COOH$.

29. (a) $CH_3CHClCOOH$; (b) $ClCH_2COOCH_3$; (c) $BrCH_2COOCH_2CH_3$;
$\quad\quad$ *a* $\quad$ *b* $\quad\quad$ *c* $\quad\quad\quad$ *b* $\quad\quad$ *a* $\quad\quad\quad$ *b* $\quad\quad$ *c* $\quad$ *a*

(d) $CH_3CH_2CHBrCOOH$; (e) $CH_3CH_2OCH_2COOH$.
$\quad$ *a* $\quad$ *b* $\quad$ *c* $\quad\quad$ *d* $\quad\quad$ *a* $\quad$ *b* $\quad$ *c* $\quad\quad$ *d*

30. (a) Crotonic acid; (b) mandelic acid; (c) *p*-nitrobenzoic acid.

CHAPTER 19

19.1 $RCH(OH)_2$.

19.2 See answer to Problem 7.5(a), page 231. Carry out hydrolysis at reflux (reduced pressure if temperature below 100° is desired) under a distilling column so that *sec*-BuOH—water azeotrope distills out as rapidly as the alcohol is formed; use a non-volatile acid (H_2SO_4, $HClO_4$) to catalyze the hydrolysis. After drying over anhyd. K_2CO_3, measure specific rotation of alcohol layer in a polarimeter, and compare the value obtained with the specific rotation of the alcohol used to form the ester in the first place.

19.3 No, because one has to make the cadmium compound from the Grignard reagent, and the nitro group would interfere with any attempts to form that reagent.

19.4 (a) Acetic, propionic, and *n*-butyric acids; (b) adipic acid (hexanedioic acid).

19.5 (a) and (b), one fraction, inactive, resolvable (racemic modification);

(c) one fraction, inactive, non-resolvable (single compound);
(d) two fractions, each active, each single compound (diastereomers);
(e) two fractions, each inactive, each resolvable (racemic modifications);   (f) no change.

19.6   (a) Oxidation of 1° alcohol to aldehyde; distill out aldehyde, the alcohol being higher boiling; or isolate aldehyde as bisulfite addition product.   (b) Reduction of aldehyde to 1° alcohol; shake mixture with $NaHSO_3$ (aq); separate alcohol from aqueous layer that contains the bisulfite addition product of the aldehyde.

19.7   Cyclohexanone reacts more rapidly, but the equilibrium favors the more slowly formed product derived from PhCHO.

19.8   High alcohol, low water concentrations shift hemiacetal–acetal and aldehyde–hemiacetal equilibria (page 642) to right; high water, low alcohol concentrations shift equilibria to left.

19.9   (a) Williamson synthesis of ethers;   (b) acetals (cyclic);   (c) HCHO and catechol; no reaction with base.

19.10   Convert PhCHO into water-soluble bisulfite addition product, leaving water-insoluble acetal untouched.

19.11   Acrolein acetal, $KMnO_4$ (cold dil. neut.); acidify. If acrolein itself were used, $KMnO_4$ would oxidize –CHO to –COOH.

19.12   Order of stability, and of rate of formation, of "carbonium" ion formed along with R'OH:

(a)
$$R-C\overset{OR'}{\underset{OR'}{\diagdown}} \Big]^+ > R-C\overset{^+OR'}{\underset{H}{\diagdown}} > R-CH_2^+ ;$$

from: ortho ester   acetal   ether

(b) $R_2C=\overset{+}{O}R' > RCH=\overset{+}{O}R' > H_2C=\overset{+}{O}R'$.

from: ketal   acetal   formal

In (b), R stabilizes carbonium ion (relative to reactant) more than H does because it (i) releases electrons, and (ii) is bigger and hence favors change from tetrahedral reactant to trigonal product.

19.13
$$\underset{H}{\overset{H}{R-C=O}} \overset{H^+}{\rightleftharpoons} \underset{H}{\overset{H}{R-C=\overset{+}{O}H}} \xrightarrow{H_2{}^{18}O} \underset{{}^{18}\overset{+}{O}H}{\overset{H}{R-C-OH}} \overset{-H^+}{\rightleftharpoons} \underset{{}^{18}OH}{\overset{H}{R-C-OH}}$$

$$R-\underset{\underset{^{18}OH}{|}}{\overset{\overset{H}{|}}{C}}-OH \overset{H^+}{\rightleftharpoons} R-\underset{\underset{^{18}OH}{|}}{\overset{\overset{H\quad H}{|\quad |}}{C}}-\overset{+}{OH} \overset{-H_2O}{\rightleftharpoons} R-\underset{\underset{^{18}OH^+}{|}}{\overset{\overset{H}{|}}{C}} \overset{-H^+}{\rightleftharpoons} R-\overset{\overset{H}{|}}{C}={}^{18}O$$

19.14 (a) Removal of proton from −OH by hydroxide ion; (b) loss of hydride ion yields resonance-stabilized carboxylate ion directly.

19.15 Use $R-\overset{\overset{D}{|}}{C}=O$, see if a second D shows up in alcohol, $R-\underset{\underset{D}{|}}{\overset{\overset{D}{|}}{C}}-OH$.

19.16 On both electronic and steric grounds (Sec. 19.8), one would expect Reaction (1) (page 644) to be *faster* for formaldehyde than for another aldehyde, and the position of *equilibrium* to lie farther to right. If (1) is rate-determining, formaldehyde is chief hydride-donor because it forms I faster than the other aldehyde does; if (2) is rate-determining, formaldehyde is chief hydride-donor because Equilibrium (1) provides more I derived from formaldehyde than from other aldehyde. (Kinetics studies indicate that (2) is rate-determining.)

19.17 Internal "crossed" Cannizzaro reaction:

$$Ph-\underset{\underset{O}{\|}}{\overset{\overset{H}{|}}{C}}-C=O \overset{OH^-}{\rightleftharpoons} Ph-\underset{\underset{O}{\|}}{\overset{\overset{H}{|}}{C}}-\underset{\underset{OH}{|}}{\overset{\overset{\cdot\cdot}{|}}{C}}-O^- \rightarrow Ph-\underset{\underset{-O}{|}}{\overset{\overset{H}{|}}{C}}-\underset{\underset{OH}{|}}{C}=O \rightarrow Ph-\underset{\underset{OH}{|}}{\overset{\overset{H}{|}}{C}}-COO^-.$$

19.18 $$Ph-\underset{\underset{O}{\|}}{C}-\underset{\underset{O}{\|}}{C}Ph \overset{OH^-}{\rightleftharpoons} Ph-\underset{\underset{O}{\|}}{C}-\underset{\underset{O}{|}}{\overset{\overset{Ph}{\cdot\cdot}}{C}}-OH \rightarrow Ph-\underset{\underset{-O}{|}}{\overset{\overset{Ph}{|}}{C}}-\underset{\underset{O}{\|}}{C}-OH \rightarrow Ph-\underset{\underset{OH}{|}}{\overset{\overset{Ph}{|}}{C}}-COO^-;$$

replacement of OH^- by OCH_3^- yields the ester by the same route.

19.19 $KMnO_4$: alkenes, alkynes, dienes, aldehydes, (arenes, if heated), (1° and 2° alcohols if heated), (ketones cleaved if hot, acidic). CrO_3/H_2SO_4: hot reagent, same as $KMnO_4$; cold reagent, only 1° and 2° alcohols give immediate reaction. Tollens': aldehydes.

19.20 Oxime formation consumes the base, hydroxylamine; change in pH shown by change in color of indicator.

19.21 Cold conc. H_2SO_4: aldehydes, ketones soluble; cold dil. neut. $KMnO_4$: aldehydes decolorize, give MnO_2, ketones negative; Br_2/CCl_4: slow substitution; CrO_3/H_2SO_4: aldehydes positive, ketones negative; $Ag(NH_3)_2^+$: aldehydes positive, ketones negative; Schiff: water-soluble aldehydes give color, ketones negative.

1. (a) $CH_3CH_2CH_2CH_2CHO$, n-valeraldehyde, pentanal; $CH_3CH_2CH_2COCH_3$, methyl n-propyl ketone, 2-pentanone; $CH_3CH_2COCH_2CH_3$, ethyl ketone, 3-pentanone; $CH_3CH_2CH(CH_3)CHO$, α-methylbutyraldehyde, 2-methylbutanal; $(CH_3)_2CHCH_2CHO$, isovaleraldehyde, 3-methylbutanal; $(CH_3)_2CHCOCH_3$, methyl isopropyl ketone, 3-methyl-2-butanone; $(CH_3)_3CCHO$, trimethylacetaldehyde, 2,2-dimethylpropanal. (b) $PhCH_2CHO$, phenylacetaldehyde, phenyl-ethanal; $PhCOCH_3$, acetophenone; o-$CH_3C_6H_4CHO$, o-tolualdehyde; m-$CH_3C_6H_4CHO$, m-tolualdehyde; p-$CH_3C_6H_4CHO$, p-tolualdehyde.

2. (a) CH_3COCH_3; (b) $PhCHO$; (c) $CH_3COCH_2CH(CH_3)_2$; (d) $(CH_3)_3CCHO$; (e) $PhCOCH_3$; (f) $PhCH=CHCHO$; (g) $(CH_3)_2CHCH_2CH_2CHO$; (h) $PhCH_2CHO$; (i) $PhCOPh$; (j) $C_2H_5CH(CH_3)CH_2CH(CH_3)CHO$; (k) $C_2H_5CH(CH_3)COCH_3$; (l) $CH_3CH=CHCHO$; (m) $(CH_3)_2C=CHCOCH_3$; (n) $PhCH=CHCOPh$; (o) $CH_3CH_2CHOHCH_2CHO$; (p) $PhCH_2COPh$; (q) o-HOC_6H_4CHO; (r) $(p$-$HOC_6H_4)_2CO$; (s) m-$CH_3C_6H_4CHO$.

3. (a) $PhCH_2COO^-$ and Ag mirror; (b) $PhCH_2COOH$; (c) $PhCH_2COOH$; (d) $PhCOOH$; (e) $PhCH_2CH_2OH$; (f) $PhCH_2CH_2OH$; (g) $PhCH_2CH_2OH$; (h) $PhCH_2CHOHPh$; (i) $PhCH_2CHOHCH(CH_3)_2$; (j) $PhCH_2CHOHSO_3Na$; (k) $PhCH_2CHOHCN$; (l) $PhCH_2CH=NOH$; (m) $PhCH_2CH=NNHPh$; (n) $PhCH_2CH=NNHAr$; (o) $PhCH_2CH=NNHCONH_2$; (p) $PhCH_2CH(OEt)_2$.

4. (a) No reaction; (b) no reaction; (c) no reaction; (d) adipic acid; (e) cyclohexanol; (f) cyclohexanol; (g) cyclohexanol; (h) 1-phenyl-cyclohexanol; (i) 1-isopropylcyclohexanol; (j) sodium 1-hydroxy-1-cyclohexanesulfonate; (k) cyclohexanone cyanohydrin; (l) cyclohexanoneoxime; (m) cyclohexanone phenylhydrazone; (n) cyclohexanone 2,4-dinitrophenylhydrazone; (o) cyclohexanone semicarbazone; (p) would predict no reaction; actually cyclohexanone ketal is formed.

5. (a) $PhCH_2OH$, $PhCOONa$; (b) $PhCH_2OH$, $HCOONa$; (c) $PhCHOHCN$; (d) $PhCHOHCOOH$; (e) $PhCHOHCH_3$; (f) $PhCH=CH_2$; (g) $PhCHOH^{14}CH(CH_3)_2$; (h) $PhCH^{18}O$.

6. (a) Cat. H_2 or $LiAlH_4$. (b) $KMnO_4$, heat. (c) CN^-, H^+; H_2O, H^+, heat. (d) MeMgBr; acidify. (e) PhMgBr; acidify. (f) Product (d), CrO_3/H_2SO_4. (g) Product (a), product (b), H^+, warm. (h) $(CH_3)_2CHMgBr$, then H_2O.

7. (a) Zn(Hg), HCl. (b) NaOI; acidify. (c) Cat. H_2 or $LiAlH_4$.
    (d) EtMgBr; acidify. (e) PhMgBr; acidify. (f) CN^-, H^+; H_2O, H^+, heat.

8. (a) *iso*-BuOH, $K_2Cr_2O_7$, H^+. (b) PhMgBr, ethylene oxide (from EtOH
    via ethylene); acidify; $K_2Cr_2O_7$, H^+. (c) Toluene, Br_2/Fe; separate
    p-isomer; CrO_3, HOAc, Ac_2O; H_2O, H^+, heat. (d) *sec*-BuOH,
    CrO_3/H_2SO_4. (e) $PhCH_3$, $2HNO_3$, H_2SO_4, heat; $2Cl_2$, heat; H_2O,
    warm. (f) p-$O_2NC_6H_4COOH$ (page 345), $SOCl_2$, heat; C_6H_6, $AlCl_3$;
    H^+. (g) $(CH_3)_2CHCOOH$ (from iso-BuOH), $SOCl_2$, heat; Et_2Cd (from
    EtMgBr). (h) MeMgBr, $PhCH_2CHO$ (from b); acidify; neut. $KMnO_4$,
    warm. (i) m-$O_2NC_6H_4COOH$ (page 345), $SOCl_2$, heat; C_6H_6, $AlCl_3$;
    H^+. (j) *n*-BuOH, $KMnO_4$, heat; acidify; $SOCl_2$, warm; toluene, $AlCl_3$;
    H^+. (k) *sec*-BuMgBr, HCHO (from MeOH); acidify; CrO_3/H_2SO_4.
    (l) *iso*-BuMgBr, CO_2; acidify; $SOCl_2$, heat; n-Bu_2Cd (from *n*-BuMgBr).
    (m) Toluene, HNO_3, H_2SO_4; separate *p*-isomer; $K_2Cr_2O_7$, H_2SO_4, heat;
    $SOCl_2$, heat; Me_2Cd (from MeMgBr). (n) *m*-Nitrobenzoic acid (page
    345), $SOCl_2$, heat; toluene, $AlCl_3$; acidify. (o) *p*-Nitrobenzoic acid
    (page 345), $SOCl_2$, heat; Et_2Cd (from EtMgBr).

9. (a) *n*-BuOH, $KMnO_4$, heat; acidify; $SOCl_2$, heat; C_6H_6, $AlCl_3$; acidify;
    Zn(Hg), HCl, heat. (b) *n*-PrCHO (from *n*-BuOH, $K_2Cr_2O_7$, H^+), CN^-,
    H^+; H_2O, H^+, heat. (c) *iso*-BuMgBr, *n*-PrCHO (made in b); acidify; H^+,
    heat; cat. H_2. (d) *iso*-BuOH, $KMnO_4$, heat; acidify; $SOCl_2$; *iso*-Bu_2Cd
    (from *iso*-BuOH via *iso*-BuMgBr); MeMgI; acidify. (e) Toluene, HNO_3,
    H_2SO_4; separate *p*-isomer; $2Cl_2$, heat; H_2O; CN^-, H^+; H_2O, H^+, heat.
    (f) Acetic acid (from EtOH), PCl_5, heat; C_6H_6, $AlCl_3$; acidify;
    $PhCH_2MgCl$; acidify. (g) PhCOOH (from toluene), PCl_5, heat; PhBr,
    $AlCl_3$, heat; acidify; EtMgBr; acidify. (h) *iso*-BuMgBr, CO_2; acidify;
    Br_2, P; base, warm; acidify.

10. A, $PhC(CH_3)_2CH_2COCl$; B,

    ;

    D, $PhCH_2CH_2C(OH)(CH_3)_2$.

11. If allowed to remain in reaction mixture, RCHO reacts with unconsumed
    RCH_2OH to form the hemiacetal, $RCH(OH)OCH_2R$. The —CHOH— of
    this is rapidly oxidized to —CO—, giving the ester $RCO-OCH_2R$.

12. See Figure 34.6, page 1090. I is D-(—)tartaric acid; J is *meso*-tartaric
    acid.

13. (a) K is bicyclic ketal. (b) Too hard to form $-C(CH_3)_2-$ bridge be-
    tween *trans* oxygens.

14. $PhCHO \xrightleftharpoons{^{18}OH^-} Ph-\overset{\overset{\displaystyle H}{|}}{\underset{\underset{\displaystyle {}^{18}OH}{|}}{C}}-O^- \xrightleftharpoons{H_2O} Ph-\overset{\overset{\displaystyle H}{|}}{\underset{\underset{\displaystyle {}^{18}OH}{|}}{C}}-OH \xrightleftharpoons{-H^+} Ph-\overset{\overset{\displaystyle H}{|}}{\underset{\underset{\displaystyle {}^{18}O_-}{|}}{C}}-OH$

$$\xrightleftharpoons{-OH^-} PhCH^{18}O.$$

15. $R-\overset{\overset{\displaystyle H}{|}}{C}=\overset{\overset{\displaystyle H}{|}}{C}-OR' \xrightleftharpoons{H^+} R-\overset{\overset{\displaystyle H}{|}}{\underset{\underset{\displaystyle H}{|}}{C}}-\overset{+}{C}=OR' \xrightleftharpoons{H_2O} RCH_2-\overset{\overset{\displaystyle H}{|}}{\underset{\underset{\displaystyle {}^+OH_2}{|}}{C}}-OR' \xrightleftharpoons{-H^+} RCH_2-\overset{\overset{\displaystyle H}{|}}{\underset{\underset{\displaystyle OH}{|}}{C}}-OR'$

Hemiacetal

$RCH_2-\overset{\overset{\displaystyle H}{|}}{\underset{\underset{\displaystyle OH}{|}}{C}}-OR' \xrightleftharpoons{H^+} RCH_2-\overset{\overset{\displaystyle H}{|}}{\underset{\underset{\displaystyle \overset{+}{O}H}{|}}{C}}-OR' \xrightleftharpoons{-R'OH} RCH_2-\overset{\overset{\displaystyle H}{|}}{C}=\overset{+}{O}H \xrightleftharpoons{-H^+} RCH_2CHO$

Hemiacetal cleaved with great ease.

16. (a) $H_2O + ROBs \xrightarrow{\text{Inversion}} H_2\overset{+}{O}R \rightarrow OBs^-$

$$\rightarrow H^+ + ROH$$
Inversion

$+ ROBs \xrightarrow{\text{Inversion}}$

Inversion | H_2O

$+ R\overset{+}{O}H_2 \rightarrow H^+ + ROH$
Net retention

(b) (1) $CH_3-\overset{\overset{\displaystyle CH_3}{|}}{C}=O + ROBs \rightarrow CH_3-\overset{\overset{\displaystyle CH_3}{|}}{C}=\overset{+}{O}R + OBs^-$

$\downarrow CH_3OH$

$CH_3-\overset{\overset{\displaystyle CH_3}{|}}{\underset{\underset{\underset{\displaystyle H}{|}}{\displaystyle CH_3\overset{+}{O}}}{C}}-OR \rightarrow CH_3-\overset{\overset{\displaystyle CH_3}{|}}{\underset{\underset{\displaystyle CH_3O}{|}}{C}}-OR + H^+$

I
Mixed ketal

$$(2)\ \text{I} + \text{H}^+ \rightarrow \underset{\underset{\text{CH}_3\text{O}}{|}}{\overset{\overset{\text{CH}_3}{|}}{\text{CH}_3-\overset{+}{\underset{|}{\text{C}}}-\overset{+}{\text{O}}\text{R}}} \rightarrow \underset{\underset{\text{CH}_3\text{O}^+}{\|}}{\overset{\overset{\text{CH}_3}{|}}{\text{CH}_3-\text{C}}} + \text{ROH}$$

2-Octanol

↓ CH$_3$OH

$$\underset{\underset{\underset{\text{H}}{|}}{\overset{\text{CH}_3\text{O}^+}{|}}}{\overset{\overset{\text{CH}_3}{|}}{\text{CH}_3-\text{C}-\text{OCH}_3}} \rightarrow \underset{\underset{\text{CH}_3\text{O}}{|}}{\overset{\overset{\text{CH}_3}{|}}{\text{CH}_3-\text{C}-\text{OCH}_3}} + \text{H}^+$$

II

Ketal

$$(3)\ \text{I} + \text{H}_2\text{O} + \text{H}^+ \rightarrow (\text{CH}_3)_2\text{C=O} + \text{ROH} + \text{CH}_3\text{OH}$$

↳ 2,4-dinitrophenylhydrazone

Mixed ketal I is formed (1) and, in presence of H$^+$ formed along with it, undergoes methanolysis (2) to yield 2-octanol (and ketal II). When the base pyridine is present to consume H$^+$, mixed ketal I persists and is the substance isolated in impure form; it contains no carbonyl group but, in the acidic 2,4-dinitrophenylhydrazine solution, is hydrolyzed (3) to acetone, which then gives a 2,4-dinitrophenylhydrazone.

17. $\text{I} + \text{Br}_2 \rightleftarrows \text{CH}_3\overset{+}{\text{O}}$=⟨⟩$\overset{\text{Br}}{\underset{}{\text{CHOH}}}$—⟨O⟩$\text{G}$ + Br$^-$ *(reversible)*

↓

II + G ⟨O⟩ $\underset{\underset{\text{H}}{|}}{\text{C}=\overset{+}{\text{O}}\text{H}}$ (electron-release by G sta-
bilizes oxonium ion, and
transition state leading
to it)

↓ − H$^+$

III

18. Hydride transfer from Ph$_2$CHO$^-$ to excess PhCHO;

$$\text{PhCHO} \xrightarrow{\text{PhMgBr}} \underset{\underset{\text{Ph}}{|}}{\text{Ph}-\overset{\overset{\text{H}}{|}}{\text{C}}-\text{O}^-} + \underset{\underset{\text{H}}{|}}{\text{Ph}-\text{C}=\text{O}} \rightarrow \underset{\underset{\text{O}}{\|}}{\text{Ph}-\text{C}-\text{Ph}} + \text{PhCH}_2\text{O}^-$$

↓ H$_2$O

PhCH$_2$OH

19. (a) Isoeugenol, see page 791; vanillin, see page 792; L, acetate of isoeugenol; M, acetate of vanillin.   (b) Shift of double bond into

conjugation with ring (see Sec. 12.16). (c) KOH, strong heat; $K_2Cr_2O_7$, H^+, warm.

20. Protonated aldehyde is electrophile, double bond is nucleophile; ring closure gives six-membered ring; hydration of resulting carbonium ion produces diol.

21. Chair: in N, all $-CCl_3$ equatorial; in O, two equatorial, one axial.

22.

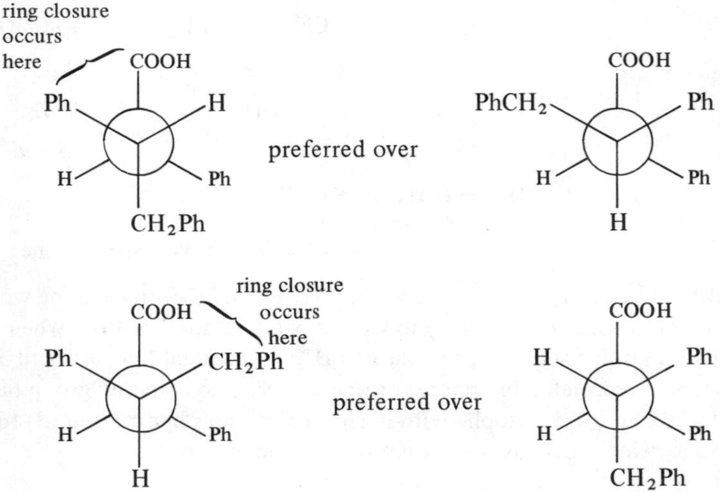

ring closure occurs here

Ph — COOH — H — H — Ph — CH_2Ph preferred over   PhCH$_2$ — COOH — Ph — H — Ph — H

ring closure occurs here

Ph — COOH — CH_2Ph — H — Ph — H   preferred over   H — COOH — Ph — H — Ph — CH_2Ph

23. (a)

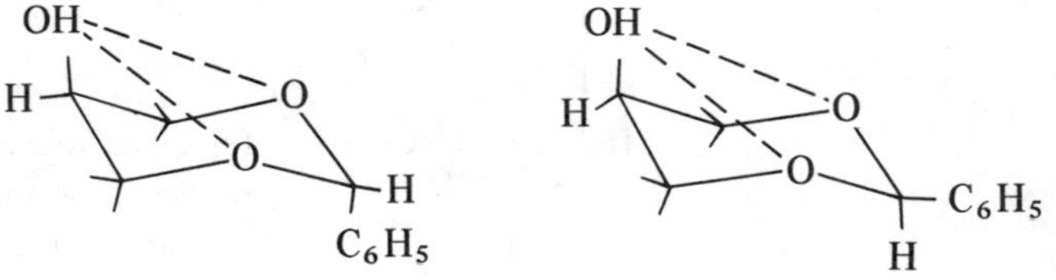

OH — H — O — O — H — C_6H_5

trans

OH — H — O — O — C_6H_5 — H

cis

(b) *trans*-isomer; intramol. H-bonding.

24. (a) Tollens' reagent; (b) Tollens' reagent; (c) 2,4-dinitrophenylhydrazine; (d) iodoform test; (e) Schiff or Tollens test; (f) Tollens test; (g) acid, then Schiff or Tollens test; (h) iodoform test; (i) 2,4-dinitrophenylhydrazine, or CrO_3/H_2SO_4; (j) acid, then Schiff or Tollens test; (k) acid and heat, then Schiff or Tollens test.

25. (a) Acetophenone gives a positive iodoform test; phenylacetaldehyde gives positive Tollens test; oxidize the isomeric tolualdehydes to the

toluic or phthalic acids and identify by m.p.   (b) *n*-Caprylic acid gives CO_2 with $NaHCO_3$(aq); the methyl ketone gives a positive iodoform test; the hydrocarbon is insol. in cold conc. H_2SO_4; the ester dissolves slowly when heated with NaOH(aq); the alcohol can be oxidized to PhCOOH (m.p. 122°).   (c) Isophorone decolorizes Br_2/CCl_4; *n*-dodecane is insol. in cold conc. H_2SO_4; ethyl benzoate and *m*-cresyl acetate dissolve slowly when heated with NaOH(aq), but of these only ethyl benzoate yields a ppt. (of PhCOOH) when the alkaline mixture is acidified; the alcohol gives an immediate green color with CrO_3/H_2SO_4.   (d) The benzylic chloride gives AgCl with $AgNO_3$; the ketone gives a positive iodoform test; the ester slowly dissolves in hot NaOH(aq); the nitro compound gives a positive test for N after sodium fusion.

26. $(CH_3)_2C=CHCH_2CH_2C(CH_3)=CHCHO$; citral *a* has H and CH_3 *trans,* citral *b* has H and CH_3 *cis.*

27.   Carvotanacetone, 5-isopropyl-2-methyl-2-cyclohexen-1-one.

28.   (a) 2-Butanone;   (b) isobutyraldehyde;   (c) 3-buten-2-ol.

29.   (a) 2-Pentanone;   (b) methyl isopropyl ketone;   (c) methyl ethyl ketone.

30.   P, *p*-methoxybenzaldehyde;   Q, *p*-methoxyacetophenone; R, isobutyrophenone.

CHAPTER 20

20.1   (a) Carbonyl addition of OH^-; CX_3^- good leaving group; net result is substitution;   (b) carbonyl addition of NH_2^-; $(C_6H_4F)^-$ better leaving group than $(C_6H_5)^-$.

20.2   The —COOH groups are the same distance apart in *cis-* and *trans-*1,2-cyclohexanedicarboxylic acids, and the ring is flexible enough to take up strain of formation of cyclic anhydride from either acid.

20.3   Maleic acid is *cis-* and fumaric acid is *trans-*butenedioic acid, HOOCCH=CHCOOH.

20.4   G, naphthalene. See Fig. 30.2, page 987.

20.5   Final product is 1-phenylnaphthalene. Compare Problem 30.18i (page 988).

20.6   9,10-Anthraquinone (see Sec. 30.18). Friedel-Crafts acylation to give a cyclic ketone.

20.7   (a) *o*-(*p*-Toluyl)benzoic acid (page 993);
(b) 2-methyl-9,10-anthraquinone (page 993).

20.8   (a) *cis*-Acid: the only one capable of forming a cyclic anhydride.
(b) In both acids, the two —COOH groups are the same distance apart.   (c) Yes.

20.9   (±)-*sec*-BuOH and phthalic acid give (±)-*sec*-butyl hydrogen phthalate, which still contains —COOH. This becomes (±)-HA of page 237. After separation of (+)-HA from (−)-HA, each ester is hydrolyzed by base (with cleavage as in Sec. 20.17) to give one of the enantiomeric alcohols.

20.10   Analogous to synthesis of phthalimide on page 672.

20.11   Stabilization of anion of phthalimide by accommodation of negative charge by nitrogen and two electronegative oxygens is greater than stabilization of anion of benzamide (nitrogen and one oxygen) or of ammonia (nitrogen, no oxygen).

20.12   The mixture is shaken with benzene which extracts ester and benzoic acid; treatment of the benzene extract with aqueous sodium carbonate removes benzoic acid as water-soluble sodium salt; distillation of wet benzene layer removes water and benzene first, and the dry ester is finally collected at $200°$.

20.13   (a) A cyclic diester with a six-membered ring containing two oxygen atoms.   (b) $\sim\!\!\sim\!\text{O(CH}_2)_9\text{COO(CH}_2)_9\text{COO(CH}_2)_9\text{CO}\!\sim\!\!\sim$.

20.14   (a) Electron withdrawal by G disperses developing negative charge on oxygen (cf. page 662).   (b) Activating; deactivating; deactivating.
(c) *p*-Nitrophenyl acetate > phenyl acetate > *p*-methylphenyl acetate > *p*-aminophenyl acetate.

20.15   (a) Steric effect, and electron release by alkyl groups.   (b) Methyl formate > methyl acetate > methyl propionate > methyl isobutyrate > methyl trimethylacetate.

20.16   Basicity of the leaving group is one factor: $Cl^- < RCOO^- < OR^- < NH_2^-$.

20.17   Structure II in Sec. 20.17.

20.18   Crowding in the tetrahedral intermediates by bulky groups makes them less stable, and the corresponding transition states more difficult to achieve, thus decreasing reaction rates.

20.19 (a) Hydrolysis of the ester of a 3° alcohol apparently proceeds via a 3° cation, acetic acid being split off intact. Because there is some shielding by the departing group, complete racemization of the optically active ester cannot take place. (b) The ease of formation of a 3° cation via an S_N1 mechanism, and the difficulty of bimolecular attack at the carbonyl carbon of a 3° ester, make these results what we might have expected.

20.20 (a) n-BuCOOH, $SOCl_2$; Et_2Cd; EtMgBr; acidify. (b) n-BuCOOH, CH_3OH, H^+; 2EtMgBr; acidify.

20.21 (a) Esters of formic acid, HCOOR. (b) HCOOH, CH_3OH, H^+; n-PrMgBr (from n-PrOH); acidify.

20.22 1-Octadecanol and 1-butanol.

20.23 (a) Phosgene, 2-pentanol (one mole); NH_3. (b) Phosgene, $PhCH_2OH$ (one mole).

20.24 Great resonance stabilization of cation, $[C(NH_2)_3]^+$, by contribution from three equivalent structures, with accommodation of positive charge by three nitrogens.

20.25 $\left[\,^=:\ddot{N}–C\equiv N:\quad :N\equiv C–\ddot{N}:^=\quad ^-:\ddot{N}=C=\ddot{N}:^-\,\right]$. Linear; bonds of equal length (longer than triple, shorter than single); charge equally distributed between nitrogens.

20.26 Hydrolysis of nitrile and amide; urea (intermediate), calcium carbonate, ammonia are products.

20.27 (a) Carbon-nitrogen triple bond (nitrile group); (b) nucleophilic addition (followed by tautomerization). (c) Water, methanol, hydrogen sulfide, ammonia are nucleophilic reagents that add to the carbon-nitrogen triple bond of cyanamide. In acid, protonation of $\equiv N$ occurs first; in aqueous base, OH^- is nucleophile.

20.28 (a) RCOCl; (b) $RCOO^-NH_4^+$, $RCONH_2$, RCN, amides of low mol. wt. amines; (c) $RCOO^-NH_4^+$; (d) $(RCO)_2O$; (e) RCOOR′.

20.29 (a) 102; (b) isopropyl acetate, n-butyl formate, isobutyl formate, *sec*-butyl formate, *tert*-butyl formate, ethyl propionate, methyl n-butyrate, methyl isobutyrate; (c) 4; (d) no, because of the greater number of possibilities.

20.30 (a) Two, 97; (b) S.E. = mol.wt./number ester groups per molecule; (c) 297.

1. (a) Methyl *n*-butyrate, methyl isobutyrate, ethyl propionate, *n*-propyl acetate, isopropyl acetate, *n*-butyl formate, isobutyl formate, *sec*-butyl formate, *tert*-butyl formate; (b) methyl benzoate, phenyl acetate, benzyl formate, *o*-cresyl formate, *m*-cresyl formate, *p*-cresyl formate; (c) methyl pentanedioate; methyl methylsuccinate; methyl ethyl-malonate.

2. (a) *n*-Butyric acid; (b) isopropyl *n*-butyrate; (c) *p*-nitrophenyl *n*-butyrate; (d) *n*-butyramide; (e) *n*-propyl *p*-tolyl ketone (*p*-methyl-*n*-butyrophenone); (f) no reaction; (g) sodium *n*-butyrate; (h) AgCl + ethyl *n*-butyrate; (i) N-methyl-*n*-butyramide; (j) N,N-dimethyl-*n*-butyramide; (k) no reaction; (l) N-phenyl-*n*-butyramide (*n*-butyranilide); (m) *n*-butyrophenone (*n*-propyl phenyl ketone); (n) *n*-propyldiphenylcarbinol.

3. In (b), (c), (e), and (l) an equimolar amount of acetic acid is formed along with the indicated product. (a) Two moles of acetic acid; (b) isopropyl acetate; (c) *p*-nitrophenyl acetate; (d) acetamide and ammonium acetate; (e) methyl *p*-tolyl ketone; (f) no reaction; (g) sodium acetate; (h) ethyl acetate and silver acetate; (i) N-methyl-acetamide and methylammonium acetate; (j) N,N-dimethylacetamide and dimethylammonium acetate; (k) no reaction; (l) acetanilide (N-phenylacetamide).

4. (a) Sodium succinate; (b) $NH_4OOC(CH_2)_2CONH_2$; (c) $HOOC(CH_2)_2CONH_2$; (d) succinimide; (e) $HOOC(CH_2)_2COOCH_2Ph$, benzyl hydrogen succinate; (f) $p\text{-}CH_3C_6H_4COCH_2CH_2COOH$; (g) N-phenylsuccinimide.

5. (a) $PhCH_2COOH + NH_4Cl$; (b) $PhCH_2COONa + NH_3$.

6. (a) $PhCH_2COOH + NH_4Cl$; (b) $PhCH_2COONa + NH_3$.

7. In each case an equimolar amount of methanol is formed along with the indicated product. (a) *n*-Butyric acid; (b) potassium *n*-butyrate; (c) isopropyl *n*-butyrate; (d) benzyl *n*-butyrate; (e) *n*-butyramide; (f) *n*-propyldiphenylcarbinol; (g) *n*-propyldiisobutylcarbinol; (h) *n*-butyl alcohol; (i) *n*-butyl alcohol; (j) *n*-butyl alcohol.

8. (a) CH_3Br, $H_2{}^{18}O$; benzoyl chloride. (b) Benzonitrile, $H_2{}^{18}O$, H^+, heat; $SOCl_2$, heat; methanol. (To conserve $H_2{}^{18}O$, a better way: benzotrichloride + one mole $H_2{}^{18}O$ gives labeled acid chloride directly.) (c) $CH_3{}^{18}OH$ from (a), $PhC^{18}OCl$ from (b). Hydrolysis of $PhCO^{18}OCH_3$ gives $CH_3{}^{18}OH$; hydrolysis of $PhC^{18}OOCH$ gives CH_3OH.

9. (a) $MeMgBr$, $^{14}CO_2$; acidify; $SOCl_2$, heat; Et_2Cd. (b) $^{14}CH_3OH$,

PBr_3; Mg, anhyd. ether; $CdCl_2$; propionyl chloride. (c) MeMgBr, $^{14}CO_2$; acidify; $LiAlH_4$; PBr_3; Mg, anhyd. ether; $CdCl_2$; acetyl chloride. (d) $^{14}CH_3OH$, PBr_3; Mg, anhyd. ether; HCHO; acidify; PBr_3; Mg, anhyd. ether; $CdCl_2$; acetyl chloride. (e) PhMgBr, $^{14}CO_2$; acidify; $SOCl_2$, heat; Me_2Cd; Zn(Hg), HCl, heat. (f) $^{14}CH_3OH$, PBr_3; Mg, anhyd. ether; $CdCl_2$; benzoyl chloride; Zn(Hg), HCl, heat. (g) CH_3CN, $H_2^{18}O$, H^+, heat; $SOCl_2$, heat; Et_2Cd.

10. (a) $HOCH_2CH_2CH_2CONH_2$; (b) $HOCH_2CH_2CH_2CH_2OH$; (c) $HOCH_2CH_2CH_2COOEt$.

11. Of the three steps, first and third cannot involve cleavage of *sec*-Bu—O bond. Inversion *must* have occurred in attack by benzoate ion on *sec*-butyl tosylate, evidently an S_N2 reaction.

12. Bimolecular attack at carbonyl carbon and retention, in 5N NaOH; S_N1, via a resonance-stabilized allylic ion (the same from both esters), with racemization, in dil. NaOH.

13. The toluates and phenylacetate can be distinguished by hydrolysis and determination of m.p. of the resulting acid. The two benzoates can be distinguished by saponification equivalents, or by m.p. of 3,5-dinitro-benzoate ester of the alcohol formed upon hydrolysis. Benzyl acetate is the only one that gives a liquid, water-soluble acid upon hydrolysis.

14. (a) $NaHCO_3$(aq); (b) EtOH gives pleasant smelling ester with RCOCl; RCOCl also gives CO_2 from $NaHCO_3$(aq); (c) NaOH, heat, test for NH_3 by litmus; (d) Br_2/CCl_4, or $KMnO_4$; (e) NaOH, heat, test for NH_3 by litmus, and see slow dissolution of nitrile; (f) $NaHCO_3$(aq), warm; (g) CrO_3/H_2SO_4; (h) NH_4 salt gives immediate evolution of NH_3 by action of cold NaOH(aq); (i) alcoholic $AgNO_3$.

15. (a) $NaHCO_3$(aq); separate layers; acidify squeous layer, collect benzoic acid on filter; dry organic layer, distill ester. (b) $NaHCO_3$(aq); separate layers; evaporate aqueous layer to dryness, add H_2SO_4, distill out *n*-valeric acid; dry organic layer, distill nitrile. (c) Ether; collect ammonium benzoate on filter; evaporate filtrate to dryness.

16. THP ester formed by acid-catalyzed addition of RCOOH to double bond, made easy by stability of intermediate cation, actually an oxonium ion.

Acid-catalyzed hydrolysis is reverse of this process, easy for the same reason.

17. A is racemic modification; it gives monolactone I, in which —COOH
    and —OH are *cis* and can react to form second lactone ring.   B is *meso*;
    it would give monolactone II.

and enantiomer   and enantiomer

I   II

18. C, Na_2CO_3;   D, ethyl urethane, $H_2NCOOC_2H_5$;   E, PhMgBr;
    F, $PhCH_2CH_2OH$;   G, $PhCH_2CH_2Br$;   H, $PhCH_2CH_2CN$;
    I, $PhCH_2CH_2COOH$;   J, $PhCH_2CH_2COCl$;   K, 1-indanone (see Problem
    10(o), page 723;   L, 1-indanol (alcohol related to K);   M, indene (see
    answer to Problem 26, Chapter 12);   N, *trans*-2-methyl-1-cyclohexyl
    acetate;   O, *trans*-2-methylcyclohexanol.

19. (a) Progesterone (below).   P, acetate of stigmasterol;   Q, ring dibromide
    of P;   R, acid from cleavage by ozonolysis at double bond in side chain;
    S, debromination product from R;   T, ethyl ester of acid S;   U, 3°
    alcohol from Grignard on T;   V, dehydration of 3° alcohol U;   W, ring
    dibromide followed by oxidative cleavage at side-chain double bond to
    give methyl ketone at C-17;   X, debromination product from W;
    Y, alcohol from hydrolysis of acetate;   Z, ring dibromide followed by
    oxidation to ketone at C-3; final step, debromination of Z.   (b) Pro-
    gesterone has double bond conjugated with C-3 ketone group; in last
    step, double bond has shifted to yield more stable product.

Progesterone

20. AA, 1,3-propanediol;   BB, 1,2-propanediol;   CC, 2-methoxyethanol;
    DD, dimethoxymethane (dimethylacetal of formaldehyde);
    EE, α-hydroxypropionaldehyde;   FF, hydroxyacetone (α-hydroxy-
    ketones reduce Tollens' reagent);   GG, β-hydroxypropionaldehyde;
    HH, propionic acid;   II, ethyl formate;   JJ, methyl acetate;
    KK, *cis*-1,2-cyclopropanediol;

LL, (epoxide structure with O) ; MM, $CH_2-CH-CH_2OH$ (with O bridging the first two carbons).

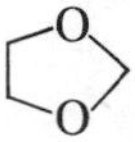

21. (a) Methyls are *trans* in NN, PP; *cis* in OO, QQ, RR.   (b) NN is resolvable.

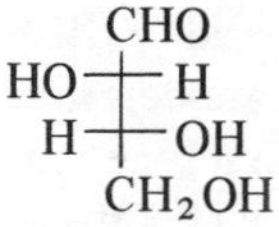

22. (a) 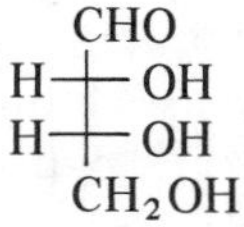

    | CHO | | CHO | |

    H—OH
    H—OH (or enantiomer
    CH_2OH
    Erythrose

    HO—H
    H—OH (or enantiomer)
    CH_2OH
    Threose

    (b) Structures shown above, not their enantiomers.

23. (a) Ethyl acetate;   (b) methacrylic acid;   (c) phenylacetamide.

24. (a) *n*-Propyl formate;   (b) methyl propionate;   (c) ethyl acetate.

25. SS, benzyl acetate;   TT, methyl phenylacetate;   UU, hydrocinnamic acid.

26. Ethyl *p*-methoxybenzoate.

27. VV, vinyl acetate.

28. (a) Ethyl adipate;   (b) ethyl ethylphenylmalonate;   (c) ethyl acetamidomalonate.

CHAPTER 21

21.1   III, in which the negative charge resides on oxygen, the atom that can best accommodate it.

21.2   Hydrogen on the carbon lying between the two carbonyl groups is the most acidic. Removal of proton yields an anion that is highly stabilized by accommodation of the negative charge by two oxygens (rather than by only one).

21.3   Order of decreasing resonance stabilization of the anion.

21.4   (a)

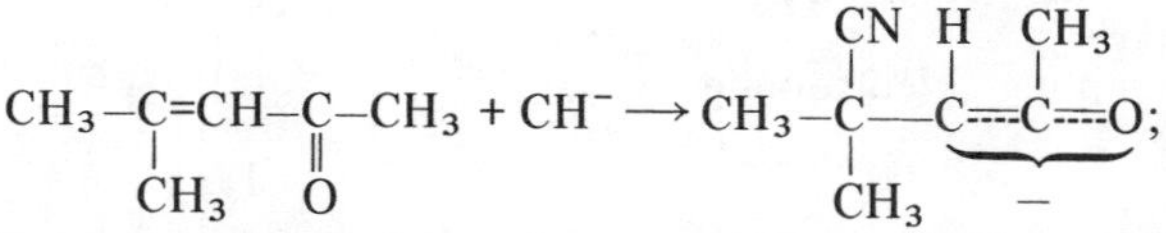

$$CH_3-C=CH-C-CH_3 + CH^- \rightarrow CH_3-C—C=C—O; \text{ addition}$$

(with CH_3, O substituents on left; CN, H, CH_3, CH_3 substituents on right)

to the end of the conjugated system that gives the more stable product, an anion in which the charge is partly accommodated by oxygen, the atom best able to do so;   (b) this anion may give an enol upon acidification, but through tautomerization finally gives the ketone

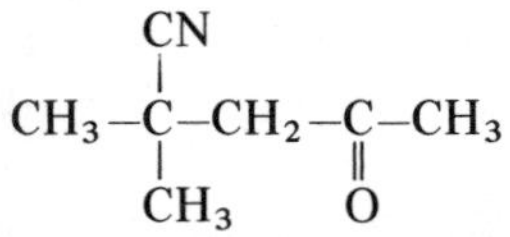

$$\underset{\underset{CH_3}{|}}{\overset{\overset{CN}{|}}{CH_3-C}}-CH_2-\underset{\overset{||}{O}}{C}-CH_3 \quad \text{(compare Sec. 27.5)}.$$

21.5 (a) Rate-determining step in both reactions is formation of flat, achiral hybrid carbanion. (b) II can give a carbanion which loses configuration readily. III has no α-hydrogen, cannot form a carbanion. (c) Rate-determining step in both reactions is formation of carbanion, which is achiral and which abstracts deuteron from solvent to generate labeled ketone.

21.6 (a) Via a carbanion, with accommodation of negative charge by acyl oxygen; (b) doubly charged anion (carbanion and carboxylate ion) more difficult to produce than singly charged anion; (c) very slow (if at all), since there is no α-hydrogen available for removal to yield carbanion.

21.7 Expect rate of racemization twice the rate of exchange. (See answer to Problem 14, page 488.)

21.8 (a) Both reactions go through the same slow Step (2), formation of the enol; (b) same as (a).

21.9 (a) HSO_4^-; (b) B:H (H_2O or D_2O when base is OH^- or OD^-).

21.10 (a) $CH_3CH_2CHOHCH(CH_3)CHO$; (b) $(CH_3)_2C(OH)CH_2COCH_3$; (c) $PhC(CH_3)(OH)CH_2COPh$ (which undergoes dehydration to give $PhC(CH_3)=CHCOPh$); (d) 2-(1-hydroxycyclohexyl)cyclohexanone (e) $PhCH_2CHOHCH(Ph)CHO$.

21.11 Gives a mixture of aldol products.

21.12 $$CH_3-\underset{\overset{||}{O}}{C}-H + H^+ \rightleftarrows CH_3-\underset{\overset{||}{+OH}}{C}-H \rightleftarrows CH_2=\underset{\overset{|}{OH}}{C}-H + H^+$$

$$CH_2=\underset{\overset{|}{OH}}{C}-H + CH_3-\underset{\overset{||}{+OH}}{C}-H \rightleftarrows CH_3-\underset{\overset{|}{OH}}{\overset{\overset{H}{|}}{C}}-CH_2-\underset{\overset{||}{+OH}}{C}-H \rightleftarrows$$

Nucleophile Electrophile

$$CH_3-\underset{\overset{|}{OH}}{\overset{\overset{H}{|}}{C}}-CH_2-\underset{\overset{||}{O}}{C}-H + H^+$$

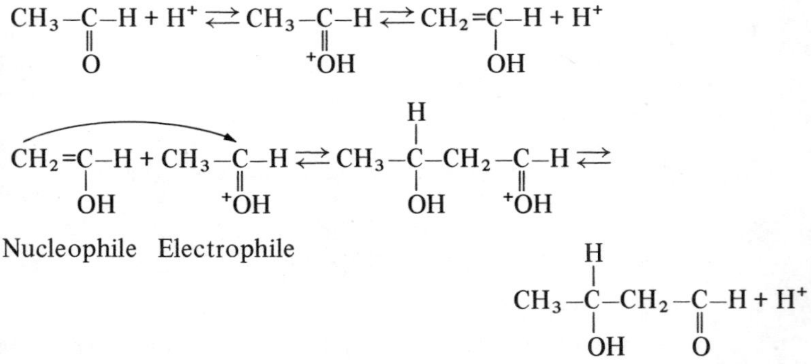

21.13 (a) Step (2) is much faster than the reverse of Step (1); as soon as a carbanion is formed (Step 1) it reacts with a second acetaldehyde molecule (Step 2) before it can react with water (reverse of Step 1) to form an acetaldehyde molecule which, in D_2O, would contain deuterium.   (b) Second-order: first-order in acetaldehyde and first-order in base.   (c) Rate of Step (2) depends on acetaldehyde concentration, and is slowed down; rate of reverse of Step (1) is unaffected, and becomes relatively more important.   (d) Step (2), carbonyl addition, is slower for a ketone, and is no longer much faster than the reverse of Step (1).

21.14   Reverse of aldol condensation of acetone (*retrograde aldol*); according to principle of microscopic reversibility (Problem 5.8, page 170), all steps in the aldol condensation are involved, in reverse order:

$$CH_3-\underset{\underset{OH}{|}}{\overset{\overset{CH_3}{|}}{C}}-CH_2-\underset{\overset{||}{O}}{C}-CH_3 + OH^- \rightleftharpoons CH_3-\underset{\underset{O_-}{|}}{\overset{\overset{CH_3}{|}}{C}}-CH_2-\underset{\overset{||}{O}}{C}-CH_3 + H_2O$$

$$CH_3-\underset{\underset{O_-}{|}}{\overset{\overset{CH_3}{|}}{C}}-CH_2-\underset{\overset{||}{O}}{C}-CH_3 \rightleftharpoons CH_3-\overset{\overset{CH_3}{|}}{C}=O + [CH_2COCH_3]^-$$

$$[CH_2COCH_3]^- + H_2O \rightleftharpoons CH_3-\overset{\overset{CH_3}{|}}{C}=O + OH^-.$$

21.15   Overlap of π orbitals of carbon–carbon and carbon–oxygen double bonds much as in conjugated dienes and in alkenylbenzenes.

21.16   (a) *n*-PrOH, $K_2Cr_2O_7$, H^+; aldol cond.; $- H_2O$; cat. H_2.   (b) As in (a), but start with *iso*-PrOH.   (c) Start with cyclohexanol.   (d) Start with 2-phenylethanol.   (e) Start with 1-phenylethanol; reduce with $NaBH_4$.

21.17   "6-12": *n*-BuOH, Cu, heat; aldol cond.; cat. H_2.
2-Methyl-2,4-pentanediol: acetone, aldol cond.; cat. H_2.

21.18   *n*-BuOH, $K_2Cr_2O_7$, H^+; CH_3CHO, OH^-, aldol cond. (four different combinations); $- H_2O$; cat. H_2.

21.19   (a) Toluene, $2Cl_2$, heat; H_2O; acetone (from *iso*-PrOH), crossed aldol; $- H_2O$; cat. H_2.   (b) $PhCOCH_3$ (page 623), PhCHO (as in a), crossed aldol; $- H_2O$; cat. H_2.   (c) Product b, acid, heat; cat. H_2.   (d) Toluene, Cl_2, heat; NaCN; H_2O, H^+; PCl_3; $LiAlH(Bu-t)_3$; PhCHO (as in a), crossed aldol; $- H_2O$; cat. H_2.   (e) Acetone (from *iso*-PrOH), 2PhCHO (as in a), crossed aldol; $- 2H_2O$.

21.10 (a) γ-Hydrogen will be acidic, since negative charge of anion is accommodated by electronegative oxygen through the conjugated
system. (b) PhCHO, $CH_3CH=CHCHO$, crossed aldol; $- H_2O$.

21.21 Basic OEt^- removes proton from acidic α-position of ethyl acetate.
Resulting anion adds to carbonyl group of PhCHO to give alkoxide of
"aldol" product. Proton transfer gives "aldol", followed by loss of
water to give ethyl cinnamate.

21.22 Addition to aldehyde or ketone of one of the following anions, protonation of "aldol" alkoxide, and dehydration:
(a) $(CH_2NO_2)^-$; (b) $(PhCHCN)^-$; (c) $[2,4-(O_2N)_2C_6H_3CH_2]^-$;
(d) $HC\equiv C^-$; (e) $[CH_3CO-O-COCH_2]^-$; (f) $[CH(COOEt)_2]^-$;
(g) $[CH(CN)(COOEt)]^-$.

21.23 Elimination $\longrightarrow$ 1- and 2-butene.

21.24 (a) $Ph_3P=CHC_3H_7$ + 2-butanone (Preparation of $Ph_3P=C(CH_3)C_2H_5$
for alternative combination accompanied by much elimination. Compare Problem 21.23.) (b) $PhCOCH_3 + Ph_3P=CHCH_2Ph$. (c) PhCHO +
$Ph_3P=CHPh$. (d) Cyclopentanone + $Ph_3P=CHCH_3$. (e) PhCH=
$CHCHO + Ph_3P=CHPh$. (f) $CH_2=CHCHO + Ph_3P=C(CH_3)COOCH_3$.

21.25 (a) *n*-BuOH, PBr_3; Ph_3P; base. *sec*-BuOH, CrO_3/H_2SO_4. (b) Benzene,
acetic anhydride, $AlCl_3$. Benzene, ethylene oxide (from EtOH via
ethylene), $AlCl_3$; PBr_3; Ph_3P; base. (c) Toluene, $2Cl_2$, heat; H_2O.
Toluene, Cl_2, heat; Ph_3P; heat. (d) Cyclopentanol, CrO_3/H_2SO_4.
EtOH, PBr_3; Ph_3P; base. (e) Benzaldehyde (as in c), CH_3CHO (from
EtOH), base. $Ph_3P=CHPh$ (as in c). (f) Glycerol, $NaHSO_4$, heat
(Problem 27.5, page 867). *n*-PrOH, $KMnO_4$, heat; Br_2, P; CH_3OH,
H^+; Ph_3P; base.

21.26 A, $Ph_3P=CHOPh$; B, $C_2H_5C(CH_3)=CHOPh$; C, $C_2H_5CH(CH_3)CHO$.
A general route to aldehydes.

21.17 D, 1-phenylcyclopentene; E, $Ph_3P=CHCH_2CH=PPh_3$; F, .

21.28 G, epoxide of *trans*-2-octene; back-side nucleophilic attack by Ph_2P^-
opens to give *erythro*-RCH–CHR′;

H, *erythro*-RCH–CHR′   ;

loses $Ph_2(CH_3)PO$ by *syn* elimination to give *cis*-2-octene.

21.29 Equilibria (1) and (3) in the condensation are reversed by EtOH; when the reaction is carried out in ether, the entire condensation proceeds farther in the direction of product.

21.30 (a) Intramolecular Claisen condensation leading to cyclization; (b) 2-carbethoxycyclohexanone; (c) no, because 3- and 4-membered rings are difficult to make; (d) ethyl 2,5-dioxocyclohexane-1,4-dicarboxylate.

21.31 PhCOOEt mixed with NaOEt, then CH_3COOEt added slowly; HCOOEt and NaOEt, then CH_3COOEt slowly; EtOOCCOOEt and NaOEt, then CH_3COOEt slowly; ethyl carbonate and NaOEt, then $PhCH_2COOEt$ slowly.

21.32 (a) Replace anion I of Sec. 21.11 by $^-CH_2COCH_3$, formed from acetone by action of OEt^-; (b) 2,4-hexanedione; (c) 1,3-phenyl-1,3-propanedione (dibenzoylmethane); (d) 2-(EtOOCCO)cyclohexanone.

21.33 (a) PhCOOEt and $PhCH_2COOEt$; (b) EtOOCCOOEt and ethyl glutarate; (c) ethyl phthalate and CH_3COOEt.

21.34 (a) CH_3CH_2CHO, $BrCH_2COOEt$, Zn, anhyd. Et_2O; H^+; $- H_2O$; cat. H_2. (b) $(CH_3)_2CHCHO$, $CH_3CHBrCOOEt$, Zn, anhyd. Et_2O; then as in (a). (c) PhCHO, $BrCH_2COOEt$, Zn, anhyd. Et_2O; H^+. (d) PhCHO, $CH_3CHBrCOOEt$, Zn, anhyd. Et_2O; then as in (a).

21.35 (a) Zn, anhyd. Et_2O; H^+; $- H_2O$; hydrolyze ester; cat. H_2. (b) As in (a); then $SOCl_2$, heat; $LiAlH(Bu-t)_3$. (c) As in (b); then $BrCH_2COOEt$, Zn, anhyd. Et_2O; H^+; $- H_2O$; hydrolyze ester; cat. H_2.

21.36 A, $EtOOCCOCH_2COOEt$; B, $EtOOCC(OH)(CH_2COOEt)_2$; C, citric acid, $(HOOCCH_2)_2C(OH)COOH$.

1. (a) $PhCH_2CHOHCH(Ph)CHO$; (b) $PhCH_2CH=C(Ph)CHO$; (c) same as a; (d) PhCHBrCHO; (e) $PhCH_2CH=CH_2$ (allylbenzene).

2. (a) 2-(1-hydroxycyclohexyl)cyclohexanone (aldol product); (b) 2-cyclohexylidenecyclohexanone (dehydration of a); (c) same as a; (d) 2-bromocyclohexanone; (e) methylenecyclohexane (see page 705).

3. (a) No reaction; (b) $PhCH_2OH$, PhCOONa; (c) PhCH=CHCHO, cinnamaldehyde; (d) $PhCH=C(CH_3)CHO$; (e) $PhCH=CHCOCH_3$, benzalacetone; (f) PhCH=CHCOCH=CHPh, dibenzalacetone; (g) PhCH=CHCOPh, benzalacetophenone; (h) PhCH=CHCOOH, cinnamic acid; (i) PhCH=CHCOOEt, ethyl cinnamate;

(j) PhCH=C(Ph)COOEt;   (k) PhCH$_2$OH, HCOONa;
(l) PhCH=CH–CH=CHCHO;   (m) PhCH=CH–CH=CH$_2$,
1-phenyl-1,3-butadiene;   (n) PhCH=CHOPh;   (o) PhCH$_2$CHO,
phenylacetaldehyde.

4. (a) OH$^-$, aldol cond.   (b) Product a, $-$ H$_2$O; cat. H$_2$.   (c) Product a,
$-$ H$_2$O.   (d) Product c, NaBH$_4$; acidify.   (e) Product a, cat. H$_2$.
(f) Product b, KMnO$_4$, heat.   (g) PhCHO, OH$^-$, aldol cond.; $-$ H$_2$O.
(h) D$_2$O, OD$^-$.   (i) H$_2$^{18}O, H$^+$.   (j) Ph$_3$P=CHCH(CH$_3$)$_2$.

5. (a) NaOI; acidify.   (b) OH$^-$, aldol cond.; $-$ H$_2$O.   (c) Product b, cat. H$_2$.
(d) Product b, NaBH$_4$; acidify.   (e) PhCHO, OH$^-$, crossed aldol; $-$ H$_2$O.
(f) PhOCH$_2$Cl, Ph$_3$P, t-BuO$^-$K$^+$; then acetophenone; dilute acid.

6. (a) CH$_3$CH$_2$CH$_2$COCH(C$_2$H$_5$)COOEt;   (b) PhCH$_2$COCH(Ph)COOEt;
(c) (CH$_3$)$_2$CHCH$_2$COCH(COOEt)CH(CH$_3$)$_2$;   (d) HCOCH(CH$_3$)COOEt;
(e) EtOOCCOCH(COOEt)CH$_2$COOEt and [EtOOCCH$_2$CH(COOEt)CO]$_2$;
(f) PhCOCH(Ph)COOEt;   (g) 2-(CH$_3$CH$_2$CO)cyclohexanone;
(h) PhCH$_2$COCH$_2$COPh;   (i) PhCOCH$_2$COCH$_2$COPh.

7. (a) CH$_3$COCH$_2$COOEt, CH$_3$COCH(CH$_3$)COOEt,
CH$_3$CH$_2$COCH(CH$_3$)COOEt;   (b) not good for either of the symmetrical
products, and not very good for the unsymmetrical product through
losses in forming the symmetrical products.

8. (a) PhCOOEt and CH$_3$CH$_2$COOEt;   (b) 2PhCH$_2$COOEt;   (c) (COOEt)$_2$
and 1CH$_3$CH$_2$COOEt;   (d) HCOOEt and PhCH$_2$COOEt;   (e) ethyl
isobutyrate and acetone;   (f) PhCOOEt and acetone;   (g) PhCOOEt
and cyclohexanone;   (h) 1HCOOEt and ethyl succinate.

9. *trans*-Cinnamic acid, Br$_2$/CCl$_4$; KOH(alc); NaNH$_2$/NH$_3$; H$_2$, Lindlar's
catalyst.

10. (a) Acetone, OH$^-$, aldol cond.   (b) Product a, $-$ H$_2$O; cat. H$_2$.
(c) CH$_3$CHO, OH$^-$, aldol cond.; $-$ H$_2$O.   (d) CH$_3$CHO, PhCHO, OH$^-$,
crossed aldol; $-$ H$_2$O; NaBH$_4$; acidify.   (e) CH$_3$CHO, p-O$_2$NC$_6$H$_4$CHO,
OH$^-$, crossed aldol; $-$ H$_2$O.   (f) CH$_3$CHO, OH$^-$, aldol cond.; cat. H$_2$.
(g) Product a, $-$ H$_2$O; NaOI; acidify.   (h) Acetone, BrCH$_2$COOEt, Zn,
anhyd. Et$_2$O; H$^+$; $-$ H$_2$O.   (i) sec-BuOH, CrO$_3$/H$_2$SO$_4$; HC≡C$^-$Na$^+$
(from acetylene); acidify.   (j) Allyl chloride, Ph$_3$P, t-BuO$^-$K$^+$; then
cinnamaldehyde (page 704).   (k) Cinnamaldehyde (page 704), CH$_3$CHO,
OH$^-$ $\longrightarrow$ PhCH=CHCH=CHCHO; then Ph$_3$P=CHPh (from PhCH$_2$Cl,
Ph$_3$P, t-BuO$^-$K$^+$).   (l) Reformatsky reaction with methyl ethyl ketone
(from sec-BuOH) and CH$_3$CHBrCOOEt.   (m) Ethylene oxide, PhMgBr;
acidify; K$_2$Cr$_2$O$_7$, H$^+$; BrCH$_2$COOEt, Zn, anhyd. Et$_2$O; acidify.
(n) n-PrCHO (from n-BuOH), (CH$_3$)$_2$CBrCOOEt, Zn, anhyd. Et$_2$O;

acidify; $-H_2O$; cat. H_2.   (o) Cinnamic acid (page 714), cat. H_2; $SOCl_2$, heat; HF, heat.   (p) *trans*-Cinnamic acid (page 714), HCO_2OH.

11. An "aldol condensation" leads to a γ-hydroxy acid, $CH_3CHOHCH(COOH)CH_2COOH$, that subsequently forms the γ-lactone, γ-methylparaconic acid.

12. Acetone $\longrightarrow$ mesityl oxide (page 711); then controlled catalytic hydrogenation of the carbon–carbon double bond.

13. (a) $PhCOCH_2COCH_2CH_3$ and $PhCOCH(CH_3)COCH_3$;   (b) iodoform test.

14. (a) Hydration of triple bond.   (b) Acetylene, $NaNH_2$; MeBr; MeMgBr; CO_2; acidify; EtOH, H^+.

15. CH_3CHO, 3HCHO, OH^-, in triple aldol cond.; then HCHO, OH^-, in crossed Cannizzaro reaction.

16.

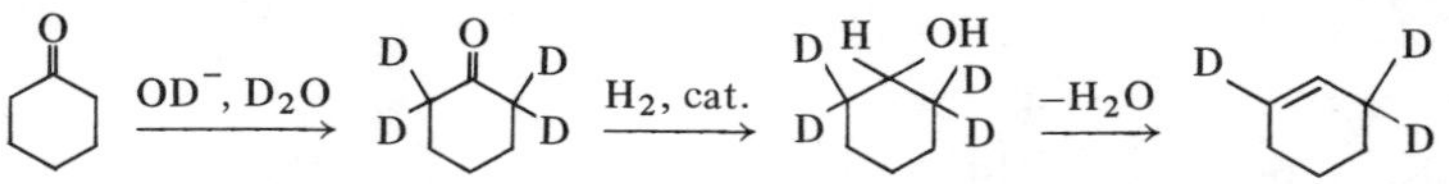

17. (a) Electron withdrawal by halogen makes hydrogens on carbon to which halogen has already become attached more acidic and hence more readily removed by base to give further substitution.

$$\text{(b) } R-\underset{\underset{O}{\|}}{C}-CX_3 + OH^- \longrightarrow R-\underset{\underset{O_-}{|}}{\overset{\overset{OH}{|}}{C}}-CX_3 \longrightarrow RCOOH + CX_3^- \longrightarrow$$

$$RCOO^- + HCX_3.$$

Electron withdrawal by three halogens makes CX_3^- comparatively weakly basic (for an alkide ion) and hence a good leaving group.

18. Dehydrocitral, $(CH_3)_2C=CHCH=CHC(CH_3)=CHCHO$, formed by aldol cond. on γ-carbon of α,β-unsaturated aldehyde (see Problem 21.20, page 713).

19. $Ph_3P=CHCH_2CH(CH_3)_2$ (from isopentyl bromide); cat. H_2; CrO_3, H_2SO_4; $Ph_3P=CHCH=CH_2$ (from allyl chloride).

20. $CH_3COCH_2COOEt + CH_3MgI \longrightarrow CH_4\uparrow + (CH_3COCHCOOEt)^-(MgI)^+$.

21. (a) Base-catalyzed tautomerization:

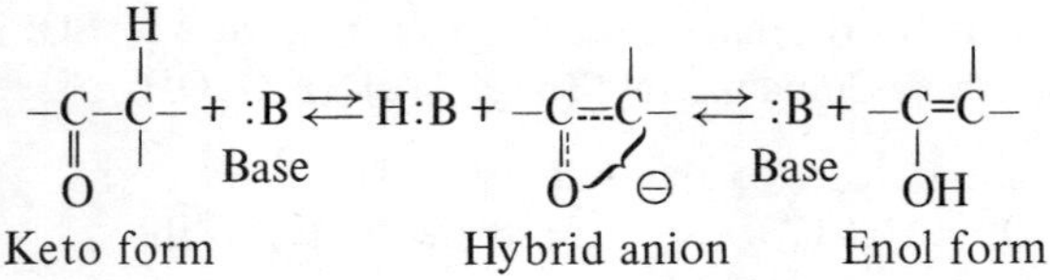

$$-\overset{\underset{|}{\text{O}}}{\overset{||}{C}}-\overset{\underset{|}{H}}{C}- + :B \rightleftarrows H:B + -\overset{\underset{\overset{\ominus}{\diagup}}{\text{O}}}{\overset{||}{C}}\!\!\cdots\!\!\overset{|}{C}- \rightleftarrows :B + -\overset{|}{C}=\overset{\underset{|}{\text{OH}}}{C}-$$

Keto form   Base   Hybrid anion   Base   Enol form

Acid-catalyzed tautomerization:

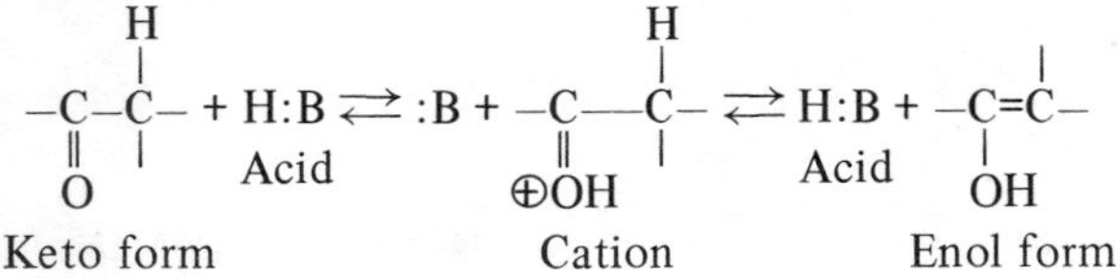

$$-\overset{\underset{|}{\text{O}}}{\overset{||}{C}}-\overset{\underset{|}{H}}{C}- + H:B \rightleftarrows :B + -\overset{\underset{\oplus\text{OH}}{||}}{C}-\overset{\underset{|}{H}}{C}- \rightleftarrows H:B + -\overset{|}{C}=\overset{\underset{|}{\text{OH}}}{C}-$$

Keto form   Acid   Cation   Acid   Enol form

(b) and (c) Enol stabilized by conjugation and intramolecular H-bonding:

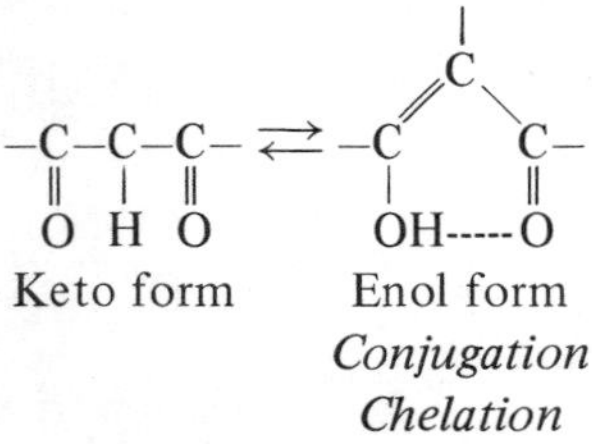

Keto form   Enol form

Conjugation

Chelation

1,3- or β-Dicarbonyl compounds

22. A,

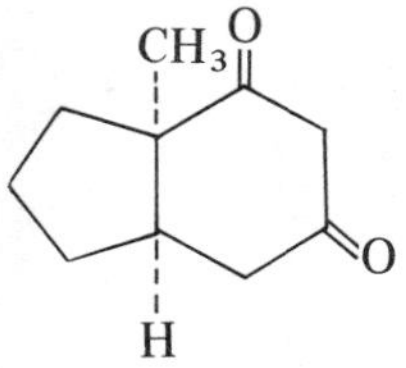

;   B,

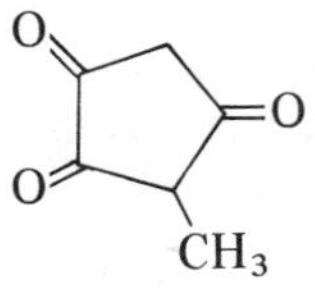

a triketone.

23. (a) *a*, enol $-CH_3$; *b*, keto $-CH_3$; *c*, keto $-CH_2-$; *d*, enol $-CH=$; *e*, enol $-OH$. Ratios *a:b* and *2d:c* are equal (5.5 and 5.6) and show 85% enol. (b) All enol; conjugation with ring.

CHAPTER 22

22.1   Treat ether solution of the liquid mixture with aq. $NaHCO_3$; separate layers. Acidify aqueous layer, extract with ether; dry, distill ether and then *n*-valeric acid. Treat ether layer with aq. HCl; separate layers;

distill ether and then the hydrocarbon. Treat acidic aqueous layer with NaOH, extract with ether; dry, distill ether and then amine.

Treat the mixture of the three solids with aq. $NaHCO_3$, and filter. Acidify filtrate; collect pptd. acid on filter. Treat the mixture of base-insoluble solids with aq. HCl; collect the insoluble ether on filter; make filtrate alkaline and collect pptd. amine on filter.

22.2 At room temperature, inversion about nitrogen is slow enough that nmr "sees" two kinds of ring protons: two protons *cis* and two protons *trans* to ethyl. At 120°, inversion is so fast that all four protons are seen in average positions: they are equivalent.

22.3 In both cases inversion evidently negligible at temperatures involved. (a) $-CH_3$ and $-Cl$ can be *cis* or *trans*. (b) Optically active reagent favors preponderance of one of the enantiomers, which would be inter-convertible through inversion.

22.4 Carbanion, like ammonia, has low, easily surmountable energy barrier between mirror-image pyramidal arrangements. Attachment of fourth group to the carbanion can occur to either arrangement, and thus give the racemic modification.

22.5 *n*-Caproic acid, $SOCl_2$, heat; NH_3; OBr^-. *n*-Butyl alcohol, PBr_3; NaCN; $2H_2$, Ni, heat, pressure. *n*-Pentyl alcohol, PBr_3; NH_3. *n*-Pentyl alcohol, $K_2Cr_2O_7$, H^+; NH_3, H_2, Ni, heat, pressure.

22.6 (a) Toluene, Cl_2, heat; NH_3. (b) Toluene, acetic anhydride, BF_3; NH_3, H_2, Ni, heat, pressure. (c) Toluene, Cl_2, heat; NaCN; $2H_2$, Ni, heat, pressure. (d) Toluene, HNO_3, H_2SO_4; isolate *p*-nitrotoluene; Fe, H^+ or cat. H_2. (e) Toluene, $KMnO_4$, OH^-, heat; acidify; PCl_5; NH_3; Br_2, OH^-.

1. (a) *n*-Butylamine (1°), *sec*-butylamine (1°), isobutylamine (1°), *tert*-butylamine (1°), methyl-*n*-propylamine (2°), methylisopropylamine (2°), diethylamine (2°), dimethylethylamine (3°); (b) benzylamine (1°), *o*-toluidine (1°), *m*-toluidine (1°), *p*-toluidine (1°), N-methylaniline (2°).

2. (a) $CH_3CH_2CH(CH_3)NH_2$; (b) o-$CH_3C_6H_4NH_2$; (c) $C_6H_5NH_3^+Cl^-$; (d) $(C_2H_5)_2NH$; (e) p-$H_2NC_6H_4COOH$; (f) $C_6H_5CH_2NH_2$; (g) $(CH_3)_2CHNH_3^+$ $^-OOCC_6H_5$; (h) o-$C_6H_4(NH_2)_2$; (i) $C_6H_5N(CH_3)_2$; (j) $HOCH_2CH_2NH_2$; (k) $C_6H_5CH_2CH_2NH_2$; (l) cyclo-$C_6H_{11}N(CH_3)_2$; (m) $(C_6H_5)_2NH$; (n) 2,4-$(CH_3)_2C_6H_3NH_2$; (o) $(n$-$C_4H_9)_4N^+I^-$; (p) p-$CH_3OC_6H_4NH_2$.

3. (a) Excess NH_3.   (b) $K_2Cr_2O_7$, H^+; NH_3, cat. H_2.   (c) NH_3, cat. H_2.
    (d) Fe, H^+, heat.   (e) $2H_2$, Ni, heat, pressure.   (f) OBr^-.   (g) $KMnO_4$,
    heat; acidify; $SOCl_2$; NH_3; OBr^-.   (h) HBr; NaCN; cat. H_2. Aniline: (d),
    (a) with difficulty. Benzylamine: all (last step only of (h)).

4. (a) iso-PrOH, CrO_3/H_2SO_4; NH_3, cat. H_2.   (b) n-BuOH, HBr; NaCN;
    cat. H_2.   (c) Toluene, HNO_3, H_2SO_4; Fe, H^+, heat.   (d) Benzene,
    HNO_3, H_2SO_4, warm; HNO_3, H_2SO_4, heat; NH_4SH, warm.   (e) EtOH,
    $KMnO_4$, heat; $SOCl_2$; benzene, $AlCl_3$; NH_3, cat. H_2.   (f) Toluene, Cl_2,
    heat; NaCN; cat. H_2.   (g) Benzene, HNO_3, H_2SO_4, warm; Cl_2, Fe, heat;
    Fe, H^+.   (h) Toluene, HNO_3, H_2SO_4; $K_2Cr_2O_7$, H_2SO_4, heat; Fe, H^+.
    (i) n-PrOH, $KMnO_4$, heat; $SOCl_2$; n-Bu_2Cd (from n-BuOH via bromide
    and Grignard); NH_3, cat. H_2.   (j) Benzene, HNO_3, H_2SO_4, warm; Fe,
    H^+; EtI (from EtOH); OH^-.   (k) Benzene, Cl_2, Fe; HNO_3, H_2SO_4, heat;
    HNO_3, H_2SO_4, heat; NH_3, warm.   (l) Toluene, Cl_2, heat; NaCN; H_2O,
    H^+, heat; $SOCl_2$; Me_2Cd (from MeOH); NH_3, cat. H_2.   (m) Toluene,
    HNO_3, H_2SO_4: Cl_2, heat; NH_3.   (n) Toluene, $2Cl_2$, heat; H_2O; CN^-,
    H^+; cat. H_2.

5. (a) $LiAlH_4$; acidify; PBr_3; excess NH_3.   (b) $LiAlH_4$; acidify; PBr_3;
    NaCN; cat. H_2.   (c) $SOCl_2$; NH_3; OBr^-.   (d) $LiAlH_4$; acidify; PBr_3,
    heat; Mg, anhyd. Et_2O; $CdCl_2$; palmitoyl chloride (from palmitic acid +
    $SOCl_2$); NH_3, cat. H_2.

6. (a) Putrescine, 1,4-diaminobutane;   (b) cadaverine, 1,5-diaminopentane.

7. $2CN^-$; $5H_2$, cat.

8. Succinic anhydride, NH_3, heat; OBr^-; acidify carefully.

9. Pair of enantiomers, a, c, e, f; one inactive compound, b; inactive *cis-
    trans* pair, d.

10. (a) Phenyl group *cis* or *trans* to $-OH$;   (b) hindered rotation about
    double bond due to overlap of *p* orbitals that form the π bond;   (c) no;
    yes; yes.

11. (a) A, potassium phthalimide;   B, N-n-propylphthalimide;
    C, n-propylamine;   D, phthalic acid.   (b) Primary amines free from
    secondary or tertiary. Acidity.

CHAPTER 23

23.1 (a) Nitro group at *o*- and *p*-position stabilizes amine through structures like — $\left\{\begin{array}{c} O \\[2pt] \diagdown \\ O \end{array}\right.$ N=$\bigcirc$=NH$_2^+$; (b) no such structures possible for

the *m*-isomer.

23.2 $(CH_3)_3\overset{+}{N}:\overset{-}{B}F_3$.

23.3 (a) 4-Methyl-2-butene, Me$_3$N; (b) ethylene, ethyldi-*n*-propylamine;
(c) vinyl chloride, dimethylethylamine; (d) ethylene, dimethyl-
n-propylamine.

23.4 (a) Strong base, ethoxide, causes E2 elimination, with Hofmann
orientation. With weak base, ethanol, elimination is E1, with Saytzeff
orientation. (b) Ethyl *tert*-pentyl ether, by (S$_N$1) reaction of *tert*-
pentyl cation with solvent. (c) Methyl ethyl ether, from S$_N$2 attack
by ethoxide at least hindered position.

23.5 (a) I gives *n*-C$_5$H$_{11}$NMe$_2$, II gives $CH_3CH_2CH(CH_3)CH_2NMe_2$;
(b) 1-bromopentane, Me$_2$NH; 1-bromo-2-methylbutane, Me$_2$NH.

23.6 1,3-Pentadiene (from thermal isomerization of 1,4-pentadiene);
2-methyl-1,3-butadiene (isoprene).

23.7 (a) Instead of —H the —SO$_3$H group is displaced from ring by an electrophilic reagent (Br$^+$ or $^+$NO$_2$) in a typical electrophilic aromatic
substitution in which —NH$_2$ and —OH activate the ring and are
ortho,para-directing. (b) Resonance stabilization of anion with dispersal of its negative charge.

Anion from   Anion from
an amide   diacetamide

23.8 (i) Attack at trigonal acyl carbon to form tetrahedral intermediate is
easier than at tetrahedral sulfonyl sulfur to form pentacovalent intermediate. (ii) Attack at alkyl carbon is easier in a sulfonate ester,
where leaving group is weakly basic sulfonate ion, than in a carboxylate ester, where leaving group is more strongly basic carboxylate ion.

23.9 Free amine is powerfully activated molecule; anilinium ion is power-fully deactivated by $-NH_3^+$ with its positive charge.

23.10 An aromatic $-NH_2$ group is too weakly basic appreciably to neutralize the $-COOH$ group.

23.11 (a) *n*-Butyl cation; (b) *n*-butyl cation reacts with Cl^- or H_2O, or loses a proton; *n*-butyl cation rearranges by hydride shift to *sec*-butyl cation which then reacts with Cl^- or H_2O, or loses a proton.

23.12 (a) Isobutyl alcohol, isobutyl chloride, isobutylene, *tert*-butyl alcohol, *tert*-butyl chloride; (b) 2-methyl-2-butene, 2-methyl-1-butene, *tert*-pentyl alcohol.

23.13 (a) $HONO + HCl \longrightarrow H_2\overset{+}{O}-N{=}O + Cl^-$;
(b) leaving groups $Cl^- > H_2O > OH^-$;
(c) $NO_2^- + H^+ \rightleftarrows HONO$

$HONO + H^+ \rightleftarrows H_2\overset{+}{O}-N{=}O$

$H_2\overset{+}{O}-N{=}O + Cl^- \longrightarrow H_2O + Cl-N{=}O$;

(d) separation of weak base Cl^- from $^+N{=}O$ easier than separation of strong base OH^- (Cl^- a better leaving group than OH^-).

23.14 (a) Neither is likely. (b) Most likely initial step is attachment of NO^+ to most nucleophilic center, amino nitrogen. With secondary amine, this is followed by loss of proton to give N-nitroso product. With tertiary amine, nitrogen has no proton to lose; NO^+ is regenerated and (probably more slowly) attacks ring carbon, which *has* a proton to lose.

23.15 Aceto-*p*-toluidide (page 760), HNO_3, H_2SO_4; H_2O, H^+, heat; HONO; H_3PO_2. *m*-Nitrotoluene (as above), Fe, H^+; HONO; KI. *p*-Toluidine (page 770), $2Br_2(aq)$; HONO; H_3PO_2. Aniline, $3Br_2(aq)$; HONO; H_3PO_2. *o*-Toluidine (page 770), HONO; CuCN; H_2O, H^+, heat. *m*-Nitrotoluene (as above), Fe, H^+; HONO; CuCN; H_2O, H^+, heat. *p*-Toluidine (page 770), HONO; CuCN; H_2O, H^+, heat. *o*-Toluidine (page 770), HONO; H_2O, H^+, warm. *m*-Nitrotoluene (as above), Fe, H^+; HONO; H_2O, H^+, warm. *p*-Toluidine (page 770), HONO; H_2O, H^+, warm.

-23.16 Nitrobenzene, Br_2, Fe, heat; Fe, H^+; HONO; CuBr. As first synthesis, except KI is used instead of CuBr.

23.17 *p*-Nitrotoluene (from toluene), $2Br_2$, Fe; Fe, H^+; HONO; H_3PO_2. *p*-Nitroaniline (page 760), $2Br_2$, HOAc; HONO; H_3PO_2.

23.18 (a) Electron withdrawal by nitro groups makes diazonium ion more electrophilic; (b) less effective due to electron release by $-CH_3$.

23.19 To prevent coupling of diazonium ion with unconsumed amine: by increasing concentration of protonated amine, decreasing concentration of free amine.

23.20 PhNHR + ArN$_2^+$ $\rightleftharpoons$ H$^+$ + PhNR–N=N–Ar (I)

PhNHR + ArN$_2^+$ $\longrightarrow$ H$^+$ + Ar–N=N–C$_6$H$_4$NHR (II)

Attack at N to yield I is faster; attack at C yields more stable product, II. Acid required to reverse formation of I. (N is more reactive site toward either electrophile, ArN$_2^+$ or H$^+$; formation of I is fast, but so is reversal. II is formed slowly but, once formed, tends to persist.)

23.21 (a) 2'-Bromo-4-hydroxy-3,4'-dimethylazobenzene. (b) *p*-Toluidine (page 770), acetic anhydride; Br$_2$; H$_2$O, H$^+$, heat; HONO; couple this diazonium salt with *o*-cresol (page 766).

23.22 Reduction with SnCl$_2$ of azo compound formed by coupling of N,N-dimethylaniline with some diazonium salt (usually $^-$O$_3$SC$_6$H$_4$N$_2^+$ from sulfanilic acid, because when sulfanilic acid is regenerated in the reduction step its solubility characteristics differ enough from those of the desired amine to permit easy separation).

23.23 (a) Nucleophilic attack by trimethylamine on methyl carbon of C$_6$H$_5$SO$_2$N(CH$_3$)$_3^+$. (b) C$_6$H$_5$SO$_2$NR$_2$ by reaction in (a). Incorrect conclusion: unknown is 2°.

23.24 (a) That unknown is 2°. (b) Separate alkaline aqueous phase, acidify, and look for precipitate.

1. (a) *n*-Butylammonium chloride; (b) *n*-butylammonium hydrogen sulfate; (c) *n*-butylammonium acetate; (d) no reaction;
(e) N-(*n*-butyl)acetamide and *n*-butylammonium acetate;
(f) N-(*n*-butyl)isobutyramide and *n*-butylammonium chloride;
(g) N-(*n*-butyl)-*p*-nitrobenzamide and pyridinium chloride;
(h) sodium salt of N-(*n*-butyl)benzenesulfonamide; (i) ethyl-, diethyl-, and triethyl-*n*-butylammonium bromides; (j) benzyl-, dibenzyl-, and tribenzylammonium bromides; (k) no reaction; (l) trimethyl-*n*-butylammonium hydroxide; (m) 1-butene and trimethylamine;
(n) isopropyl-*n*-butylamine; (o) see Problem 23.11, page 763;
(p) N-(*n*-butyl)phthalamic acid, *o*-HOOCC$_6$H$_4$CONHC$_4$H$_9$;
(q) N-(*n*-butyl)glycine, *n*-C$_4$H$_9$NHCH$_2$COOH; (r) N-(*n*-butyl)-2,4,6-trinitroaniline (N-(*n*-butyl)picramide).

2. (a) Cyclohexylamine > ammonia > aniline; (b) ethylamine > 3-amino-1-propanol > 2-aminoethanol; (c) *p*-methoxyaniline (*p*-anisidine) >

aniline > *p*-nitroaniline; (d) *m*-ethylbenzylamine > benzylamine > *m*-chlorobenzylamine; (e) *p*-chloro-N-methylaniline > 2,4-dichloro-N-methylaniline > 2,4,6-trichloro-N-methylaniline.

3. An aqueous solution of Me_4NOH, because the $4°$ compound is completely ionized and OH^- is a stronger base than Me_3N.

4. (a) All three form soluble ammonium salts; (b) aniline dissolves with the formation of a diazonium salt, methylaniline yields a neutral yellow N-nitroso compound, dimethylaniline gives green *p*-nitroso compound; (c) all three form $4°$ ammonium salts; (d) aniline gives solution, methylaniline gives solid, dimethylaniline does not react; (e) neutral amides from aniline and methylaniline, no reaction with dimethylaniline; (f) same as (e); (g) all three show rapid formation of tribromo substitution products.

5. (a) All three form soluble ammonium salts; (b) ethylamine gives N_2, diethylamine yields a neutral yellow N-nitroso compound, triethylamine yields the same N-nitroso compound and cleavage products; (c) all three form $4°$ ammonium salts; (d) ethylamine gives solution, diethylamine gives solid, triethylamine does not react; (e) neutral amides from ethylamine and diethylamine, no reaction with triethylamine; (f) same as (e); (g) N-bromoamines from $1°$ and $2°$ amines (reaction not studied by us, but not surprising), no reaction with $3°$ amine.

6. (a) $p\text{-}CH_3C_6H_4N_2^+$; (b) $p\text{-}ONC_6H_4NEt_2$; (c) 1-propanol, 2-propanol, propylene; (d) $p\text{-}^-O_3SC_6H_4N_2^+$; (e) $C_6H_5N(CH_3)NO$; (f) 2-methyl-2-butene; (g) $p\text{-}^+N_2C_6H_4-C_6H_4N_2^+\text{-}p$; (h) $C_6H_5CH_2OH$.

7. (a) 2,4-Diamino-4'-nitroazobenzene; (b) *p*-nitrophenol + N_2; (c) *p*-bromonitrobenzene + N_2; (d) 2-hydroxy-5-methyl-4'-nitroazobenzene; (e) *p*-iodonitrobenzene + N_2; (f) *p*-chloronitrobenzene + N_2; (g) *p*-nitrobenzonitrile + N_2; (h) *p*-fluoronitrobenzene, N_2, BF_3; (i) nitrobenzene, N_2, H_3PO_3.

8. (a) H_3PO_2, H_2O; (b) H_2O, H^+, heat, steam-distilling the cresol immediately; (c) CuCl; (d) CuBr; (e) KI; (f) HBF_4, isolate ArN_2BF_4, and heat dry salt; (g) CuCN; (h) N,N-dimethylaniline in slightly acidic medium; (i) resorcinol (1,3-dihydroxybenzene) in slightly alkaline medium.

9. (a) N-Methyl-*n*-butyramide and methylammonium chloride; (b) N-methylacetanilide and acetic acid; (c) propylene and tri-*n*-propylamine; (d) N,N-diethylisovaleramide and Et_2NH_2Cl; (e) MeOH and trimethylamine; (f) trimethylammonium acetate; (g) acetic acid and dimethylammonium chloride; (h) aniline and sodium benzoate;

(i) MeOH and formanilide;   (j) N,N′-dimethylurea (CH$_3$NHCONHCH$_3$) and MeNH$_3$Cl;   (k) N-nitroso-N-methyl-*m*-nitroaniline;   (l) 2,4,6-tribromoaniline;   (m) 2,4,6-tribromo-3-methylaniline;   (n) 2,6-dibromo-4-methylaniline;   (o) *p*-toluenediazonium chloride;   (p) *o*- and *p*-nitroacetanilide;   (q) 2-nitro-4-methylacetanilide;   (r) N,N,N-trimethyl-*p*-ethylanilinium iodide;   (s) N-(*p*-bromophenyl)benzamide and *o*-isomer.

10. (a) *p*-Nitrotoluene (page 383), Br$_2$, Fe; Fe, H$^+$.   (b) *p*-Toluidine (page 738), acetic anhydride (from EtOH via acetic acid); Br$_2$, Fe; H$_2$O, H$^+$, heat.   (c) Acetanilide (page 746), chlorosulfonic acid; aniline (page 733); H$_2$O, H$^+$, heat.   (d) Acetanilide (page 746), HNO$_3$, H$_2$SO$_4$; Fe, H$^+$.
(e) Aniline (page 733), 2EtI (from EtOH); NaNO$_2$, HCl.   (f) *p*-Toluidine (page 738), acetic anhydride (from EtOH via acetic acid); KMnO$_4$, warm, careful buffering to prevent hydrolysis; HNO$_3$, H$_2$SO$_4$; H$_2$O, H$^+$, heat.
(g) Benzene, iso-PrBr (from iso-PrOH), AlCl$_3$; HNO$_3$, H$_2$SO$_4$; Fe, H$^+$; Br$_2$(aq).   (h) *p*-Nitrotoluene (page 383), Cl$_2$, heat; NH$_3$; Fe, H$^+$.
(i) Aniline (page 733), iso-PrBr (from iso-PrOH); NaNO$_2$, HCl.
(j) EtOH, HBr, heat; NH$_3$ (excess); MeI (from MeOH); *n*-valeroyl chloride (from *n*-BuOH via HBr, NaCN, hydrolysis, SOCl$_2$).
(k) *n*-BuOH, HBr, heat; Mg, anhyd. Et$_2$O; ethylene oxide (from EtOH); acidify; PBr$_3$; NH$_3$.   (l) *n*-BuOH, KMnO$_4$, heat; acidify; SOCl$_2$; benzene, AlCl$_3$; remove Al salts; NH$_3$, cat. H$_2$.   (m) EtOH, KMnO$_4$, heat; acidify; Cl$_2$, P; SOCl$_2$; NH$_3$.   (n) EtOH, KMnO$_4$, heat; acidify; Cl$_2$, P; NH$_3$; benzoyl chloride (from toluene via benzoic acid).

11. (a) 2,3-Dibromotoluene: *o*-toluidine (page 770), acetic anhydride; HNO$_3$, H$_2$SO$_4$; H$_2$O, H$^+$, heat; Br$_2$; HONO; CuBr; Fe, H$^+$, heat; HONO; H$_3$PO$_2$. 2,4-Dibromotoluene: *p*-nitrotoluene (from toluene), Br$_2$, Fe, heat; Fe, H$^+$; HONO; CuBr. 2,5-Dibromotoluene: *o*-toluidine (page 770), acetic anhydride; Br$_2$; H$_2$O, H$^+$, heat; HONO; CuBr. 2,6-Dibromotoluene: *p*-nitrotoluene (from toluene), 2Br$_2$, Fe, heat; Fe, H$^+$; HONO; H$_3$PO$_2$. 3,4-Dibromotoluene: aceto-*p*-toluidide (page 771), Br$_2$; H$_2$O, H$^+$, heat; HONO; CuBr. 3,5-Dibromotoluene: *p*-toluidine (page 770), 2Br$_2$(aq); HONO; H$_3$PO$_2$.   (b) *o*-Chlorobenzoic acid: *o*-toluidine (page 770), HONO; CuCl; KMnO$_4$, OH$^-$, heat; acidify. *m*-Chlorobenzoic acid: *m*-nitrotoluene (as in Problem 23.15), Fe, H$^+$; HONO; CuCl; KMnO$_4$, OH$^-$, heat; acidify. *p*-Chlorobenzoic acid: *p*-toluidine (page 770), HONO; CuCl; KMnO$_4$, OH$^-$, heat; acidify.   (c) *o*-Bromofluorobenzene: bromobenzene, HNO$_3$, H$_2$SO$_4$, heat; isolate *o*-isomer; Fe, H$^+$; HONO; HBF$_4$; heat. *m*-Bromofluorobenzene: *m*-bromonitrobenzene (page 344), Fe, H$^+$; HONO; HBF$_4$; heat. *p*-Bromofluorobenzene: as for *o*-isomer except isolate *p*-bromonitrobenzene.

12. (a) *p*-Toluidine (page 770), HONO; HBF$_4$; heat. (b) *m*-Nitrotoluene (as in Problem 23.15), Fe, H$^+$; HONO; HBF$_4$; heat. (c) *p*-Toluidine (page 770), HONO; KI; KMnO$_4$, OH$^-$, heat; acidify. (d) *m*-Bromonitrobenzene (page 344), Fe, H$^+$. (e) *p*-Toluic acid (page 769), Br$_2$, Fe, heat. (f) Aceto-*p*-toluidide (page 771), Br$_2$; H$_2$O, H$^+$, heat; HONO; CuCN; H$_2$O, H$^+$, heat. (g) From ethylbenzene (page 395) to *m*-nitroethylbenzene as for *m*-nitrotoluene in Problem 23.15; then Fe, H$^+$; HONO; H$_2$O, H$^+$, warm. (h) *p*-Nitroaniline (page 760), 2Br$_2$, HOAc; HONO; H$_3$PO$_2$; Fe, H$^+$. (i) Aceto-*p*-toluidide (page 771), Br$_2$; H$_2$O, H$^+$, heat; HONO; KI. (j) Aceto-*p*-toluidide (page 771), HNO$_3$, H$_2$SO$_4$; H$_2$O, H$^+$, heat; HONO; H$_2$O, H$^+$, warm; Fe, H$^+$. (k) *p*-Nitroaniline (page 760), 2Br$_2$, HOAc; HONO; KI; Fe, H$^+$; HONO; H$_3$PO$_2$. (l) Aceto-*p*-toluidide (page 771), HNO$_3$, H$_2$SO$_4$; H$_2$O, H$^+$, heat; HONO; KI. (m) *p*-Nitrobenzyl chloride (from *p*-nitrotoluene), NaCN; H$_2$O, H$^+$, heat; Fe, H$^+$; HONO; H$_2$O, H$^+$, warm. (n) *p*-Nitrotoluene (from toluene), Br$_2$, Fe; Fe, H$^+$, heat; HONO; CuCl.

13. (a) ∼∼CO(CH$_2$)$_4$CONH(CH$_2$)$_6$NH∼∼; a substituted amide.
    (b) Acidic hydrolysis of amide linkages.

14.

Poor leaving group (OH$^-$) converted into a good leaving group (OTs$^-$).

15. (a) Reaction of C$_6$H$_5$N$_2^+$ is S$_N$1-like. Reaction of *p*-O$_2$NC$_6$H$_4$N$_2^+$ is S$_N$2-like. Electron withdrawal by —NO$_2$ slows down formation of Ar$^+$ so that bimolecular reaction predominates. (b) N$_2$ is an extraordinarily good leaving group.

16. (a) Hinsberg test; (b) HONO, then β-naphthol; (c) Hinsberg test; (d) Hinsberg test; (e) 3° salt with OH$^-$ gives odor or basic vapors of amine; (f) AgNO$_3$; (g) CrO$_3$/H$_2$SO$_4$; (h) HCl(aq); (i) BaCl$_2$; (j) AgNO$_3$; (k) HCl(aq); (l) BaCl$_2$ or H$_2$O or NaOH.

17. (a) Shake with aq. HCl; separate layers; dry hydrocarbon, distill; add NaOH to aqueous layer, shake with ether, separate layers, dry ether layer, distill. (b) Shake with aq. HCl; separate layers; dry anisole, distill; add NaOH to aqueous layer, shake with ether, separate layers, dry ether layer, distill. (c) Shake with aq. HCl; collect amide on filter; make filtrate alkaline, separate organic layer, dry, distill amine. (d) Shake with aq. HCl; collect sulfanilic acid on filter; make filtrate

alkaline, collect amine on filter.   (e) Treat with acetic anhydride, then aq. HCl; collect amide on filter, hydrolyze in hot alkaline medium, collect, dry, and distill amine; make acidic filtrate alkaline, separate, dry, and distill 3° amine.   (f) Shake ether solution with aq. NaOH; separate layers; acidify aqueous layer, extract with ether, dry, distill ether, then acid; treat ether layer with aq. HCl, separate hydrocarbon in one layer, make aqueous layer alkaline, extract with ether, dry, and distill amine. (g) Follow procedure in (c).   (h) Follow procedure in (c).

18. (a) Diazotization and coupling for aniline; then Hinsberg test. (b) HCl(aq).   (c) Hinsberg test to distinguish 3° and 2° amines; only one of the 1° amines will give a diazotization and coupling test.   (d) Hot NaOH(aq) gives NH_3 from ethyl oxamate.   (e) Formamide soluble in water; 3° amine soluble in HCl(aq), but nitrile insoluble.   (f) Amine soluble in HCl(aq); hot NaOH(aq) on nitrile gives NH_3; nitrobenzene unreactive.   (g) Elemental analysis distinguishes tosyl chloride and the two sulfonamides, which can be further distinguished by NaOH(aq); elemental analysis distinguishes *p*-chloroaniline and *p*-nitrobenzyl chloride which can be further distinguished by $AgNO_3$; of the compounds remaining, only the 3° amine is colorless, *o*-nitroaniline is more soluble than 2,4-dinitroaniline in HCl(aq), and 2,4-dinitroaniline readily gives NH_3 when warmed with NaOH(aq).

19. Test amine by Hinsberg procedure. If 3°, test for Cl. If 2°, make acetyl derivative, determine m.p.; if m.p. is 54-55°, make *p*-toluenesulfonamide to distinguish between possibilities. If 1°, test for Cl.

20. (a) Choline, $HOCH_2CH_2N(CH_3)_3{}^+ OH^-$;   (b) acetylcholine, $CH_3COOCH_2CH_2N(CH_3)_3{}^+ OH^-$.

21. (a) Novocaine, $p\text{-}H_2NC_6H_4COOCH_2CH_2N(C_2H_5)_2$.   (b) *p*-Nitrobenzoic acid (page 345), $SOCl_2$; $HOCH_2CH_2NEt_2$ (from ethylene oxide and Et_2NH); cat. H_2.

22. D, N-methyl-N-phenyl-*p*-toluamide;   E, N-methylaniline;   F, *p*-toluic acid;   G, N-methylbenzenesulfonanilide.

23. H, Alcohol;   I, unsaturated;   J, 4° hydroxide;   K, diene and 3° amine; L, 4° hydroxide;   M, 1,3,5-cyclooctatriene;   N, 5,8-dibromo-1,3-cyclooctadiene;   O, ditertiary amine;   P, diquaternary hydroxide; Q, 1,3,5,7-cyclooctatetraene.

24. (a) R, $HOCH_2C(CH_3)_2CHO$;   S, $HOCH_2C(CH_3)_2CHOHCN$; T, $HOCH_2C(CH_3)_2CHOHCOOH$;   U, γ-lactone of T; V, $HOCH_2C(CH_3)_2CHOHCOONa$; pantothenic acid, $HOCH_2C(CH_3)_2CHOHCONHCH_2CH_2COOH$.   (b) Succinic anhydride, NH_3; NaOBr.

25. W, anilinium chloride, $PhNH_3^+ Cl^-$; liquid, aniline.

26. (a) n-Butylamine; (b) N-methylformamide; (c) m-anisidine.

27. (a) α-Phenylethylamine; (b) β-phenylethylamine; (c) p-toluidine.

28. X, p-phenetidine (p-ethoxyaniline); Y, N-ethylbenzylamine;
    Z, Michler's ketone, p,p'-bis(dimethylamino)benzophenone,
    p-$(CH_3)_2 NC_6 H_4 \underset{\underset{O}{\|}}{C} C_6 H_4 N(CH_3)_2$-$p$.

CHAPTER 24

24.1 Intermolecular H-bonding in m- and p-isomers reduced or eliminated by dilution; intramolecular H-bond in o-isomer unaffected.

24.2 o-Nitroaniline, salicylic acid, salicyladehyde, o-fluorophenol. (Geometry is wrong for o-hydroxybenzonitrile: the $-C\equiv N$ group, with digonal carbon, is linear.)

24.3 Shake ether solution of mixture with $NaHCO_3$(aq); separate layers (Aq. 1, Ether 1). Acidify Aq. 1 with HCl, collect p-toluic acid on funnel. Shake Ether 1 with NaOH(aq); separate layers (Aq. 2, Ether 2). Acidify Aq. 2 with HCl, extract with ether, dry, distill ether and then p-cresol. Shake Ether 2 (containing amine and nitro compound) with HCl; separate layers (Aq. 3, Ether 3). Evaporate Ether 3, collect nitro compound on funnel. Make Aq. 3 alkaline with NaOH, extract with ether, dry, distill ether and then amine.

24.4 Benzene, propylene (from cracking), HF.

24.5 (a) Toluene, HNO_3, H_2SO_4; Fe, H^+; HONO; H_2O, H^+, warm.
    (b) Toluene, $Tl(OOCCF_3)_3$; $Pb(OAc)_4$, Ph_3P; H_2O, OH^-, heat; H^+.
    (c) m-Nitrotoluene (as in Problem 23.15), HONO; H_2O, H^+, warm.
    (d) Toluene, $Tl(OOCCF_3)_3$, $73°$; $Pb(OAc)_4$, Ph_3P; H_2O, OH^-, heat; H^+.

24.6 Acidity of phenols high enough (due to acid-strengthening nitro groups) to permit reaction with weakly basic HCO_3^-.

24.7 Phenol (via cumene hydroperoxide, Sec. 24.4 and Problem 24.4), H_2SO_4, low temp. (Problem 24.13); isolate o-isomer; $2Cl_2$, Fe; desulfonate by H_2O, H^+, steam distillation; NaOH; $ClCH_2COONa$ (from acetic acid via HVZ reaction); acidify with HCl(aq).

24.8 Benzene, Cl_2, Fe; HNO_3, H_2SO_4, warm; HNO_3, H_2SO_4, heat; NaOH heat; acidify; *n*-PrBr, NaOH; NH_4SH, warm.

24.9 *p*-Bromophenyl benzoate, *p*-$BrC_6H_4OOCC_6H_5$.

24.10 Volatility of *o*-isomer greater due to intramol. H-bonding.

24.11 Resorcinol, $CH_3(CH_2)_4COCl$, $ZnCl_2$; Zn(Hg), HCl, heat.

24.12 (a) The $-SO_3H$ group is displaced by electrophilic reagents, in this case by nitronium ion; (b) can use stronger nitrating agent without fear of destructive oxidation.

24.13 *o*-Isomer formed more rapidly but reversibly; *p*-isomer more stable than *o*-isomer; and *m*-isomer formed too slowly to be important.

24.14 Phenol, $NaNO_2$, H_2SO_4, 7-8°; oxidation by HNO_3.

24.15 Aspirin: salicylic acid, acetic anhydride, H^+. Methyl salicylate: salicylic acid, MeOH, H^+, warm.

24.16 (a) Removal of proton easier from $CHCl_3$, which is more acidic than CH_2Cl_2; impossible for CCl_4, which has no protons; confirms Step (1). (b) Removal of proton from $CHCl_3$ occurs to form an an anion that can acquire D from D_2O to yield $CDCl_3$; confirms Step (1), and its reversibility. (c) Reversal of Step (2) and hence also Step (1) by excess Cl^-; confirms Step (2), and its reversibility. (d) Reversal of Step (2), and hence also Step (1), but this time by I^-; necessity of removing proton by base is shown; confirms Steps (1) and (2), and their reversibility. (e) Addition of nucleophilic CCl_3^- to carbonyl group; confirms Step (1).

24.17 ArONa, $ClCH_2COONa$, warm; acidify. Neutralization equivalents of the aryloxyacetic acids would be useful in identifying phenols.

1. (a) 2,4-$(O_2N)_2C_6H_3OH$; (b) *m*-$CH_3C_6H_4OH$; (c) *p*-$C_6H_4(OH)_2$; (d) *m*-$C_6H_4(OH)_2$; (e) 4-*n*-hexyl-1,3-dihydroxybenzene; (f) *o*-$C_6H_4(OH)_2$; (g) 2,4,6-$(O_2N)_3C_6H_2OH$; (h) $CH_3COOC_6H_5$; (i) $C_6H_5OCH_3$; (j) *o*-HOC_6H_4COOH; (k) *o*-$HOC_6H_4COOC_2H_5$.

2. (a) HONO; H_2O, H^+, warm. (b) Benzene, $Tl(OOCCF_3)_3$; $Pb(OAc)_4$, Ph_3P; H_2O, OH^-, heat; H^+. (c) NaOH, strong heat; acidify. (d) O_2; H_2SO_4, H_2O, rearr.

3. (a) HBr, heat. (b) H_2SO_4, low temp.; NaOH; NaOH, strong heat; acidify. (c) $2SO_3$, H_2SO_4, heat; NaOH; NaOH, strong heat; acidify.

(d) HNO_3, H_2SO_4, heat; HNO_3, H_2SO_4, stronger heat; NaOH(aq), heat; acidify; HNO_3, H_2SO_4, heat. (e) $2Me_2SO_4$, NaOH.

4. (a) *o*-Toluidine (page 770), HONO; H_2O, H^+, warm. (b) *m*-Nitrotoluene (as in Problem 23.15), Fe, H^+; HONO; H_2O, H^+, warm. (c) *p*-Toluidine (page 770), HONO; H_2O, H^+, warm. (d) *p*-Nitroaniline (page 760), HONO; KI; Fe, H^+; HONO; H_2O, H^+, warm. (e) Nitrobenzene, Br_2, Fe; Fe, H^+; HONO; H_2O, H^+, warm. (f) Benzene, Br_2, Fe; HNO_3, H_2SO_4, heat; isolate *o*-isomer; Fe, H^+; HONO; H_2O, H^+, warm. (g) *p*-Nitrotoluene (from toluene), Br_2, Fe; Fe, H^+; HONO; H_2O, H^+, warm. (h) Aceto-*p*-toluidide (page 771), Br_2; H_2O, H^+, heat; HONO; H_2O, H^+, warm. (i) Aceto-*p*-toluidide (page 771), HNO_3, H_2SO_4; H_2O, H^+, heat; HONO; CuBr; Fe, H^+; HONO; H_2O, H^+, heat. (j) *o*-Nitrotoluene (from toluene), Br_2, Fe; Fe, H^+; HONO; H_2O, H^+, warm. (k) Benzene, Cl_2, Fe; HNO_3, H_2SO_4, heat; HNO_3, H_2SO_4, higher heat; NaOH(aq), heat; acidify. (l) Cumene (Problem 24.4), HNO_3, H_2SO_4; isolate *p*-isomer; Fe, H^+; HONO; H_2O, H^+, warm. (m) Cumene (Problem 24.4), HNO_3, H_2SO_4; isolate *p*-isomer; Fe, H^+; $2Br_2$(aq); HONO; H_2O, H^+, warm. (n) *p*-Toluidine (page 770), HONO; H_2O, H^+, warm; $CHCl_3$, OH^-; acidify. (o) *o*-HOC_6H_4CHO (page 804), MeI, OH^-; HCHO (from MeOH), OH^-, crossed Cannizzaro.

5. (a) Sodium *o*-cresoxide, *o*-$CH_3C_6H_4ONa$; (d) *o*-methylanisole, *o*-$CH_3C_6H_4OCH_3$; (e) *o*-tolyl benzyl ether, *o*-$CH_3C_6H_4OCH_2C_6H_5$; (g) *o*-tolyl 2,4-dinitrophenyl ether; (h) *o*-cresyl acetate, *o*-$CH_3C_6H_4OOCCH_3$ (must shift equilibrium, Sec. 18.16); (i) *o*-cresyl acetate, *o*-$CH_3C_6H_4OOCCH_3$; (j) *o*-cresyl hydrogen phthalate; (k) *o*-cresyl *p*-nitrobenzoate; (l) *o*-cresyl benzenesulfonate; (m) 3-methyl-4-hydroxyphenyl methyl ketone; (o) color produced; (p) 2-methylcyclohexanol; (q) 4-nitro-2-methylphenol; (r) 3-methyl-2-hydroxybenzenesulfonic acid; (s) 3-methyl-4-hydroxybenzenesulfonic acid; (t) 4,6-dibromo-2-methylphenol; (u) 4-bromo-2-methylphenol; (v) 4-nitroso-2-methylphenol; (w) 4-nitro-2-methylphenol; (x) 3-methyl-4-hydroxy-4'-nitroazobenzene (also named as 4-(4-nitrophenylazo)-2-methylphenol); (y) 3-methyl-2-hydroxybenzoic acid; (z) 3-methyl-2-hydroxybenzaldehyde. No reaction: b, c, f, n.

6. (c) Phenol and methyl bromide; (p) cyclohexyl methyl ether; (r) *o*- and *p*-methoxybenzenesulfonic acid; (s) *o*- and *p*-methoxybenzenesulfonic acid; (t) *o*- and *p*-bromoanisole; (u) *o*- and *p*-bromoanisole. All others: no reaction.

7. (c) Benzyl bromide; (h) benzyl acetate; (i) benzyl acetate; (j) benzyl hydrogen phthalate; (k) benzyl *p*-nitrobenzoate;

(l) benzyl benzenesulfonate; (n) benzyl chloride.
All others: no reaction.

8. (a) $PhSO_3H > PhCOOH > PhOH > PhCH_2OH$; (b) $H_2SO_4 > H_2CO_3 >$
   PhOH H_2O; (c) $m\text{-}NO_2 > m\text{-}Br >$ unsubstd. $> m\text{-}CH_3$;
   (d) 2,4,6- $>$ 2,4- $> p\text{-}$.

9. (a) NaOH(aq). (b) NaOH(aq) to detect the phenol; then CrO_3/H_2SO_4
   to distinguish between the alcohol and the ether. (c) $NaHCO_3$(aq) to
   detect the acid; then cold NaOH(aq) to distinguish between the phenol
   and the ester. (d) Dilute HCl. (e) The two acids are soluble in
   $NaHCO_3$(aq), but only one of them gives a color with $FeCl_3$. Of the
   remaining compounds, only ethyl salicylate is soluble in cold NaOH(aq).
   (f) $NaHCO_3$(aq) to detect the acid; then NaOH(aq) to detect the phenol;
   then dilute HCl to detect the amine.

10. (a) Shake with NaOH(aq); separate and dry hydrocarbon layer; acidify
    aqueous layer, extract with ether, dry, distill ether and then phenol.
    (c) Shake ether solution of mixture with $NaHCO_3$(aq); separate aqueous
    layer, acidify, collect acid on filter; shake ether layer with cold
    NaOH(aq); separate and acidify alkaline layer, collect phenol on filter;
    dry and distill ether and then ester. (d) Shake ether solution of mix-
    ture with HCl(aq); separate aqueous layer, make alkaline, extract with
    ether, dry, distill; dry ether layer, distill. (f) Shake solid mixture with
    $NaHCO_3$(aq), filter, collect residue; acidify filtrate, collect pptd. acid;
    treat residue with NaOH(aq), filter, collect solid; acidify filtrate, collect
    pptd. phenol; treat remaining mixture of amine and nitro compound
    with HCl(aq), filter, collect nitro compound on filter; make filtrate
    alkaline, collect pptd. amine on filter.

11. (a) HNO_3, H_2SO_4, heat; HNO_3, H_2SO_4, higher heat; NaOH(aq), heat;
    Sn, H^+. (b) $2Me_2SO_4$, OH^-; HNO_3, H_2SO_4, warm; Fe, H^+.
    (c) $2H_2SO_4$; isolate 4,6-dihydroxy-1,3-benzenedisulfonic acid; HNO_3,
    H_2SO_4, heat, introducing an $-NO_2$ group between the $-OH$'s;
    desulfonate by H_2O, H^+, heat. (d) HNO_3, H_2SO_4; Fe, H^+; HONO;
    H_2O, H^+, warm. (e) Isobutylene, acid catalyst. (f) Diisobutylene
    (page 200), acid catalyst. (g) PhOH, NaOH, $BrCH_2CH_2Br$. (h) Product
    g, KOH, strong heat. (i) PhOH and CH_3CHO. (j) Me_2SO_4, OH^-;
    tert-BuCl, $AlCl_3$; HNO_3, H_2SO_4, heat, to give dinitration at both posi-
    tions *ortho* to $-OMe$. (k) *p*-Toluidine (page 770), $2SO_3$, H_2SO_4,
    heat; HONO; H_3PO_2; NaOH, strong heat; acidify.

12. (a) Vanillin, Ac_2O, NaOAc, heat; HBr, heat (cleave ether).
    (b) Anethole $\longrightarrow$ *p*-$CH_3OC_6H_4CHO$ (compare Problem 19, page 650);

CH_3NO_2, OH^- (see Problem 21.22a); cat. H_2; HI.   (c) Vanillin, hot HBr; CN^-, H^+; $2H_2$, Ni, heat, pressure.

13.   Phenoxide ion contains two sites of nucleophilic reactivity: the $-O^-$, and the π electrons of the ring. It is an example of what Professor Nathan Kornblum (of Purdue University) has called *ambident* anions (L.: *ambi,* both; *dens,* tooth).   (a) Nucleophilic aliphatic substitution on benzylic carbon, with phenoxide $-O^-$ as nucleophile.   (b) Nucleophilic aliphatic substitution, as before, but now phenoxide ring competes with $-O^-$ as nucleophile. (From standpoint of ring, reaction is electrophilic aromatic substitution.)   (c) In aprotic solvents, $-O^-$ is only weakly solvated and hence highly reactive; in water, solvation through H-bonding lowers nucleophilic power of $-O^-$, and ring begins to compete successfully with it.   (d) Acidic protons of phenol and 2,2,2-trifluoroethanol H-bond strongly; methanol and ethanol less effective than water.

14.   Strong acid converts phloroglucinol reversibly into protonated species, hybrid of II and corresponding structures

$R =$ H, Me, or Et

with charge on *o*-OR groups. Spectrum is due to protons *a* ($\delta 4.15$) and *b* ($\delta 6.12$), allylic and vinylic protons, respectively, deshielded by positive charge. In D_2SO_4 all ring protons are gradually replaced by deuterons in electrophilic aromatic substitution via intermediates like II. From 1,3,5-trimethoxybenzene in D_2SO_4, would expect to isolate 1,3,5-trimethoxybenzene-2,4,6-d_3.

15.   (Numbering in citral will be retained throughout.)   (i) Protonation of carbonyl oxygen; electrophilic attack on ring of chavebetol by C-1 (compare page 1044) to yield RCHOHAr.   (ii) Acid converts RCHOHAr into carbonium ion, which adds to C-6 to generate $3°$ cation with charge at C-7.   (iii) Cation combines with phenolic $-OH$; proton lost from oxygen to yield final product.

16.   (a) A, *p*-nitrophenyl ethyl ether (*p*-nitrophenetole);   B, *p*-ethoxyaniline (*p*-phenetidine);   C, *p*-(*p*-ethoxyphenylazo)phenol (4-hydroxy-4'-ethoxyazobenzene);   D, 4,4'-diethoxyazobenzene;   E, 2 moles

p-ethoxyaniline; phenacetin, *p*-CH$_3$CONHC$_6$H$_4$OC$_2$H$_5$.   (b) F,
o-HOC$_6$H$_4$CH$_2$CH$_2$Br; coumarane (below);   (c) G, C$_6$H$_5$OCH$_2$COOH,
phenoxyacetic acid; H, C$_6$H$_5$OCH$_2$COCl; 3-cumaranone (below);

       Coumarane   3-Cumaranone

(d) I, 5-isopropyl-2-methylbenzenesulfonic acid;
J, 2-isopropyl-5-methylbenzenesulfonic acid; carvacrol,
5-isopropyl-2-methylphenol; thymol, 2-isopropyl-5-methylphenol;
K, 5-carboxy-2-methylbenzenesulfonic acid.
(e) L, *p*-CH$_3$OC$_6$H$_4$CHBrCH$_2$CH$_3$; M, 3,4-bis(*p*-methoxyphenyl)hexane;
hexestrol, 3,4-bis(*p*-hydroxyphenyl)hexane.

17. N, 3,4-(HO)$_2$C$_6$H$_3$COCH$_2$Cl; O, 3,4-(HO)$_2$C$_6$H$_3$COCH$_2$NHCH$_3$;
adrenaline, 3,4-(HO)$_2$C$_6$H$_3$CHOHCH$_2$NHCH$_3$.

18. (a) P, *p*-isopropylbenzenesulfonic acid; Q, *p*-isopropylphenol;
R, 4-isopropylcyclohexanol; S, ketone from R; T, cyanohydrin from
S; U, acetate ester of T; V, unsaturated nitrile; W, acid from V;
X, acid chloride from W; phellandral, aldehyde from X, 4-isopropyl-
3,4,5,6-tetrahydrobenzaldehyde.   (b) Two configurations about C-4
produced in hydrogenation step.   (c) Dihydrophellandric acid, *cis*-
and *trans*-4-isopropylcyclohexanecarboxylic acids, each of which is
achiral.

19. Y, *m*-cresol.

20. (a) *cis*- or *trans*-*p*-CH$_3$OC$_6$H$_4$CH=CHCH$_3$, *p*-CH$_3$OC$_6$H$_4$CH$_2$CH=CH$_2$,
p-CH$_3$OC$_6$H$_4$C(CH$_3$)=CH$_2$; (b) *cis*- or *trans*-*p*-CH$_3$OC$_6$H$_4$CH=CHCH$_3$;
p-CH$_3$OC$_6$H$_4$CH$_2$CH=CH$_2$; (c) ozonolysis, or isomerization of one
into the other by strong heating with KOH; (d) Z, *p*-allylanisole,
p-CH$_3$OC$_6$H$_4$CH$_2$CH=CH$_2$; (e) AA, *p*-propenylanisole,
p-CH$_3$OC$_6$H$_4$CH=CHCH$_3$; (f) *p*-bromoanisole, Mg, anhyd. Et$_2$O;
CH$_3$CH$_2$CHO; acidify; H$^+$, heat.

21. (a) BB, isopropyl salicylate; CC, salicylic acid; (b) hot alkali
hydrolyzed ester to sodium salicylate and iso-PrOH, which was dis-
tilled off and gave an iodoform test.

22. Chavibetol, 2-methoxy-5-allylphenol; DD, methyl ether of chavibetol;
EE, 2-methoxy-5-propenylphenol; FF, methyl ether of EE.

23. (a) An amide;

(b)

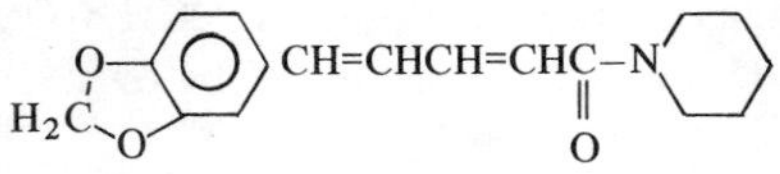

Piperine 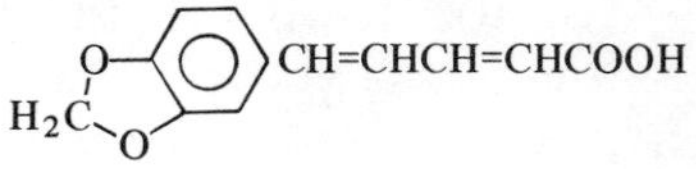   Piperonylic acid

24. (a) Hordinene, p-$HOC_6H_4CH_2CH_2N(CH_3)_2$ or
p-$HOC_6H_4CH(CH_3)N(CH_3)_2$ (actually, the former); KK, 3° amino
group free; LL, phenolic group methylated. (b) p-$HOC_6H_4CH_2CHO$,
Me_2NH, cat. H_2.

25. MM, sulfonation *ortho* to $-CH_3$; NN, replacement of $-SO_3H$ by $-OH$;
OO, hydrogenation of ring; PP, replacement of alcoholic $-OH$ by $-Br$;
QQ, dehydrohalogenation of PP; RR, ethyl ester of QQ; a-terpineol,
2-(4-methyl-3-cyclohexenyl)-2-propanol.

26. Coniferyl alcohol, 3-(4-hydroxy-3-methoxyphenyl)-2-propen-1-ol;
SS, its dibenzoate; TT, its methyl ether (phenolic).

27. (a) A ketal and lactone. Electrophilic attack by Br^+ at C-4 of ring
generates benzenonium ion, which combines (at C-1 of ring) with
carboxylate group.

(b)

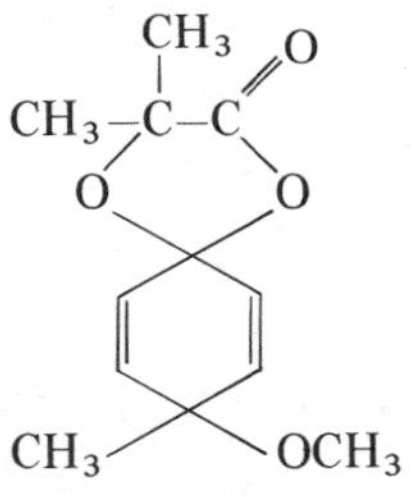

VV 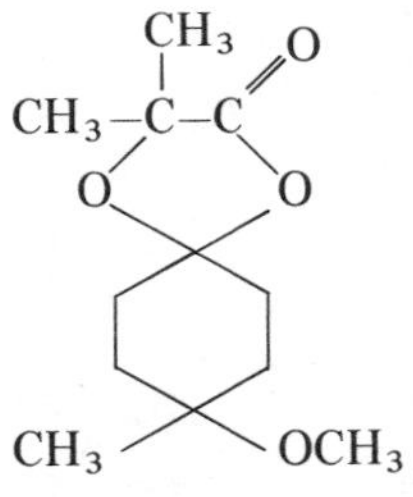   WW 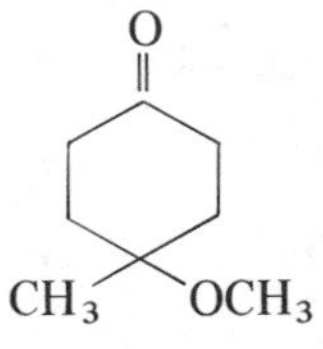   XX

(c) Synthesis of a variety of non-benzenoid cyclic compounds from
benzenoid starting materials.

28. AAA, piperonal, page 650; BBB, vanillin, page 792; CCC, eugenol,
page 791; DDD, thymol, page 792; EEE, isoeugenol, page 791;
FFF, safrole, page 792.

CHAPTER 25

25.1 (a) See Sec. 11.21. (b) See Problem 11.13 (page 367) and its answer.

25.2 (a) Toluene, Br_2, $Tl(OOCCF_3)_3$. (b) Toluene, $Tl(OOCCF_3)_3$, $25°$; KI. (c) See page 771. (d) Toluene, $Tl(OOCCF_3)_3$, $73°$; KI. (e) Toluene, HNO_3, H_2SO_4; isolate o-isomer; Fe, H^+; HONO; CuBr.

25.3 Stronger C—O bond in phenols: partial double-bond character to Ar—O bond and/or sp^2 hybridization of aromatic carbon.

25.4 (a) Salt of p-nitrosophenol; (b) nucleophilic aromatic substitution; (c) electron withdrawal — or, more properly, electron acceptance — by nitroso group, and stabilization of intermediate anion. (d) $PhNO_2$, Fe, H^+; make alkaline; 2EtI (from EtOH); nitrous acid (from $NaNO_2$); KOH, heat.

25.5 (a) Nucleophilic aromatic substitution of —OH for $—OCH_3$; activation by the two $—NO_2$ groups *ortho* and *para* to $—OCH_3$. (b) Alkaline medium brings about nucleophilic displacement of $—NH_2$ of p-nitroaniline to give p-nitrophenol, thus decreasing yield of amine. (c) Nucleophilic displacement of —Cl by $—SO_3Na$; the reagent, SO_3^{--}, has an unshared electron pair on sulfur where SO_3 (sulfur trioxide) has none. (d) Not a general method, and cannot be used to prepare $PhSO_3H$. (e) Nucleophilic displacement of o- or p-NO_2 by $—SO_3Na$ gives a water-soluble nitrobenzenesulfonate salt; m-isomer inactive, remains insoluble.

25.6 Dispersal of developing charge, negative or positive, in transition state leading to:

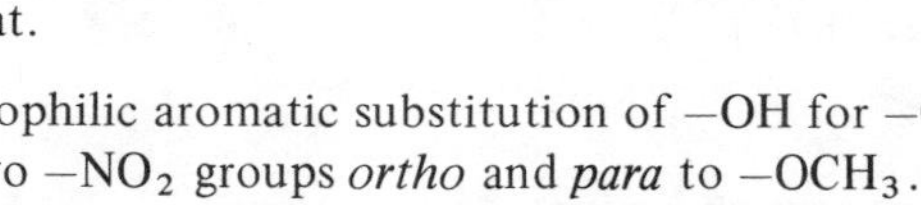

25.7

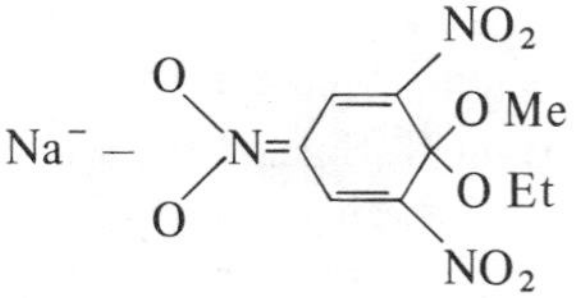

(and corresponding structures involving o-NO_2 groups)

25.8 o-Fluoroanisole, which has two electron-withdrawing, acid-strengthening substituents, is a stronger acid than benzene; the phenyl anion is a stronger base than the anion that carries two electron-withdrawing, base-weakening substituents.

25.9 Organolithium compound, like Grignard reagent, reacts (a) with CO_2 to give carboxylic acid, and (b) with a ketone to yield a tertiary alcohol.

(c)

25.10 (a) AgNO$_3$; (b) AgNO$_3$; (c) Br$_2$/CCl$_4$ or KMnO$_4$; (d) iodoform test, or CrO$_3$/H$_2$SO$_4$; (e) iodoform test.

25.11 (a) Oxidation to acids, and determination of their m.p.'s or neutralization equivalents; (b) ozonolysis, or isomerization of allylic compound by hot KOH.

1. (a) Phenylmagnesium bromide; (h) *o*- and *p*-BrC$_6$H$_4$NO$_2$; (i) *o*- and *p*-BrC$_6$H$_4$SO$_3$H; (j) *o*- and *p*-BrC$_6$H$_4$Cl; (m) *o*- and *p*-BrC$_6$H$_4$C$_2$H$_5$. No reaction: b, c, d, e, f, g, k, l, n, o.

2. (a) *n*-Butylmagnesium bromide; (b) *n*-butyl alcohol; (c) 1-butene; (d) 1-hexyne; (e) *n*-butyl ethyl ether; (f) *n*-butylamine; (g) *n*-valeronitrile; (l) *n*- and *sec*-butylbenzene. No reaction: h, i, j, k, m, n, o.

3. (b) 2,4-Dinitrophenol; (e) 2,4-dinitrophenyl ether; (f) 2,4-dinitroaniline; (g) 2,4-dinitrobenzonitrile.

4. (a) Mg, anhyd. Et$_2$O; H$_2$O. (b) HNO$_3$, H$_2$SO$_4$. (c) Cl$_2$, Fe. (d) SO$_3$, H$_2$SO$_4$. (e) Br$_2$, Fe; Br$_2$, Fe, heat. (f) CH$_3$Cl, AlCl$_3$. (g) Mg, anhyd. Et$_2$O; HCHO; H$_2$O. (h) Mg, anhyd. Et$_2$O; CH$_3$CHO; H$_2$O. (i) Mg, anhyd. Et$_2$O; acetone; H$_2$O. (j) HNO$_3$, H$_2$SO$_4$, warm; HNO$_3$, H$_2$SO$_4$, heat; NaOH(aq), heat. (k) Mg, anhyd. Et$_2$O; allyl bromide. (l) Mg, anhyd. Et$_2$O; CO$_2$; acidify. (m) NaNH$_2$/NH$_3$.

5. (a) C$_6$H$_6$; (b) C$_6$H$_6$; (c) C$_6$H$_6$; (d) allylbenzene; (e) PhCH$_2$OH; (f) PhCHOHCH$_3$; (g) PhCHOHPh; (h) *p*-CH$_3$C$_6$H$_4$CHOHPh; (i) 2-phenyl-2-propanol; (j) 1-phenylcyclohexanol; (k) 1-phenyl-3,3-dimethylcyclohexanol; (l) methyldiphenylcarbinol; (m) Ph$_3$COH, triphenylcarbinol; (n) optically active *sec*-butyldiphenylcarbinol; (o) C$_6$H$_6$ + HC≡CMgBr. Racemic modifications: f, h, k. Optically active single compound: n. All others: optically inactive single compounds.

6. (a) 2,4,6-Trinitrochlorobenzene > 2,4-dinitrochlorobenzene > *o*-chloronitrobenzene > *m*-chloronitrobenzene, chlorobenzene; (b) toluene > benzene > chlorobenzene > nitrobenzene; (c) 3-bromo-1-butene > 4-bromo-1-butene > 1-bromo-1-butene;

(d) toluene $>$ *p*-bromotoluene $>$ bromobenzene $>$ *p*-dibromobenzene;
(e) benzyl chloride $>$ ethyl chloride $>$ chlorobenzene;
(f) $PhCHBrCH_3$ $>$ $PhCH_2CH_2Br$ $>$ $PhCH=CHBr$. Products from most active compounds: (a) picric acid (2,4,6-trinitrophenol); (b) *o*- and *p*-nitrotoluene; (c) $CH_3CH(OEt)CH=CH_2$ and $CH_3CH=CHCH_2OEt$; (d) *o*- and *p*-$CH_3C_6H_4SO_3H$; (e) $PhCH_2CN$, phenylacetonitrile; (f) α-phenylethyl ethyl ether.

7. $NaHCO_3$, to minimize nucleophilic substitution leading to 2,4-dinitrophenol.

8. (a) $CH_2=CBrCH_2OH$; (b) *p*-$BrC_6H_4CH_2NH_2$; (c) *p*-ClC_6H_4COOH; (d) *m*-$BrC_6H_4CHBrCH_2Br$; (e) 2-chloro-4-nitroanisole; (f) *p*-ClC_6H_4MgBr; (g) no reaction; (h) *p*-$BrC_6H_4CH_2Br$; (i) *o*-$ClC_6H_4CH=CH_2$; (j) *p*-$BrC_6H_4CH_2Cl$; (k) *m*-$F_3CC_6H_4NH_2$; (l) *m*-$CH_3OC_6H_4NEt_2$.

9. (a) C_6H_6, HNO_3, H_2SO_4; Cl_2, Fe, heat. (b) C_6H_6, Cl_2, Fe; HNO_3, H_2SO_4. (c) $C_6H_5CH_3$, $KMnO_4$, heat; acidify; Br_2, Fe. (d) $C_6H_5CH_3$, Br_2, Fe; $KMnO_4$, heat; acidify. (e) $C_6H_5CH_3$, $3Cl_2$, heat; Cl_2, Fe. (f) C_6H_6, Br_2, Fe; HNO_3, H_2SO_4; Br_2, Fe. (g) $C_6H_5CH_3$, Br_2, Fe; $2Cl_2$, heat. (h) C_6H_6, Cl_2, Fe; HNO_3, H_2SO_4, heat; HNO_3, H_2SO_4, stronger heating; NH_3, warm. (i) C_6H_6, C_2H_4, HF; Br_2, Fe; Cl_2, heat; KOH(alc), heat. (j) $C_6H_5CH_3$, Br_2, Fe; Br_2, Fe; $KMnO_4$, heat; acidify. (k) Toluene, $Tl(OOCCF_3)_3$, 73°; KI. (l) C_6H_6, Br_2, Fe; SO_3, H_2SO_4. (m) $C_6H_5CH_3$, Cl_2, Fe; Cl_2, heat; NaOH(aq), warm. (n) $C_6H_5CH_3$, Br_2, Fe; Mg, anhyd. Et_2O; acetone; H_2O; acid, heat; cat. H_2.

10. Nitrogen can accommodate the negative charge of the anion (see Sec. 31.10).

11. Protonated chloral, $Cl_3C\overset{+}{C}HOH$, attacks the ring of chlorobenzene in an electrophilic aromatic substitution to give *p*-$ClC_6H_4CHOHCCl_3$. With acid this gives an oxonium ion, *p*-$ClC_6H_4CH(CCl_3)OH_2^+$, that ionizes with loss of water to *p*-$ClC_6H_4\overset{+}{C}HCCl_3$, an ion that attacks a second molecule of chlorobenzene in an electrophilic aromatic substitution to give DDT.

12. Phenoxide ion can add to intermediate benzyne in two ways: (i) with attachment at oxygen to give diphenyl ether; and (ii) with attachment at *p*-carbon (electrophilic substitution from viewpoint of phenoxide ion) to give *p*-phenylphenol. (Compare answer to Problem 13, Chapter 24.)

13. In carbanions and transition states leading to their formation, electron-withdrawing inductive effect of fluorine depends on distance from

negative carbon, and is *much* stronger from *ortho* position than from *meta* or *para*.

14. $-N_2^+$ activates ring toward nucleophilic aromatic substitution; chloride ion displaces much bromide before reduction occurs.

15.

$$ArX + R_2NH \underset{(1)}{\rightleftharpoons} \underset{\substack{\overset{\displaystyle X}{\diagup} \\ Ar^- \diagdown \\ \overset{+}{N}HR_2}}{} \xrightarrow{(2)} X^- + Ar\overset{+}{N}HR_2$$

$$\longrightarrow ArNR_2$$

$$\underset{\substack{\overset{\displaystyle X}{\diagup} \\ (3) \Big\downarrow \; :B}}{}$$

$$\underset{\substack{\overset{\displaystyle X}{\diagup} \\ Ar^- \diagdown \\ NR_2}}{} \xrightarrow{(4)} X^- + ArNR_2$$

$$XI$$

Bunnett (page 478), who did this work, has given essentially the following interpretation. (There is additional evidence to help rule out certain alternative interpretations.)

When X = F, intermediate X is formed reversibly (1). Some of X goes on to products (2) by loss of X^-, but some reverts to ArX by loss of weakly basic R_2NH; this reversal of (1) retards the over-all reaction. Via (3), base converts the intermediate X into XI, which rapidly goes on (4) to products by loss of X^- rather than revert to ArX by loss of the strongly basic R_2N^- anion.

When X = Br, (2) is much faster because of weaker C—Br bond. X is formed irreversibly, all of it rapidly going on to product with or without action of base.

16. (a) Primary isotope effect. Consider answer to preceding problem, with X = OPh or ^{18}OPh. Steps (2) and (3) are slower for heavier isotope, and more of intermediate reverts to starting material via reverse of step (1). (b) Piperidine speeds up (3) relative to reverse of (1), so that higher fraction of intermediate goes on to product, regardless of whether OPh^- or $^{18}OPh^-$ is being lost.

17. In the aprotic solvent, azide ion is weakly solvated (no H-bonding) and hence a stronger nucleophile.

18. (a) 28, N_2; 44, CO_2; 76, benzyne, C_6H_4; 152, biphenylene, dimer of benzyne. (b) o-Aminobenzoic acid.

Biphenylene

19. Tetraphenylmethane; KNH_2/NH_3 produces benzyne from chloroben-zene; benzyne then adds the $Ph_3C:^-$ anion. The resonance-stabilized Ph_3C^- is too weakly basic to produce benzyne, and too weakly nucleophilic to bring about bimolecular displacement.

20. (a) At 340°, reaction proceeds (at least partly) via an aryne, which adds H_2O to give both *p*- and *m*-cresol; at 250°, reaction is direct displacement to give only *p*-cresol. (b) Addition of *t*-BuOH to the aryne XII. (c) Addition of CH_3CN (as $^-CH_2CN$) or NH_3 to the aryne XIII.

COOH

O_2N

XII   XIII

21. II and III give the same aryne, which adds the amino side chain to yield 1-methyl-2,3-dihydroindole.

CH_3

1-Methyl-2,3-dihydroindole

22. (a) Only 1,5-dibromopentane will react with $AgNO_3$; only *p*-bromo-styrene reacts with $KMnO_4$. (b) Oxidize to acid and determine m.p.: *o*-, 148°; *m*-, 156°; *p*-, 254°. (c) Only benzyl chloride will react with $AgNO_3$; *o*-dichlorobenzene will not react with (hot) $KMnO_4$. (d) Only 4-octyne decolorizes Br_2/CCl_4; the alcohols react with CrO_3/H_2SO_4, and can be distinguished by elemental analysis; of remaining compounds only ethylcyclohexane contains no Cl, only chlorobenzene is soluble in fuming sulfuric acid. (e) Aryl halide is negative to $AgNO_3$; oxidize others to acids and distinguish them by m.p.'s of these products.

23. $Ar^- + Ar'{-}Br \rightleftharpoons Ar{-}Br + Ar'^-$

Only carbanions with negative charge *ortho* to halogen are involved. Hardest part: base can form carbanion from V, but this cannot abstract Br from another molecule of V, since this would not generate carbanion with charge *ortho* to halogen.

CHAPTER 26

26.1 (a) *n*-Valeric acid: use *n*-PrBr. Isovaleric acid: use *iso*-PrBr. α-Methylbutyric acid: use MeBr and EtBr in successive steps. Cannot make trisubstituted acetic acids by malonic ester synthesis, because only two alkyl groups can be introduced. (b) Alkylate malonic ester with *iso*-BuBr; hydrolysis; then Br_2; excess NH_3; decarboxylation. (Bromination and ammonolysis best carried out on free isobutyl-malonic acid rather than on ester.) (c) As in (b), except use *sec*-BuBr.

26.2 (a) In synthesis of adipic acid, excess of monosodium salt ensures displacement of both bromine atoms. In synthesis of cyclic acid, excess of halide ensures monosubstitution to give (β-bromoethyl)malonic ester; addition then of second mole of ethoxide generates carbanion which, by intramolecular nucleophilic attack, closes ring in second alkylation. (b) Excess 1,4-dibromobutane, one mole sodiomalonic ester; one mole sodium ethoxide; hydrolysis; acidification; decarboxylation.

26.3 (a) Ethyl benzalmalonate, $PhCH=C(COOEt)_2$. The amine abstracts a proton from malonic ester to give a carbanion that adds to benzaldehyde. Protonation and loss of water lead to final product.
(b) Cinnamic acid. (c) See Problem 21.22e.

26.4 (a)

⬡=C–COOEt.   Acetate ion abstracts a proton from
  |
  CN

cyanoacetic ester to give a carbanion that adds to cyclohexanone. Protonation and loss of water lead to final product.
(b)

⬡=CHCOOH.

26.5 See Sec. 27.7.

26.6 Nucleophilic substitution (S_N2); $1° > 2° >> 3°$ (or none); aryl halides not used.

26.7 (a) $CH_3COCH_2CH_2COOH$, a γ-keto acid. (Bromoacetic acid would simply convert sodio compound into acetoacetic ester.)
(b) $PhCOCH_2COCH_3$; $CH_3COCH_2CH_2COCH_3$; both are diketones.

26.8 (a) Use *n*-PrBr to alkylate ethyl acetoacetate; (b) *iso*-PrBr; (c) MeBr and EtBr in successive alkylations; (d) can make only mono- or disubstituted acetones by acetoacetic ester synthesis and this is a

trisubstituted acetone; (e) acetyl chloride and ethyl socioaceto-
acetate; (f) chloroacetone and ethyl sodioacetoacetate; or
$2Na[CH_3COCHCOOEt], I_2$; (g) $PhCOCH_2Cl$ and
$Na[CH_3COCHCOOEt]$.

26.9 Crossed Claisen condensation, followed by hydrolysis and decarboxylation of a β-keto acid. A, $EtOOCCOCH(CH_3)COOEt$.

26.10 (a) Ethyl isovalerate and ethyl oxalate; (b) $PhCH_2COOEt$ and ethyl
oxalate; (c) ethyl succinate and ethyl oxalate; (d) product a, NH_3,
cat. H_2; (e) product c, NH_3, cat. H_2.

26.11 (a) Charged end loses CO_2; resulting anion, $HO-C=CH_2$, is stabilized

through accommodation of the negative charge by oxygen.
(b) Doubly-charged carbanion, $^-OOC-CH_2^-$, would be less stable and
the transition state leading to it would be reached with difficulty.

26.12 Loss of CO_2 yields carbanion stabilized by three powerfully electron-
withdrawing groups.

26.13 Intermediates that can react with Br_2 and I_2 are involved; both the
proposed intermediates in decarboxylation (the carbanion and the
enol) are known to react with halogens (Secs. 21.3 and 21.4).

26.14 $HO-C-CH_2-COOH \rightarrow HO-C-CH_2-COO^- \rightarrow HO=CH_2 + CO_2$

26.15 $Ph-C\equiv CCOO^- \rightarrow CO_2 + PhC\equiv C:^-$ (relatively stable anion).

26.16 In general synthesis on page 855: (a) R is Me, R′ is Et; (b) R is Me,
R′ is Me, R″ (in second halide) is Me; (c) R is Et, R′ is Me; (d) R is
Me, R′ is $PhCH_2$.

26.17 (a) A is I (page 855) with R = n-$C_6H_{13}CH(O^-Li^+)$−; B is
n-$C_6H_{13}CHOHCH_2COOEt$. (b) As in (a), except use n-Pr_2CO
instead of aldehyde. (c) As in (a), except use I (R = Et) and PhCHO.

26.18 (a)

    HO⟨ ⟩Oxaz   O=⟨ ⟩Oxaz   Ph⟨ ⟩COOEt
       C   D   E

(b) Benzene, succinic anhydride, $AlCl_3$. (c) As in (b);

2-amino-2-methyl-1-propanol; EtMgBr; EtOH, H_2SO_4; $- H_2O$.
(d) *p*-Bromobenzoic acid, 2-amino-2-methyl-1-propanol; Mg, Et_2O;
EtCHO; EtOH, H_2SO_4.   (e) As in (d), except use PhCHO in place
of EtCHO.

26.19   From acid-base complex via six-membered cyclic transition state.

(a)

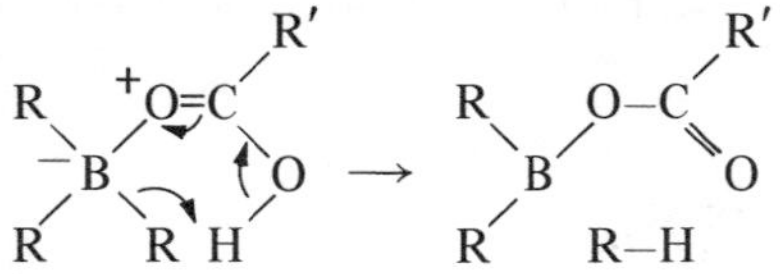

(b)

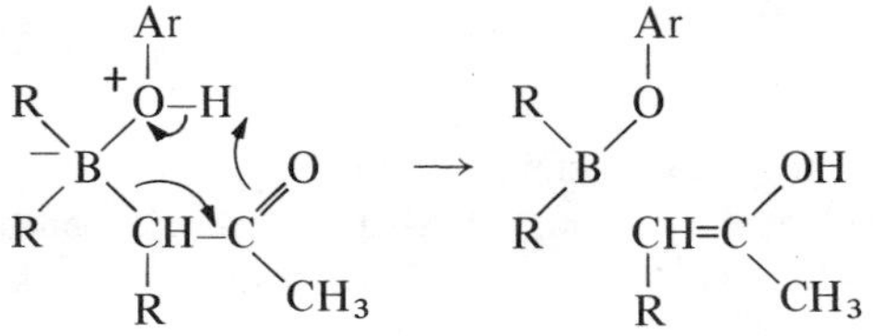

(enol)

26.20   (a) 1-Butene, 9-BBN; $BrCH_2COCH_3$, base.   (b) Isobutylene, 9-BBN;
$BrCH_2COOEt$, base.   (c) As in (a), except start with 2-butene.
(d) As in (a), except start with cyclohexene.   (e) As in (b), except
start with 1-methylcyclopentene.   (f) As in (b), except use
$PhCOCH_2Br$.   (g) Cyclopentene, 9-BBN; t-$BuCOCH_2Br$, base.

26.21   (a) Alkylate enamine of cyclohexanone with benzyl bromide.
(b) Alkylate enamine of isobutyraldehyde with allyl bromide.
(c) As in (a), except use ethyl α-bromopropionate.   (d) As in (a),
except use bromoacetone.   (e) As in (a), except use 2,4-dinitro-
bromobenzene.   (f) As in (b), except use acetyl chloride.

26.22

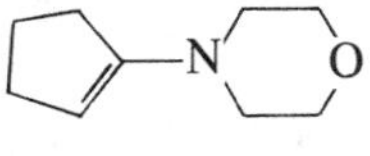

A 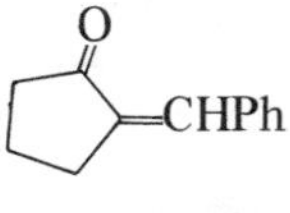   B

C, $Me_2CHCH=N-Bu$-*t*;   D, $(Me_2C=CH-N-Bu$-*t*$)^- (MgBr)^+$;
E, C_2H_6;   F, $PhCH_2C(CH_3)_2CHO$.

1.   (a) *n*-BuBr;   (b) 2MeBr;   (c) iso-PrBr;   (d) MeBr and iso-PrBr;
(e) 2EtBr;   (f) 2$PhCH_2Br$;   (g) MeBr and $CH_3CHBrCOOEt$;

(h) CH_2Br_2 and 2 malonic ester;   (i) excess 1,3-dibromopropane, one mole malonic ester, NaOEt; NaOEt.

2. (a) MeBr.   (b) 2EtBr.   (c) EtBr and *n*-PrBr.   (d) $C_2H_5CH(CH_3)CH_2Br$. (e) MeBr and isopentyl bromide.   (f) $CH_3CHBrCOOEt$ (ketonic cleavage); or MeBr and CH_3COCH_2Cl (acidic cleavage, Problem 11, page 862).   (g) $ClCH_2COOEt$; then cat. H_2 on product of ketonic cleavage.   (h) MeBr and *n*-PrBr; then cat. H_2 on ketone.   (i) Acetoacetic ester, NaOEt, 1-bromo-2-methylbutane; ketonic cleavage; MeMgBr; H_2O; acid, heat; cat. H_2.   (j) 2-Bromopentane (acidic cleavage). (k) iso-PrBr (acidic cleavage).   (l) $CH_3CHBrCOOEt$ (acidic cleavage). (m) 2 acetoacetic ester, 2NaOEt; I_2; ketonic cleavage; cat. H_2.

3. Cyclopentanone. 2-Carbethoxycyclopentanone, NaOEt; MeBr; dil. OH^-, warm (ketonic cleavage).

4. (a) A, $(EtOOC)_2CH(CH_2)_3CH(COOEt)_2$;   B, ethyl 1,1,3,3-cyclohexanetetracarboxylate;   C, 1,3-cyclohexanedicarboxylic acid;   (b) D, $(EtOOC)_2CH(CH_2)_2CH(COOEt)_2$;   E, ethyl 1,1,4,4-cyclohexanetetracarboxylate;   F, 1,4-cyclohexanedicarboxylic acid;   (c) G, $(EtOOC)_2CHCH(COOEt)_2$; H, succinic acid;   (d) I, ethyl 1,1,2,2-cyclobutanetetracarboxylate; J, 1,2-cyclobutanedicarboxylic acid.   (e) $BrCH_2CH_2Br$, 2 malonic ester, 2NaOEt; then 2NaOEt; CH_2I_2. $BrCH_2CH_2CH_2Br$, 2 malonic ester, 2NaOEt; then 2NaOEt; I_2. Excess $Br(CH_2)_4Br$, 1 malonic ester, 1NaOEt; then second mole of NaOEt.

5. K, 1,5-hexadiene;   L, 2,5-dibromohexane; M, $CH_3CHBrCH_2CH_2CH(CH_3)CH(COOEt)_2$; N, ethyl 2,5-dimethyl-1,1-cyclopentanedicarboxylate; O, 2,5-dimethylcyclopentanecarboxylic acid.

6. Decarboxylation to CCl_3^- easy because of relative stability of this anion. Subsequent steps same as (2) and (3) on page 311.

7. (a) 1 mole $BrCH_2CH_2Br$ to excess $Na[CH_3COCHCOOEt]$; ketonic cleavage.   (b) Intramol. aldol cond.   (c) As in (a), but using CH_2I_2. (Or by Michael reaction, Sec. 27.7.)   (d) Intramol. aldol cond. to give 3-methyl-2-cyclohexen-1-one.

8. (a) 1$(COOEt)_2$, 1 ethyl glutarate, 2NaOEt; then ketonic cleavage; (b) $(COOEt)_2$, 1$CH_3CH_2CH_2COOEt$; then ketonic cleavage.

9. (a) Dialkylation of malonic ester with EtBr; urea, NaOEt.   (b) As in (a), except use allyl bromide and 2-bromopentane in alkylation of malonic ester.   (c) As in (a), except use EtBr and isopentyl bromide in alkylation of malonic ester.

10. (a) Removal of C-5 proton from barbituric acid gives resonance-stabilized aromatic anion (six π electrons from C-5 and the two nitrogens); Veronal has no C-5 protons, cannot form such an anion.
(b) Amide with two acyl groups for each N–H group.

11. (a) Reversal of Claisen condensation by which keto ester was made; here, esters are irreversibly hydrolyzed to carboxylate salts.
(b) Alkylate acetoacetic ester before hydrolyze with concentrated alkali. (c) Use *n*-PrBr in alkylation, dil. NaOH in the ketonic cleavage; *n*-valeric acid chief acidic side-product. The crude ketone will contain water, EtOH, acetic acid, *n*-valeric acid. Remove acids by aqueous NaOH; then distill, collecting water, EtOH, ketone. Remove EtOH and some water by shaking with conc. $CaCl_2$(aq). Separate ketone from aqueous layer, dry over $MgSO_4$, and distill.

12. (a) Reversal of crossed Claisen condensation between ketones and esters (Problem 21.32, page 719); as in preceding problem, products irreversibly hydrolyzed to carboxylate anions. (b) Cyclopentanone, pyrrolidine, TsOH; PhCOCl; conc. base; N_2H_4, base (Wolff-Kishner reduction).
(c) Enamine of cyclohexanone (part b), $ClCO(CH_2)_7COOEt$; conc. base; N_2H_4, base.

13. P, $CH_3(CH_2)_5CHOHCH_2COOEt$; Q, $CH_3(CH_2)_5COCH_2COOEt$;
R, $CH_3(CH_2)_5COCH(CH_2Ph)COOEt$; S, $CH_3(CH_2)_5COCH_2CH_2Ph$,
1-phenyl-3-nonanone.

14.

I II

(a) T, mixture of I and II; U, II. (b) Equilibration through reversible hydroboration gives more stable isomer, II.

15. (a)

$$ArCHO + OH^- \rightleftarrows Ar-\underset{\underset{OH}{|}}{\overset{\overset{H}{|}}{C}}-O^- + H_2O$$

$$Ar-\underset{\underset{OH}{|}}{\overset{\overset{H}{|}}{C}}-O^- + OH^- \rightleftarrows Ar-\underset{\underset{O^-}{|}}{\overset{\overset{H}{|}}{C}}-O^- + H_2O$$

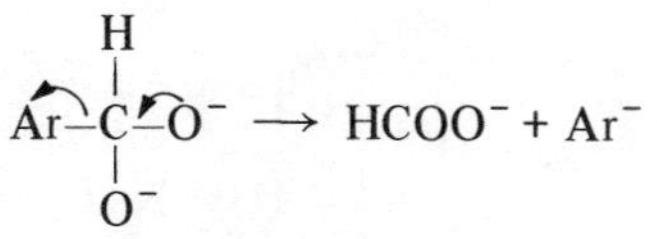

$$\underset{\underset{O^-}{|}}{\overset{\overset{H}{|}}{Ar-C-O^-}} \longrightarrow HCOO^- + Ar^-$$

$$Ar^- + H_2O \longrightarrow ArH + OH^-$$

(b) Two *o*-Cl stabilize Ar^- and transition state leading to its formation.

16.

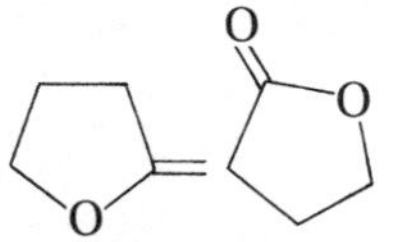

$(ClCH_2CH_2CH_2)_2C=O$

        V   W

Aldol-like condensation, dehydration gives V. Cleavage of lactone and vinylic ether, tautomerization; substitution of Cl for two OH's; decarboxylation of β-keto acid gives W. Abstraction of α-protons by base, intramolecular double nucleophilic attack by anions displaces Cl's, gives final product.

17. (a) X, $CH_3COCHRCOOEt$; Y, CH_3COCH_2R;
     Z, $RCH_2C(CH_3)(OH)C\equiv CH$; AA, nerolidol,
     $RCH_2C(CH_3)(OH)CH=CH_2$. (b) R is
     $(CH_3)_2C=CHCH_2CH_2C(CH_3)=CHCH_2-$, with $-H$ and $-CH_3$ *trans*.

18. (a) BB, 2-carbethoxy-3(or 5)-methylcyclohexanone;
     CC, 2-carbethoxy-2-isopropyl-3(or 5)-methylcyclohexanone; at this
     point, menthone could be 2-isopropyl-3-methylcyclohexanone or
     2-isopropyl-5-methylcyclohexanone; (b) 2-isopropyl-5-methylcyclo-
     hexanone; (c) menthone, 2-isopropyl-5-methylcyclohexanone.

19. DD, $CH_3COCH(CH_3)COOEt$; EE, $CH_3COC(CH_3)_2COOEt$;
     FF, $EtOOCCH_2C(CH_3)(OH)C(CH_3)_2COOEt$;
     GG, $EtOOCCH_2C(CH_3)(CN)C(CH_3)_2COOEt$;
     camphoronic acid, $HOOCCH_2C(CH_3)(COOH)C(CH_3)_2COOH$.

20. HH, $CH_3COCH(COOEt)CH_2COOEt$;
     II, $(CH_3)_2C(OH)CH(COOEt)CH_2COOEt$;
     JJ, $(CH_3)_2C(OH)CH(COOH)CH_2COOH$;
     KK, $CH_3COC(COOEt)(CH_2COOEt)_2$;
     LL, $CH_3COCH(CH_2COOH)_2$; MM, $CH_3COCH(CH_2COOEt)_2$;
     NN, $(CH_3)_2C(OH)CH(CH_2COOEt)_2$;
     OO, $(CH_3)_2C(OH)CH(CH_2COOH)_2$;

Terebic acid

Terpenylic acid

21.

$$-\overset{|}{\underset{\underset{\text{OPO}_3\text{H}_2}{|}}{\text{C}}}\overset{\text{COO}^-}{\underset{|}{\text{C}}}- \longrightarrow -\overset{|}{\text{C}}=\overset{|}{\text{C}}- + \text{CO}_2 + \text{H}_2\text{PO}_4^-$$

The dihydrogen phosphate ion, H_2PO_4^-, is a better leaving group than OH^-.

CHAPTER 27

27.1 (a) *n*-Butyric acid; (b) $\text{CH}_3\text{CH}=\text{CHCOO}^-$ and EtOH;
(c) $\text{PhCH}=\text{CHCOO}^-$ and CHI_3; (d) $\text{CH}_3\text{CH}=\text{CHCH}=\text{NNHPh}$;
(e) $\text{CH}_3\text{CH}=\text{CHCOO}^-$ and Ag; (f) PhCHO and PhCOCHO;
(g) *n*-BuOH; (h) *meso*-HOOCCHBrCHBrCOOH; (i) racemic tartaric acid, HOOCCHOHCHOHCOOH.

27.2 A, $\text{PhCH}_2\text{CH}_2\text{CHO}$; B, $\text{PhCH}_2\text{CH}_2\text{CH}_2\text{OH}$; C, $\text{PhCH}=\text{CHCH}_2\text{OH}$.

27.3 (a) Hydration; then aldol cond.; $-\text{H}_2\text{O}$. (b) PhCHO, CH_3CHO, OH^-.
(c) PhCHO, Ac_2O, NaOAc, heat. Or PhCHO, acetone, OH^-; NaOI.
(d) *iso*-BuBr + sodiomalonic ester; OH^-, heat; H^+; $-\text{CO}_2$; Br_2, P; alc. KOH.

27.4 (a) Ethylene, HOCl; CN^-; $-\text{H}_2\text{O}$. (b) Ethylene, HOCl; CN^-; MeOH, H^+; $-\text{H}_2\text{O}$. (c) Acetone, CN^-, H^+; MeOH, H^+; $-\text{H}_2\text{O}$.

(d)

Orlon   Acryloid   Lucite, Plexiglas

27.5 (a) $\text{CH}_2\text{OHCHOHCH}_2\text{OH} \rightarrow \text{CH}_2\text{OHCH}=\text{CHOH} \rightarrow \text{CH}_2\text{OHCH}_2\text{CHO}$ $\rightarrow \text{CH}_2=\text{CHCHO}$; (b) oxidation by $\text{Ag(NH}_3)_2\text{OH}$, Tollens' reagent.

27.6 All less stable than I.

27.7 An amide; formed by conjugate addition and subsequent ring closure through amide formation.

27.8 Two-step conjugate addition involving 2 moles acrylonitrile and 1 mole ammonia. First step gives $H_2NCH_2CH_2CN$ which then adds to the second mole of acrylonitrile.

27.9 Two-step conjugate addition involving 2 moles ethyl acrylate and 1 mole $MeNH_2$. First step gives $MeNHCH_2CH_2COOEt$ which then adds to the second mole of ethyl acrylate.

27.10 A, $EtOOCCH_2CH(CH_3)CH(COOEt)_2$; B, $CH_3CH(CH_2COOH)_2$; C, $EtOOCCH_2CH_2CH(COOEt)COCH_3$; D, δ-ketocaproic acid; E, $CH_3COCH_2CH_2CH(COOEt)_2$; F, $PhCH(CH_2COPh)_2$; G, $H_2C=CHCH(CN)CH_2CH_2CN$; H, $H_2C=CHCH(COOH)CH_2CH_2COOH$; I, $EtOOCCH=C(COOEt)CH(COOEt)COCH_3$; J, $HOOCCH=C(COOH)CH_2COOH$.

27.11 (a) K, $H_2C=C(COOEt)_2$; (b) Michael addn. of ethyl malonate; (c) glutaric acid.

27.12 Michael addn. gives 2-($CH_3COCH_2CH_2$)cyclohexanone; aldol cond. between carbonyl group of cyclohexanone and methyl group of side chain brings about ring closure; then $-H_2O$.

27.13 (a) Michael addn., followed by an intramol. Claisen cond. to form a six-membered ring; (b) saponification, acidification, decarboxylation of resulting β-keto acid.

27.14 Cyclopentadiene anion adds by Michael addn. to the unsaturated ketone.

27.15 1,4-Diphenyl-1,3-butadiene + maleic anhydride; 1,3-butadiene + 2-cyclopentenone; 1,3-butadiene (2 moles).

27.16 (a) 3-Ethoxy-1,3-pentadiene + *p*-benzoquinone; (b) 5-methoxy-2-methyl-1,4-benzoquinone + 1,3-butadiene.

27.17 1,4-Addition of HCl to *p*-benzoquinone, followed by a keto—enol tautomeric shift of a proton.

27.18 (a) Ease of oxidation; (b) ease of reduction.

27.19 *p*-Nitrosophenol undergoes keto—enol tautomerization to give the mono-oxime.

1. Acrolein: HCHO + CH_3CHO, crossed aldol; $-H_2O$. Crotonaldehyde: page 704. Cinnamaldehyde: page 704. Mesityl oxide: page 704. Benzalacetone: page 704. Dibenzalacetone: 2PhCHO + acetone, crossed

aldol. Benzalacetophenone: page 704. Acrylic acid: acrolein (see above), Tollens' reagent. Or ethylene, Cl_2, H_2O; CN^-; H_2O, H^+; $- H_2O$. Crotonic acid: crotonaldehyde (page 704), Tollens' reagent. Isocrotonic acid: acetylene, $NaNH_2$; $MeBr$; CO_2; acidify; H_2, Lindlar's catalyst (page 257). Methacrylic acid: page 632. Sorbic acid: $CH_3CHO + CH_3CH=CHCHO$ (page 704), crossed aldol; $- H_2O$; Tollens' reagent. Cinnamic acid: page 714. Maleic acid: succinic acid (Problem 5a, page 610), Br_2, P; KOH (alc); 250-300° (Problem 20.3, page 668); H_2O. (Actually made via maleic anhydride by cat. oxidation of benzene.) Fumaric acid: maleic acid, trace HBr, light (isomerization). Maleic anhydride: maleic or fumaric acid, heat. Methyl acrylate: Problem 27.4b, page 867. Methyl methacrylate: Problem 27.4c, page 867. Ethyl cinnamate: PhCHO + CH_3COOEt + NaOEt. Acrylonitrile: Problem 27.4a, page 867.

2. (a) $PhCH_2CH_2COCH_3$ and $PhCH_2CH_2CHOHCH_3$;
   (b) $PhCH=CHCHOHCH_3$; (c) $PhCH_2CH_2COONa$ and CHI_3;
   (d) PhCHO and CH_3COCHO; (e) $PhCHBrCHBrCOCH_3$;
   (f) $PhCHClCH_2COCH_3$; (g) $PhCHBrCH_2COCH_3$;
   (h) $PhCHOHCH_2COCH_3$; (i) $PhCH(OCH_3)CH_2COCH_3$;
   (j) $PhCH(CN)CH_2COCH_3$; (k) $PhCH(NHCH_3)CH_2COCH_3$;
   (l) $PhCH(NHPh)CH_2COCH_3$; (m) $PhCH(NH_2)CH_2COCH_3$;
   (n) $PhCH(NHOH)CH_2COCH_3$; (o) $PhCH=CHCOCH=CHPh$;
   (p) $CH_3COCH_2CH(Ph)CH(COOEt)_2$;
   (q) $CH_3COCH_2CH(Ph)CH(CN)COOEt$;
   (r) $CH_3COCH_2CH(Ph)C(CH_3)(COOEt)_2$;
   (s) $CH_3COCH_2CH(Ph)CH(COOEt)COCH_3$;
   (t) 4-aceto-5-phenylcyclohexene;

   (u)
   (v)

3. (a) $PhCOCH_2CH(Ph)CH(CN)COOEt$;
   (b) $EtOOCCH_2CH(Ph)CH(CN)COOEt$;
   (c) $EtOOCCH_2CH(COOEt)CH(COOEt)_2$;
   (d) $EtOOCCH=C(COOEt)CH(COOEt)_2$;
   (e) $CH_3COCH_2C(CH_3)_2CH(COOEt)_2$;
   (f) $CH_3COCH_2C(CH_3)_2CH(COOEt)COCH_3$;
   (g) $EtOOCCH_2CH(CH_3)C(CH_3)(COOEt)_2$;
   (h) $(EtOOC)_2CHCH_2CH(COOEt)_2$; (i) $CH_3CH[CH(COOEt)COCH_3]_2$;
   (j) $O_2NCH_2CH_2CH_2COOMe$; (k) $O_2NCH[CH(CH_3)CH_2COOEt]_2$;
   (l) $O_2NC(CH_2CH_2CN)_3$; (m) $Cl_3CH_2CH_2CN$.

4. (a) PhCOCH₂CH(Ph)CH₂COOH; (b) PhCH(CH₂COOH)₂;
(c) HOOCCH(CH₂COOH)₂; (d) HOOCCH=C(COOH)CH₂COOH;
(e) CH₃COCH₂C(CH₃)₂COOH; (f) (CH₃)₂C(CH₂COCH₃)₂;
(g) HOOCCH₂CH(CH₃)CH(CH₃)COOH; (h) glutaric acid;
(i) CH₃CH(CH₂COCH₃)₂.

5. A, [(EtOOC)₂CHCH(Ph)CH₂]₂C=O;
B, (EtOOC)₂CHCH(Ph)CH₂COCH=CHPh;
C, 4,4-dicarbethoxy-3,5-diphenylcyclohexanone.

6. (a)   (b)   (c)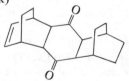

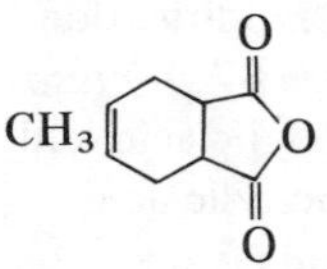

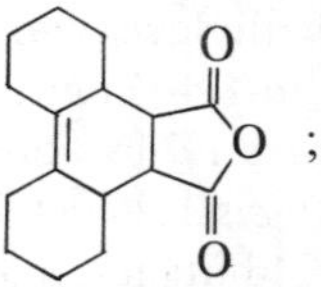

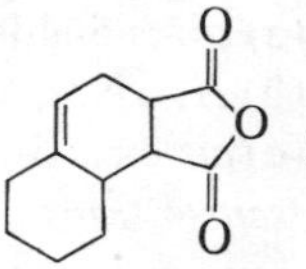

(d) 4-acetylcyclohexene; (e)   (f)

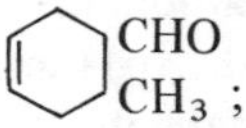

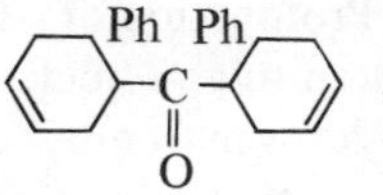

(g) 5-nitro-4-phenylcyclohexene; (h)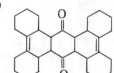

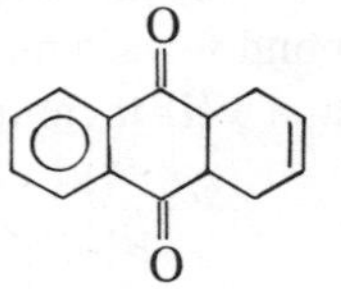

(i)   (j)   (k)

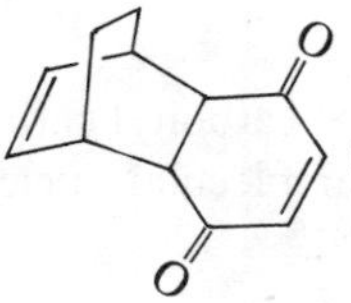

(l)   (m)   (n)

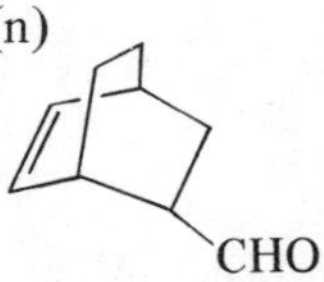

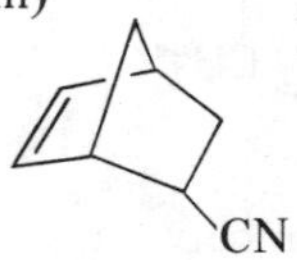

7. (a) 1,3,5-Hexatriene + maleic anhydride;
(b) 1,4-dimethyl-1,3-cyclohexadiene + maleic anhydride;
(c) 1,3-butadiene + PhCH=CHCOCH₃; (d) 1,3-butadiene +
acetylenedicarboxylic acid; (e) 1,3-cyclopentadiene + *p*-benzoquinone;

(f) 1,1′-bicyclohexenyl (I, page 880) + 1,4-naphthoquinone (II, page 880); (g) 1,3-cyclopentadiene + crotonaldehyde;
(h) 1,3-cyclohexadiene + methyl vinyl ketone; (i) 2 moles 1,3-cyclopentadiene.

8. The Diels-Alder reaction involves *syn*-addition. D is the anhydride of E, *cis*-4-cyclohexene-1,2-dicarboxylic acid; F, *cis*-1,2-cyclohexanedicarboxylic acid (unresolvable *meso* compound); G is the diacyl chloride of H, *trans*-4-cyclohexene-1,2-dicarboxylic acid; I, racemic *trans*-1,2-cyclohexanedicarboxylic acid.

9. (a) *trans*-5-aldehyde-4-methylcyclohexene: racemic modification.
(b) *cis*-5,8,9,10-tetrahydro-1,4-naphthoquinone (page 877): *meso*.
(c) *cis*-4-*cis*-5-dihydroxy-*cis*-1,2-cyclohexanedicarboxylic acid and *trans*-4-*trans*-5-dihydroxy-*cis*-1,2-cyclohexanedicarboxylic acid: 2 *meso*. (d) *meso*-1,2,3,4-butanetetracarboxylic acid: *meso*.

10. (a) Protonation of $-OH$; carbonium ion formation; Me shift; loss of proton to give double bond. (b) Carbanion formed by removal of γ-hydrogen of ethyl crotonate attacks in a Claisen cond. one ester group of ethyl oxalate. (c) Electron-withdrawing phosphonium group activates double bond toward nucleophilic attack by phenoxide ion; the addition product VIII then undergoes intramolecular Wittig reaction.

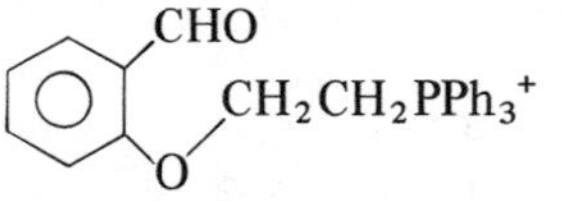

VIII

(d) Nucleophilic attack by the ylid at C-3 (instead of carbonyl carbon) to yield anion IX; PPh_3 is then displaced in an intramolecular nucleophilic substitution reaction.

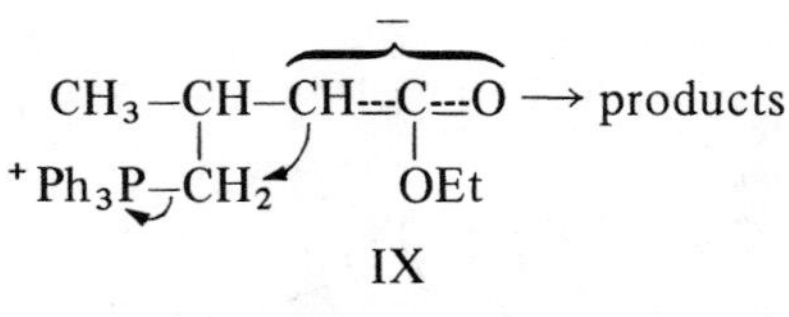

IX

(e) Diels-Alder reaction between furan and benzyne.

11. Nucleophilic addition of H_2O to α,β-unsaturated aldehyde generates the aldol, 3-hydroxy-3,7-dimethyl-6-octenal. This undergoes base-catalyzed *retroaldol* ("reverse aldol") reaction by reversal of steps (1)-(3) on pages 709−710. Equilibrium is displaced toward fragmentation by removal of one product (acetaldehyde) by distillation.

12. Conjugate addition of Grignard reagent produced
$C_6H_5CH(C_2H_5)CH_2COCH_3$, 4-phenyl-2-hexanone.

13.

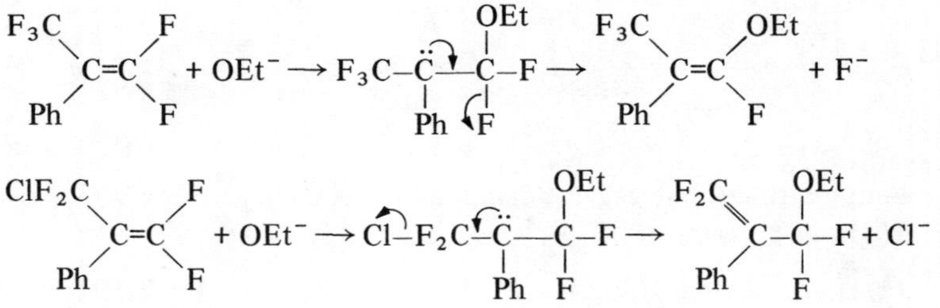

Formation of carbanion is rate-determining step, nearly identical for two similar alkenes. Then weakest C–X bond is broken, but rate does not affect overall rate; that is, there is no "element effect" (see pages 478 and 834).

14. J, Acrolein; K, $ClCH_2CH_2CH(OEt)_2$; L, $CH_2=CHCH(OEt)_2$;
M, $CH_2OHCHOHCH(OEt)_2$; N, glyceraldehyde, $CH_2OHCHOHCHO$;
O, $EtOOCCH=C(COOEt)CH(COOEt)_2$; P, aconitic acid,
$HOOCCH=C(COOH)CH_2COOH$; Q, $EtOOCCH_2CH(COOEt)CH(COOEt)_2$;
R, tricarballyic acid, $HOOCCH(CH_2COOH)_2$; S, "tetracyclone,"
tetraphenylcyclopentadienone; T, Diels-Alder adduct of S with maleic
anhydride; U, tetraphenylphthalic anhydride; V, Diels-Alder adduct
of S with phenylacetylene; W, pentaphenylbenzene;
X, $(CH_3)_2C(OH)C\equiv C-OEt$; Y, $(CH_3)_2C(OH)CH=CHOEt$;
Z, β-methylcrotonaldehyde, $(CH_3)_2C=CHCHO$. (Vinylic ether is cleaved
(Problem 15, page 649) to the β-hydroxyaldehyde, which then under-
goes dehydration); AA, $EtOOCCH_2C(CH_3)_2CH(CN)COOEt$;
BB, $(CH_3)_2C(CH_2COOH)_2$; CC, $CH_3COCH_2C(CH_3)_2CH(COOEt)_2$;
DD, $CH_3CH(OH)C\equiv CCH_3$; EE, $CH_3COC\equiv CCH_3$; FF, acetylacetone,
$CH_3COCH_2COCH_3$; GG, $(CH_3)_2C=CHCOOH$;
HH, $ClCH_2C(CH_3)(OH)CH_2Cl$; II, $NCCH_2C(CH_3)(OH)CH_2CN$;
JJ, $HOOCCH=C(CH_3)CH_2COOH$; KK, 2-carbethoxycyclopentanone;

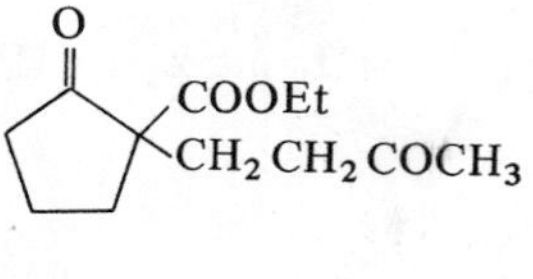

LL

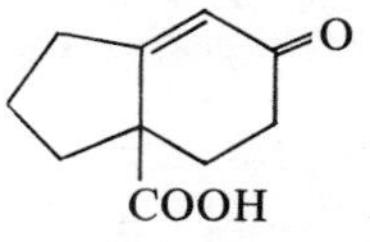

MM

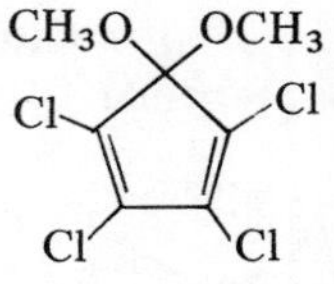

NN

OO   PP   QQ, 7—ketonorbornene

15. Acrylonitrile (2 moles), 1,4-diaminobutane, conjugate addition; $4H_2$, Ni, heat, pressure.

16. (a) HVZ reaction with $2Br_2$, P; 2KOH(alc); acidify.   (b) EtOH, HCl (see Problem 14a, formation of K); KOH(alc); Br_2/CCl_4; 2KOH(alc); acidify. (c) OH^-, crossed aldol; heat, $-H_2O$.   (d) H_2O, H_2SO_4, HgSO$_4$. (e) PhCHO, CH_3COOEt, NaOEt, Claisen cond.; ethyl malonate, NaOEt, Michael addn.; saponification; acidification; decarboxylation. (f) PhCHO, CH_3COOEt, NaOEt, Claisen cond.; CN^-, conjugate addn.; H_2O, H^+, heat.   (g) PhCHO, $2CH_3COCH_2COOEt$, NaOEt, crossed aldol followed by Michael addn.; saponification; acidification; decarboxylation $(-2CO_2)$.

17. (a) III: $CH_3CHO + CH_3COCH_2COOEt$, via aldol cond.; then second mole of CH_3COCH_2COOEt, via Michael addn. IV: cyclization of III via aldol cond. involving the two terminal CH_3CO groups.   (b) IV is correct. Nmr spectrum too complex for as symmetrical a molecule as III.

Would expect only 6 signals from III: 3H doublet, 1H multiplet, 6H triplet, 2H doublet, 6H singlet, 4H quartet.

18.

RR   SS   TT

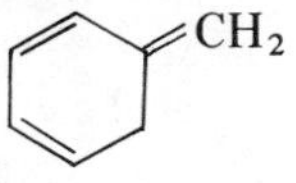

UU 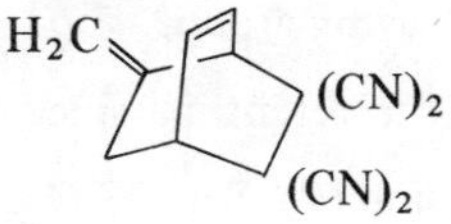   VV

19.

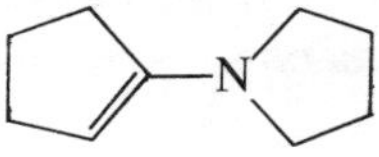

                    $CH_2CH_2COOCH_3$ $CH_2CH_2COOCH_3$
WW 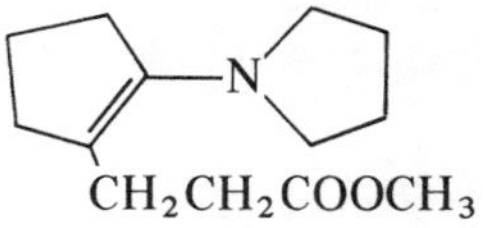   XX 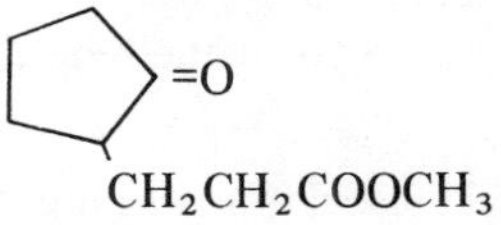   YY

   Enamine **WW** contains nucleophilic carbon (page 859), undergoes Michael addition to methyl acrylate.

20. (a) One set of 2 methyls more deshielded than the other (*exo/endo* isomerism), two 3° protons, two olefinic protons;

   (b) $(CH_3)_2\overset{\cdot}{C}-C-\overset{\cdot}{C}(CH_3)_2$
                     $\underset{O}{\overset{\|}{}}$

21.

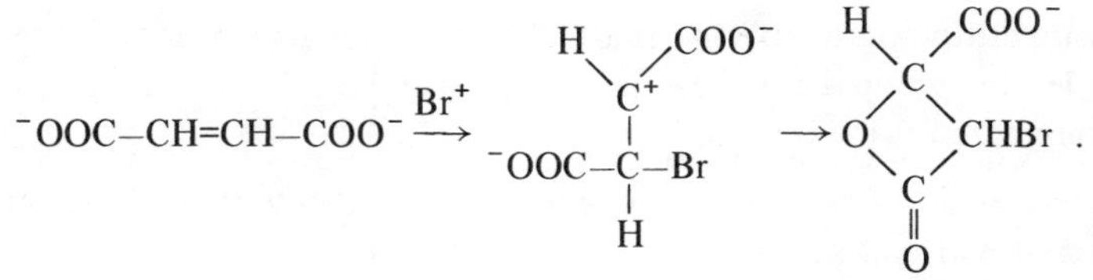

   Evidence for two-step electrophilic addition; intermediate carbonium (or perhaps bromonium) ion is trapped by basic carboxylate ion within same molecule, just as it was (Sec. 6.13) by chloride ion, bromide ion, etc.

22. Loss of N_2 and CO_2 from **IX** (compare Problem 18, page 844) gives aryne derived from aromatic cyclopentadienyl anion (Sec. 10.10). Aryne reacts with **X** to give Diels-Alder adduct, which loses CO to generate central aromatic ring of **XI**.

CHAPTER 28

28.1 (a) Ammonium ion;   (b) sulfonium ion;   (c) protonated epoxide;
     (d) epoxide;   (e) bromonium ion;   (f) benzenonium ion;
     (g) oxonium ion;   (h) ketone (dienone);   (i) cyclopropylcarbinyl
     cation.

28.2 N_2 is leaving group.

28.3 Goes with retention, since only *cis* amino acid can form lactam.

28.4 If reaction (2), Sec. 28.6, occurs, it is not reversible; in view of substituent effect, then, (2) and (3) are concerted.

28.5 (a) *p*-Methoxybenzaldehyde formed by migration of H; *p*-cresol (and formaldehyde), by migration of *p*-tolyl; (b) H migrates somewhat faster than *p*-tolyl.

28.6 H migrates much faster than alkyl.

28.7 Carbonium ion undergoes pinacol-like rearrangement.

28.8 (a) 2°ion; CH_3CH_2CHO; H migrates. (b) 3°ion; $(CH_3)_2CHCHO$; H migrates. (c) Benzylic ion; $PhCH_2CHO$; H migrates. (d) Benzylic ion; Ph_2CHCHO; H migrates. (e) Benzylic ion; $PhCH_2COCH_3$; H migrates. (f) Benzylic ion; $Ph_2C(CH_3)COCH_3$; Me migrates. (g) Benzylic ion involving 2 phenyl groups; Ph_3CCOCH_3; Ph migrates. (h) Both 3° ions; mixture of products. (i) Both benzylic ions; mixture of products.

28.9 Competition between solvent attack and rearrangement independent of leaving group; hence reaction is S_N1-like, with intermediate carbonium ion.

28.10 Intermediate is carbonium ion, which recombines with water faster than it rearranges.

28.11 (a) Charge on C-1; (b) charge on C-2.

28.12

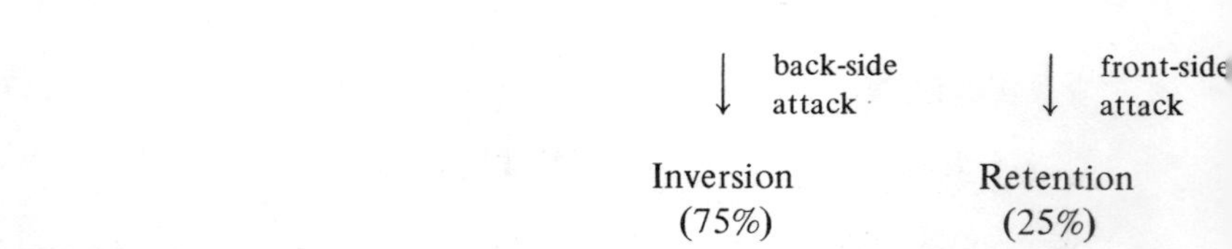

back-side attack

front-side attack

Inversion
(75%)

Retention
(25%)

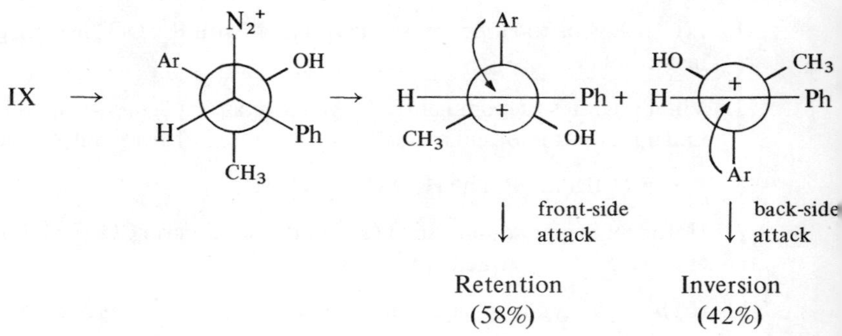

IX →

N_2^+

Ar ⟍ ⟋ OH

H ⟋ ⟍ Ph

CH$_3$

→

H———Ph +

CH$_3$ OH

Ar

H———Ph

OH

Ar

↓ front-side attack	↓ back-side attack
Retention (58%)	Inversion (42%)

Favored reaction in each case is one that involves *trans* transition state, that is, with Ph and CH$_3$ apart.

28.13 Bromonium ion as in Figure 28.5 (page 907) except that CH$_3$'s are *trans*. Attack *a* or *b* gives same product, *meso*.

28.14 Intermediate is an α-lactone.

28.15 Oxygens carry charge by *sharing* electrons.

28.16 Neighboring *trans*-Br and *trans*-I give anchimeric assistance.

28.17 (a) As in Figure 28.5 (page 907) with bridge Ph instead of Br, and nucleophile HOAc instead of Br⁻. (b) As in (a) except that CH$_3$'s are *trans*. Attack *a* or *b* gives same product, optically active *erythro* acetate.

28.18 α-Phenylethyl cation by H-shift.

28.19 (a) Intermediate is hybrid of I and II on page 915. (b) Norbornyl intermediate is symmetrical, and undergoes attack equally at C-1 and C-2. Intermediate in (a) is *not* symmetrical. Attack at C-2 regenerates starting material; attack at C-1 gives optically active product.

1. Successive H-shifts occur.

2. $CH_3COCH_2CH_2CH_2CH_2CH_2OH$, formed by migration of ring carbon.

3. (a) Methyl benzyl ketone, iodoform test; α-phenylpropionaldehyde, Tollens test; ethyl phenyl ketone, negative iodoform and Tollens. (b) Moving downfield. Methyl benzyl ketone: singlet CH$_3$, singlet CH$_2$, aromatic 5H. α-Phenylpropionaldehyde: doublet CH$_3$, quartet CH (probably split again into doublets), aromatic 5H; far downfield CHO (doublet). Ethyl phenyl ketone: triplet-quartet of C_2H_5, aromatic 5H.

4. (a) Analogous to Hofmann rearrangement, with $R'COO^-$ leaving group instead of X^-.

5. Vinyl migrates predominantly, to give adipaldehyde, most of which undergoes intramolecular aldol to cyclopentene-1-carboxaldehyde.

6. A, PhCONHPh; B, PhNH$_2$; C, PhCOOH.

7. Hofmann degradation of urea (an amide) would give CO_3^{--} and hydrazine, H_2N-NH_2, which is then oxidized.

8. (b) *p*-Methoxyphenol and benzophenone; phenol and *p*-chlorobenzophenone.

10. Two successive H-shifts.

11. R undergoes 1,2-shift, with retention of configuration, from B to O in intermediate R_3B-OOH, with displacement of OH^-.

12. (a) Both *cis*- and *trans*-alcohols give the same cyclic bromonium ion upon loss of water from an initial oxonium ion; back-side attack by Br^- on cyclic ion gives *trans*-dibromide.   (b) Nucleophilic attack by OH^- on least hindered position in each case: at $-CH_2Br$ in IV to give VI directly; at C-1 of V to form $CH_3CHBrCHCH_2OH$, which reacts
$$\qquad\qquad\qquad\qquad\qquad\qquad\qquad\quad \overset{|}{O^-}$$
further (page 563) to give VI.   (c) Three successive nucleophilic attacks: one intermolecular, and then two intramolecular.

Reactants $\longrightarrow$ $\overset{\overset{\displaystyle O}{\parallel}}{Ph\overset{\frown}{C}C(CH_3)_2CH_2-\underset{\underset{\displaystyle O_-}{|}}{CH}-CH_2Cl}$

$\underset{\underset{\displaystyle O}{\rule{3cm}{0.4pt}}}{\overset{\overset{\displaystyle ^-O\rule{2cm}{0.4pt}}{|}}{Ph\overset{}{C}C(CH_3)_2CH_2-\underset{|}{CH}-CH_2-Cl}} \longrightarrow \underset{\underset{\displaystyle O}{\rule{3cm}{0.4pt}}}{\overset{\overset{\displaystyle O\rule{2cm}{0.4pt}}{|}}{Ph\overset{}{C}C(CH_3)_2CH_2-\underset{|}{CH}-CH_2}}$

13. Tosylate poorer leaving group than N_2, requires assistance from phenyl.

14. (a) Neighboring $-OH$; (b) hydrolyzed.

15. With *p*-CH$_3$OPh, nearly all reaction via (symmetrical) bridged ion; with *p*-NO$_2$Ph, most reaction via open cation; with Ph, about 50:50.

16. (a) Equilibrium among open cations via fast migration of Ph; loss of OAc^- is rate-determining step for all reactions. If (2) involved bridged intermediate, predict 50:50 ratio of products, contrary to fact.

17. Assistance by π electrons to give following intermediates (in (b), may be nonclassical ion):

      (a)   (b)   (c)

18. (a) and (b) Norbornyl intermediate III (page 917) is symmetrical, and undergoes substitution equally at C-1 and C-2 to give enantiomers. Because of two-carbon bridge in XVII, corresponding intermediate is not symmetrical: attack at one carbon gives (optically active) XVIII, attack at other carbon gives (optically active) XIX. Formation of XX would require attack on open (or unshielded) cation.
    (c) Assistance by π electrons to give intermediate

which is attacked at either "front" carbon to give XX and enantiomer.

19. Nucleophilic attack on acyl carbon of XXII by Z to give *tetrahedral intermediate:*

XXV $\longleftarrow$ ... $\longrightarrow$ ... $\longrightarrow$ XXIII or XXIV

CHAPTER 29

29.1 First, monocation; then aromatic dication with 2 π electrons.

29.2 (a) Aromatic, with 2 π electrons:

$$ \triangleright\!\!\!-O^- + HClO_4 \longrightarrow \triangleright\!\!\!-OH \; ClO_4^- $$

(b) Product is aromatic 1,2,3-triphenylcyclopropenyl cation (see answer to Problem 10.6, page 330).

(c) $Cl_3CCOO^- \xrightarrow{\text{heat}} CO_2 + Cl_3C:^- \xrightarrow{-Cl^-} CCl_2$

29.3　(a) *Con* closure; I or III → *trans*; II → *cis*.
　　　(b) *Dis* closure; I or III → *cis*; II → *trans*.

29.4　(a) ψ_1; 2π electrons.　(b) $4n + 2$; *dis* (thermal).　(c) $4n, con$ (thermal).
　　　(d) Cation, $4n, con$; anion, $4n + 2, dis$.

29.5　(a) *Dis* opening.　(b) *Dis* closure.　(c) *Dis* closure; *con* opening; *dis* closure.　(d) *Con* opening (4 e); *dis* closure (6 e).　(e) *Dis* opening of cation (2 e), then combination with water.　(f) Protonated ketone like a cyclopentadienyl cation, with 4 π elections; *con* closure.

29.6　Via the cyclobutene, with *con* closures and openings.

29.7　(a) *cis*-3,6-Dimethylcyclohexene; [4 + 2].　(b) Methyl group is *cis* to anhydride bridge (*endo* reaction).　(c) Ph's are *cis* to each other (*syn* addition) and *cis* to anhydride bridge (*endo* reaction).　(d), (e), (f) all are tetramethylcyclobutanes; in D, one methyl is *trans* to other three.

29.8　(a) Diels-Alder; *retro*-Diels-Alder.　(b) *Endo* not *exo*.

29.9　(a) [4 + 2], not [6 + 2].　(b) Photochemical (intramolecular) *supra,supra* [2 + 2].　(c) *supra,supra* [6 + 4].　(d) *supra,supra* [8 + 2].　(e) *supra,antara* [14 + 2].

29.10　(a) *supra* [1,5]-H to either face of trigonal carbon.　(b) [1,5]-D, not [1,3]-D or [1,7]-D.　(c) [1,3]-C (*supra*) with inversion at migrating C.

1.　(a) Phenols; no.　(b) Dipolar structure is aromatic with 6π electrons (compare answer to Problem 29.2).　(d) Intramolecular H-bond.

2.　(a) *Con* opening (4 e); [1,5]-H *supra*.　(b) *Con* opening (4 e); *dis* closure (6 e).　(c) [1,7]-C *supra* and *dis* closure (4 e); [1,7]-H *supra*.　(d) [4 + 4] *supra,supra*; *retro* [4 + 2] *supra,supra* (presumably thermal).　(e) Allylic cation (2 π electrons) undergoes [4 + 2] cycloaddition, followed by loss of proton.　(f) Bridge walks around the ring in a series of *supra* [1,5]-C shifts.

3.　(a) A, *trans*-7,8-dialkyl-*cis,cis,cis*-cycloocta-1,3,5-triene.
　　(b) B, 1-isopropenyl-2,3,3-trimethylcyclobutene;
　　C, $(CH_3)_2C=C(CH_3)C(=CH_2)C(CH_3)=CH_2$.
　　(c) D, 9-methyl-9-ethyl-*trans,cis,cis,cis*-cyclonona-1,3,5,7-tetraene; the *dis* closure takes place with both possible rotations.
　　(d) E, *cis*-bicyclo[5.2.0]nona-8-ene;　F, *cis,trans*-cyclonona-1,3-diene;
　　G, *trans*-bicyclo[5.2.0]nona-8-ene.　(e) Two H's at following positions:

in H, at C-2 (via 1,7-H); in I, at C-4 (via 1,5-H either from starting material or from H); in J, at C-3 (via 1,5-H from H; via 1,7-H from I).

4. Symmetry-allowed *con* opening impossible on geometric grounds for bicyclo compound; reaction is probably not concerted.

5. K, *cis*-cicyclo[4.2.0]octa-2,4-diene; L, Diels-Alder adduct, which undergoes *retro*-Diels-Alder.

6. (a) [1,2] *supra* sigmatropic shift; π framework is a vinyl radical cation (ethylene minus one π electron); HOMO is π in Figure 29.5, page 931; predict retention in migrating group. (b) π framework is diene radical cation (diene minus one π electron); HOMO is ψ_2 in Figure 29.6, page 932; predict inversion in migrating group.

7. Symmetry-forbidden. HOMO of H_2 is σ in Figure 29.4, page 930; LUMO of ethylene is π^*. LUMO of H_2 is σ^* in Figure 29.4; HOMO of ethylene is π.

8.

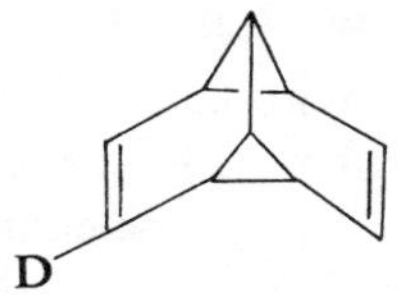

9. (a) [4 + 2] cycloaddition of benzyne and diene. (b) [2 + 2] thermal cycloaddition symmetry-forbidden; reaction non-concerted, probably via diradicals.

10.

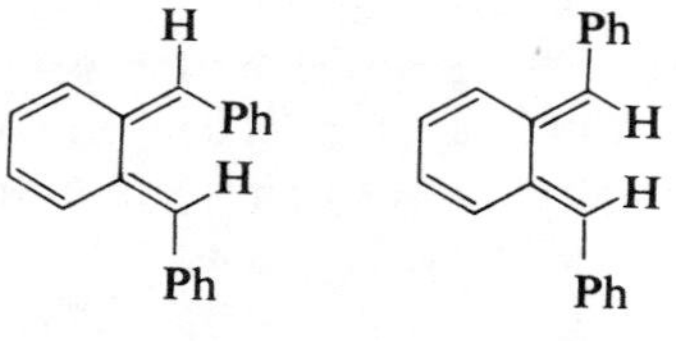

11. (a) Two successive nucleophilic substitution reactions: nucleophile is cyclopentadienyl anion in first, substituted cyclopentadienyl anion in second. Inversion both times. *Meso* dibromide gives *cis*-VII (Figure 29.26); racemic dibromide gives *trans*-VII. (b) *cis*-VII contains four non-equivalent olefinic hydrogens; *trans*-VII, two equivalent pairs.

12. (a) M and N, position isomers, both from *syn exo* addition; O and P, position isomers; R is diastereomer of Q (with OAc *cis* to D).
(b) *retro*-Diels-Alder.

13. (a) (Numbering from left to right in Fig. 29.19). Overlap between lobe

of C-3 of diene and C-3 of ene, carbons to which bonds are not being formed.   (b) Lobes corresponding to those in (a) are of opposite phase.

14. (a)

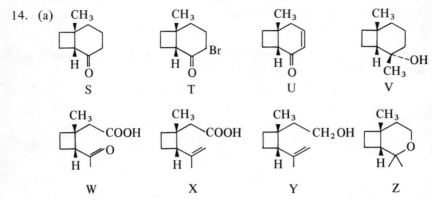

S   T   U   V

W   X   Y   Z

CH₃Li attacks U from most open side, away from fold in molecule.
(b) Intramolecular solvomercuration possible only for *cis* isomer.

15. (a) Allowed thermal *con* opening (4 e) would give impossibly strained *cis,cis,trans*-cyclohexa-1,3,5-triene; reaction must go by forbidden *dis* opening.   (b) Allowed *antara* [1,3] -H impossible on geometric grounds; reaction must go by forbidden *supra* [1,3]-H.

16. (a) *Con* opening (6 e); [1,7] -H *antara*.   (b) Analogous to products from 7-dehydrocholesterol.   (c) *Dis* closure. In ergosterol, C-1 methyl is β, C-9 H is α (see page 514). IX and X: both substituents are α in one, and both are β in other.   (d) In XI, C-1 methyl is α, C-9 H is β.

17. Photochemical *con* opening (6 e) gives *cis,cis,cis,cis,cis*-cyclodeca-1,3,5,7,9-pentaene. This is stable at −190°, but at room temperature undergoes thermal *dis* closure (6 e) to *cis*-XII.   (b) 10 π electrons fits Hückel rule, but evidently not very stable for steric reasons.

CHAPTER 30

30.1   2; 10; 14.

30.2   Friedel-Crafts acetylation, followed by the haloform reaction.

30.3   (b) *Trans,* 2 equatorial bonds; *cis,* 1 equatorial bond, 1 axial bond; *trans*-decalin more stable, both large groups (the other ring) on each ring are equatorial;   (c) *syn*-addition, rate control; *anti*-addition, equilibrium control.

30.4 Benzylic substitution; elimination of HBr to give conjugated alkenyl-benzene; benzylic-allylic substitution; elimination to give aromatic ring.

30.5 A, β-hydroxyester; B, unsaturated acid; C, aromatic acid; D, ester of C; E, alcohol; F, bromide; G, substituted malonic ester; H, monocarboxylic acid; I, acid chloride; J, cyclic ketone; K, alcohol from J; (a) cadalene, 4-isopropyl-1,6-dimethylnaphthalene; (b) cadinene has same carbon skeleton as cadalene, follows isoprene rule.

30.6 (a) Fe, H^+. (b) Product a, HONO; KI. (c) Product a, HONO; CuCN. (d) Product c, H_2O, H^+, heat. (e) Product d, $SOCl_2$. (f) Product e, Et_2Cd. (g) Product c, H_2, Ni. (h) Product f, Zn(Hg), HCl. (i) Product e, LiAlH(Bu-t)$_3$. (j) Product d, $LiAlH_4$; H^+. (k) Product j, conc. HCl. (l) Product k, CN^-; H_2O, H^+. heat. (m) Product a, acetic anhydride.

30.7 (a) Mg, anhyd. Et_2O. (b) Product a, CO_2; H^+. (c) Product a, acetone; H_2O. (d) Product c, H^+, heat; H_2, Pt. (e) Product a, HCHO; H_2O. (f) Product a, CH_3CHO; H_2O. (g) Product a, ethylene oxide; H_2O.

30.8 (a) Via aryne; addition of piperidine anion to aryne at C-2 or C-1 gives carbanion with negative charge on C-1 or on C-3; addition at C-2 favored by delocalization of negative charge on C-1 over the other aromatic ring. (b) Direct displacement of −F by the amine. (c) Both direct displacement and elimination-addition occur. Fluoronaphthalene least reactive toward aryne formation (page 838), most reactive toward direct displacement (Sec. 25.12).

30.9 1,2,4-Benzenetricarboxylic acid; 1,2,3-benzenetricarboxylic acid.

30.10 (a) $C_{10}H_8$, CH_3COCl, $PhNO_2$, $AlCl_3$; Zn(Hg), H^+. (b) $C_{10}H_8$, CH_3CH_2COCl, $PhNO_2$, $AlCl_3$; MeMgBr; H_2O. (c) Product b, H^+, heat; H_2, Pt. (d) $C_{10}H_8$, CH_3COCl, $PhNO_2$, $AlCl_3$; $NaBH_4$; H^+. (e) $C_{10}H_8$, succinic anhydride, $PhNO_2$, $AlCl_3$; Zn(Hg), HCl. (f) Product e, $LiAlH_4$; H_2O. (g) Product e, EtOH, H^+; 2MeMgBr; H_2O. (h) Product g, H^+, heat; cat. H_2. (i) $C_{10}H_8$, CH_3COCl, $PhNO_2$, $AlCl_3$; NH_3, H_2, Ni. (j) Product d, H^+, heat.

30.11 (a) See Sec. 11.12. (b) From left to right in a diagram like Fig. 8.8, page 272: high valley, α-acid; low peak, transition state leading to α-acid; trough, naphthalene and SO_3; high peak, transition state leading to β-acid; low valley, β-acid.

30.12 (a) SO_3, $160°$; OH^-, heat; Bucherer reaction; HONO; CuBr.
(b) Replace CuBr in (a) by HBF_4; heat. (c) Replace CuBr in (a) by
CuCN. (d) Product c, H_2O, H^+, heat; or product a, Mg, anhyd. Et_2O;
CO_2; H^+. (e) Product d, $SOCl_2$; $LiAlH(Bu-t)_3$. (f) Product e, acetic
anhydride, NaOAc, heat.

30.13 Replace CuBr in Prob. 30.12a by NO_2^-, catalyst.

30.14 (a) 4-Bromo-1-methylnaphthalene; (b) 4-nitro-1-methylnaphthalene;
(c) 1-(4-methylnaphthyl) methyl ketone;
(d) 1-bromo-2-methylnaphthalene, 1-nitro-2-methylnaphthalene,
1-(2-methylnaphthyl) methyl ketone; (e) 6- and
7-nitro-1-bromonaphthalene; (f) 1-bromo-2-methoxynaphthalene.

30.15 (a) Activating group at position 2 directs to position 1; (b) bulky
complex avoids hindered positions and gives β-substitution in other
ring; (c) high-temperature sulfonation gives β-substitution, with other
ring less hindered; (d) low-temperature sulfonation gives
α-substitution, at least hindered position; (e) high-temperature
sulfonation gives β-substitution; (f) nitration α, other ring from
deactivating group.

30.16 (a) HNO_3, H_2SO_4; Fe, H^+; acetic anhydride; HNO_3, H_2SO_4; H_2O,
H^+, heat. (b) Product a, HONO; NO_2^-, catalyst (see Prob. 30.13,
page 982). (c) As in (a), except nitrate a second time before hydrolysis of amide. (d) Product c, HONO; H_3PO_2. (e) β-Naphthylamine
(page 982), acetic anhydride; HNO_3, H_2SO_4; H_2O, H^+, heat; HONO;
NO_2^-, catalyst. (f) HNO_3, H_2SO_4; Fe, H^+; H_2SO_4 ($\longrightarrow$ salt); strong
heat. (g) H_2SO_4, low temp.; HNO_3, H_2SO_4; separation of 8-nitro
from 5-nitro isomer; Fe, H^+. (h) SO_3, $160°$; HNO_3, H_2SO_4 (see
Prob. 30.15f); separation from 8-nitro isomer; Fe, H^+. (i) As in (h),
except use 8-nitro isomer.

30.17 Deactivating acyl group transformed into activating alkyl group.

30.18 (a) $PhCH_3$, succinic anhydride, $AlCl_3$; Zn(Hg), HCl; HF; Zn(Hg), HCl;
Pd, heat. (b) C_6H_6, succinic anhydride, $AlCl_3$; Zn(Hg), HCl; HF;
MeMgBr; H_2O; H^+, heat; Pd, heat. (c) *p*-Xylene, succinic anhydride,
$AlCl_3$; Zn(Hg), HCl; HF; Zn(Hg), HCl, heat; Pd, heat. (d) As in (b),
except start with toluene. (e) $PhCH_3$, succinic anhydride, $AlCl_3$;
EtOH, H^+; MeMgBr (react with keto group only); H_2O; H^+, heat;
H_2O, H^+, heat (hydrolyze ester); cat. H_2; HF; Zn(Hg), HCl; Pd, heat.
(f) As in (e) through ring closure by HF; then MeMgBr; H_2O; H^+,
heat; Pd, heat. (g) As in (f) except start with benzene, and replace
MeMgBr by EtMgBr. (h) As in (b), except start with PhBr, and use
EtMgBr. (i) As in (b), except use PhMgBr.

30.19 Phenanthrene (see Sec. 30.19, and Fig. 30.3, page 995).

30.20 23 kcal/mole; 31 kcal/mole.

30.21 Attachment of $^+NO_2$ at the 9-position, followed by: (a) acetate ion
at the 10-position; (b) EtOH at the 10-position; (c) HNO_3 at the
10-position; (d) loss of H^+ from the 9-position of the initial product,
in the usual manner of aromatic substitutions.

30.22 (a) Most stable tetrahydro product; (b) reversible sulfonation yields
more stable product.

30.23 (a) *p*-Xylene, phthalic anhydride, $AlCl_3$; H_2SO_4, heat. (b) *o*-Xylene,
phthalic anhydride, $AlCl_3$; H_2SO_4, heat (20% yield); separate from
80% yield of 2,3-dimethyl isomer. (c) *m*-Xylene, phthalic anhydride,
$AlCl_3$; H_2SO_4, heat. (d) Toluene, phthalic anhydride, $AlCl_3$; Zn,
OH^- (reduction of keto group to $-CH_2-$); HF; MeMgBr; H_2O; H^+,
heat ($- H_2O$, aromatization). (e) As in (d), except start with
naphthalene (β-acylation).

30.24 (a) 1-Nitro-9,10-anthraquinone; (b) 5-nitro-2-methyl-9,10-anthra-
quinone (with some 8-nitro isomer).

30.25 (a) $1\text{-}C_{10}H_7CH_3$, succinic anhydride, $AlCl_3$ (acylation in 4-position);
Zn(Hg), HCl; HF; Zn(Hg), HCl; Pd, heat. (b) $C_{10}H_8$, succinic anhydride, $AlCl_3$ (β-acylation); Zn(Hg), HCl; HF; MeMgBr; H_2O; H^+, heat;
Pd, heat. (c) As in (b), except α-acylation. (d) As in (c), except
start with $1\text{-}C_{10}H_7CH_3$. (e) $1\text{-}C_{10}H_7CH_3$, succinic anhydride, $AlCl_3$
(acylation in 4-position); EtOH, H^+; MeMgBr (react only with keto
group); H_2O; H^+, heat; H_2O, H^+, heat (hydrolyze ester); cat. H_2 of
side chain; HF; Zn(Hg), HCl; Pd, heat. (f) $C_{10}H_8$, succinic anhydride, $AlCl_3$ (β-acylation); EtOH, H^+; MeMgBr (react only with keto
group); H_2O; H^+, heat; H_2O, H^+, heat (hydrolyze ester); cat. H_2 of
side chain; HF; MeMgBr; H_2O; H^+, heat; Pd, heat. (g) As in (f),
except start with $1\text{-}C_{10}H_7CH_3$, and use α-succinoylation product.
(h) $2\text{-}C_{10}H_7CH_3$, succinic anhydride, $PhNO_2$, $AlCl_3$ (acylation in
6-position, Prob. 30.15b); Zn(Hg), HCl; HF; Zn(Hg), HCl; Pd, heat.

30.26 A, 2-naphthyl ethyl ketone, Friedel-Crafts acylation;
B, 2-naphthyl-1-bromoethyl ketone, α-halogenation;
C, 2-naphthylCOCH(CH$_3$)CH(COOEt)$_2$, alkylation;
D, 2-naphthylCOCH(CH$_3$)CH(COO$^-$)$_2$, ester hydrolysis;
E, 2-naphthylCOCH(CH$_3$)CH(COOH)$_2$, acidification;
F, 3-(2-naphthoyl)butanoic acid, decarboxylation;
G, 4-(2-naphthyl)-3-methylbutanoic acid, Clemmensen reduction;
H, 4-keto-2-methyl-1,2,3,4-tetrahydrophenanthrene, ring closure by

intramolecular acylation; I, 2-methyl-1,2,3,4-tetrahydrophenanthrene, Clemmensen reduction; I finally subjected to aromatization by catalytic dehydrogenation.

30.27 A, $C_6H_5CH_2CH_2MgBr$, formation of Grignard reagent; B, Mg salt of 1-(2-phenylethyl)cyclohexanol, carbonyl addition; C, 1-(2-phenylethyl)cyclohexanol, acidification; D, 1-(2-phenylethyl)cyclohexene, dehydration; E, 1,2,3,4,9,10-hexahydrophenanthrene, ring closure by intramolecular Friedel-Crafts alkylation; E subjected to aromatization by dehydrogenation. β-Phenylethyl bromide: PhMgBr, ethylene oxide; H_2O; PBr_3.

30.28 A, K salt of ethyl 2-ketocyclohexanecarboxylate, acidity of α-hydrogen; B, ethyl 2-keto-1-(2-phenylethyl)cyclohexanecarboxylate, alkylation; C, salt of B, ester hydrolysis; D, 2-(2-phenylethyl)-cyclohexanone, decarboxylation; E, 2-(2-phenylethyl)cyclohexanol, reduction; F, 2-(2-phenylethyl)cyclohexene, dehydration; G, 1,2,3,4,9,10-hexahydrophenanthrene, ring closure by intramolecular Friedel-Crafts alkylation; G subjected to aromatization by dehydrogenation.

30.29 A, Reformatsky reaction; B, acidification of Reformatsky adduct; C, dehydration of ester of β-hydroxy acid; D, hydrolysis of ester; E, liberation of carboxylic acid; F, ring closure by intramolecular Friedel-Crafts acylation; G, Clemmensen reduction; pyrene, aromatization by catalytic dehydrogenation.

Pyrene

Starting material: naphthalene, succinic anhydride, $AlCl_3$ (β-acylation); Zn(Hg), HCl; HF.

30.30 1-$C_{10}H_7MgBr$, ethylene oxide; H_2O; PBr_3; Mg, anhyd. Et_2O; cyclohexanone; H_2O; H^+, heat ($-H_2O$); H_2SO_4, heat (ring closure); Se, heat.

30.31 PhMgBr, ethylene oxide; H_2O; PBr_3; Mg, anhyd. Et_2O; α-tetralone (see Fig. 30.2, page 987); H_2O; H^+, heat ($-H_2O$); H_2SO_4, heat (ring closure); Se, heat.

1. (a) 1,4-Naphthoquinone; (b) phthalic anhydride; (c) 1,4-dihydronaphthalene; (d) tetralin; (e) decalin;

(f) $1\text{-}C_{10}H_7NO_2$; (g) $1\text{-}C_{10}H_7Br$; (h) $1\text{-}C_{10}H_7SO_3H$;
(i) $2\text{-}C_{10}H_7SO_3H$; (j) $1\text{-}C_{10}H_7COCH_3$; (k) $2\text{-}C_{10}H_7COCH_3$;
(l) $2\text{-}C_{10}H_7COCH_2CH_2COOH$.

2. (a) 4-Nitro-1-methylnaphthalene; (b) 1-nitro-2-methylnaphthalene;
(c) 1,5- and $1,8\text{-}C_{10}H_6(NO_2)_2$; (d) 1,6- and $1,7\text{-}C_{10}H_6(NO_2)_2$;
(e) 5- and 8-nitro-1-naphthalenesulfonic acid; (f) 5- and
8-nitro-2-naphthalenesulfonic acid;
(g) N-(4-nitro-1-naphthyl)acetamide;
(h) N-(1-nitro-2-naphthyl)acetamide; (i) 4-nitro-1-naphthol;
(j) 1-nitro-2-naphthol; (k) 9-nitroanthracene.

3. 1-, 5-, and 8-nitro-2-methylnaphthalene.

4. (a) HNO_3, H_2SO_4; Fe, H^+; H_2O, H_2SO_4, 200°. (b) SO_3, 160°; OH^-,
H_2O, 300°; acidify. (c) HNO_3, H_2SO_4; Fe, H^+. (d) Product b,
Bucherer reaction. (e) Product c, HONO; KI. (f) Product d, HONO;
KI. (g) HNO_3, H_2SO_4. (h) Product d, HONO; NO_2^-, catalyst.
(i) Product c, HONO; CuCN; H_2O, H^+, heat. Or Br_2; Mg, anhyd. Et_2O;
CO_2; acidify. (j) Product d, HONO; CuCN; H_2O, H^+, heat.
(k) Succinic anhydride, $AlCl_3$, α-acylation; Zn(Hg), HCl. (l) Product i,
$LiAlH(Bu\text{-}t)_3$. (m) Same as (l), except start with product j. (n) $PhNH_2$,
HONO, 0°; product b, OH^-; acidify. (o) Product n, $SnCl_2$. (p) $PhNH_2$,
HONO, 0°; product a, OH^-; acidify; $SnCl_2$. (q) Product b, Me_2SO_4,
OH^-; Br_2. (r) Product g, HNO_3, H_2SO_4; excess Fe, H^+. (s) Product r,
$2Br_2$; 2HONO; 2KI. (t) SO_3, 160°; HNO_3, H_2SO_4. (u) Product d,
acetic anhydride; HNO_3, H_2SO_4; H_2O, H^+, heat; Fe, H^+. (v) Product
c, acetic anhydride; $2HNO_3$, H_2SO_4; H_2O, H^+, heat; HONO; H_3PO_2;
excess Fe, H^+. (w) O_2, V_2O_5, 475°; NH_3, heat (forming phthalimide);
OCl^-; acidify. (x) Product k, HF; Zn(Hg), HCl; Pd, heat. (y) O_2, V_2O_5,
475°; C_6H_6, $AlCl_3$; H_2SO_4, strong heat. (z) Product y, Zn, OH^-.

5. A, tetralin; B, 6-succinoyl-1,2,3,4-tetrahydronaphthalene; C, keto
group of B reduced to $-CH_2-$;
D, 4-keto-1,2,3,4,5,6,7,8-octahydrophenanthrene;
E, 1,2,3,4,5,6,7,8-octahydrophenanthrene; F, phenanthrene.

6. (a) PhOMe, succinic anhydride, $AlCl_3$; isolate *p*-isomer; EtOH, H^+;
MeMgBr (react only with keto group); H_2O; H^+, heat; H_2O, H^+, heat
(hydrolyze ester); cat. H_2 of side chain; HF; PhMgBr; H_2O; H^+, heat;
Pd, heat. (b) Naphthalene, phthalic anhydride, $AlCl_3$ (β-acylation);
H_2SO_4, heat (forming 1,2-benzanthraquinone); Zn, OH^-.
(c) *o*-Benzoylbenzoic acid (page 669), Zn, OH^- (reduction of carbonyl
group to $-CH_2-$); HF, heat; PhMgBr; acidify; H^+, heat.
(d) Naphthalene, succinic anhydride, $AlCl_3$ (α-acylation); Zn(Hg), HCl,

heat; HF, heat; PhMgBr; acidify; H⁺, heat; Pd, heat.   (e) As in (d), except start with 1-phenylnaphthalene (Problem 30.18i, page 988).

7. G, 1,2-benzanthracene;   H, chrysene.

8. 1-Naphthol. Ring closure by intramolecular acylation; aromatization by keto—enol tautomerization.

9. (a) Diels-Alder.   (b) I, an anhydride, the Diels-Alder adduct of maleic anhydride at the 9- and 10-positions of anthracene;   J, the corresponding dicarboxylic acid. Both I and J are *meso* compounds.   (c) J is a *meso* compound, K is a racemic modification.

    (d)

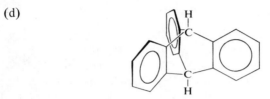

Triptycene
(Gr.: *triptychos,* consisting of three plates)

Consider one of the three aromatic rings of triptycene. In O, this ring contains two —NH₂ groups *para* to each other; in N, this ring is quinoid. M is the corresponding hydroquinone. L is the keto form of M; it is the Diels-Alder adduct of *p*-benzoquinone to the 9,10-positions of anthracene.

10. (a) 1,4-Dihydronaphthalene;   (b) 2-methoxy-1,4-dihydronaphthalene;   (c) 2-hydroxy-1,4-dihydronaphthalene, an enol;   (d) enol-to-keto tautomerization to the final product, β-tetralone (2-oxo-1,2,3,4-tetrahydronaphthalene).

11. (a) 1,6-Cyclodecanedione (III, page 317);   (b)

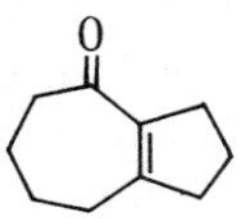

    Formed by ring closure involving an intramol. aldol cond.   (c) NaBH₄; — H₂O; Pd, heat (− 3H₂).

12. (a)

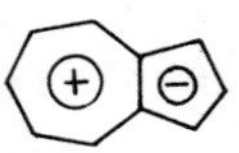

    6 π electrons in each ring.

    Azulene

    (b) From 7-ring toward 5-ring; augmented by C—Cl dipole.

13. (a)

$$d \left\{ \text{structure with } H\ H\ a,\ -H\ c,\ H\ b \right\} \qquad b \left\{ \text{structure with } D\ D,\ -H\ a,\ D \right\} \qquad \text{Aromaticity of 7-ring preserved.}$$

(b) Protonation at C-1; azulene upon neutralization. (c) Deuteration via electrophilic substitution at C-1 and C-3, and deuteration at C-1 comparable to the protonation in (b). Except 1,3-dideuterioazulene upon neutralization. (d) At C-1.

14. Nucleophilic substitution in the 7-ring at C-4 via

Aromaticity of 5-ring preserved, conjugation in 7-ring.

15. P, ethyl β-hydroxy-β-(p-isopropylphenyl)propionate; Q, dehydration product from P; R, 3-(p-isopropylphenyl)-1-propanol; S, γ-(p-isopropylphenyl)butyryl chloride; T, 7-isopropyl-1-tetralone; U, 7-isopropyl-1-methyl-1,2,3,4-tetrahydro-1-naphthol; V, 7-isopropyl-1-methyl-3,4-dihydronaphthalene; eudalene, 7-isopropyl-1-methylnaphthalene.

16. W, 2,4,5-trichlorophenol; X, 2,4,5-trichloro-6(hydroxymethyl)phenol; Y, 2,2', 3,3', 5,5'-hexachloro-6,6'-dihydroxydiphenylmethane; Z, m-CH$_3$C$_6$H$_4$MgBr; AA, 1-(m-tolyl)-4-methyl-1-cyclohexanol; BB, 1-(m-tolyl)-4-methylcyclohexene; CC, 3,4'-dimethylbiphenyl; DD, Ph$_3$COH; EE, Ph$_3$CBr; FF, compound I, p. 393; GG, 4-aminotetraphenylmethane (from Friedel-Crafts alkylation); HH, tetraphenylmethane; II, 1,3,5-triphenylbenzene.

17. $-$N$^+$ powerfully activates molecule toward nucleophilic aromatic substitution.

18. (a) JJ, methylene bridge between 9- and 10-positions of phenanthrene, formed by the addition of methylene that causes the least sacrifice of resonance stabilization. (b) Random insertion of methylene into n-pentane; driving force is restoration of resonance-stabilized aromatic system of phenanthrene. (c) Three insertion products and one addition product. (d) *cis*-1-Methyl-2-isopropylcyclopropane from the *cis*-alkene; the *trans*-isomer from the *trans*-alkene.

19. KK,

 ; Each ring contains 6 π electrons.

20. (a) Via an aryne, the same one whether from 1- or 2-chloronaphthalene.
(b) Direct displacement accompanies elimination-addition. Fluoride least reactive toward aryne formation (page 838), most reactive toward direct displacement (Sec. 25.12). Piperidine shifts equilibrium of Step 1 (page 838) to left, tends to inhibit aryne formation.

21. UU is aromatic, with 14 π electrons. Methyl protons are *inside* aromatic ring; see Fig. 13.4, page 419.

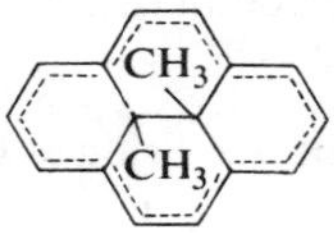

UU

CHAPTER 31

31.1 A, $Na^+ [CH_3COCHCOOEt]^-$; B, $[-CH(COOEt)COCH_3]_2$.

31.2 NaOEt, crossed Claisen; NaOEt, salt formation; I_2; H^+ heat; $- 2CO_2$, $- 2EtOH$; P_2O_5, heat.

31.3 $-COOH$ deactivates ring.

31.4 Two units of starting material linked at the 5-positions through a $-CH_2-$ group; formed via hydroxymethyl derivative (see pages 1043–1044).

31.5 Sodium furoate and furfuryl alcohol (Cannizzaro reaction).

31.6 SO_3 transferred from salt to aromatic compound to give intermediate cation typical of aromatic substitution; this loses proton to pyridine.

31.7 (a) Overlapping sextets of pyrrole and benzene rings, much as in naphthalene; (b) aromatic sextet preserved in six-ring and positive charge accommodated by nitrogen if substitution occurs in 3-position.

31.8 Tetrahydrofuran, HCl (excess), heat; $2CN^-$; resulting $NC(CH_2)_4CN$ is hydrolyzed to adipic acid, catalytically hydrogenated to hexa-methylenediamine.

31.9 (a) Simple salt; (b) no reaction; (c) amide; (d) alkali-insoluble sulfonamide; (e) N-alkylation; (f) ring scission to $(CH_3)_2NCH_2CH_2CH=CH_2$.

31.10 Hygrine, 2-acetonyl-N-methylpyrrolidine; hygrinic acid,

N-methyl-2-pyrrolidinecarboxylic acid;
A, $BrCH_2CH_2CH_2CH(COOEt)_2$; B, $BrCH_2CH_2CH_2CBr(COOEt)_2$;
C, N-methyl-2,2-dicarbethoxypyrrolidine; D, salt of dicarboxylic
acid from C; E, dicarboxylic acid from D.

31.11 Orientation ("*para*") controlled by activating $-NH_2$ group.

31.12 $KMnO_4$, heat; $SOCl_2$; NH_3; OBr^-, OH^- (Hofmann degradation of
amide).

31.13 Amine > imine > nitrile.

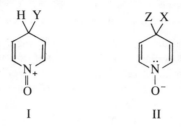

I   II

31.16 Nucleophilic substitution proceeds via an intermediate like II, in
which negative charge is carried by the electronegative element
oxygen.

31.17 4-Nitropyridine: pyridine N-oxide, HNO_3, H_2SO_4; PCl_3.
4-Bromopyridine: pyridine N-oxide, HNO_3, H_2SO_4; HBr (see Prob.
31.16); PCl_3.

31.18 Piperidine, a 2° amine, would itself be acylated.

31.19 (a) Nitrogen-containing ring is deactivated, as in pyridine; substitution
thus occurs at an α-position in the less deactivated ring (compare
Secs. 30.9 and 30.13). (b) Benzenoid ring more easily attacked by
oxidizing agents than deactivated nitrogen-containing ring.
(c) Nucleophilic substitution facilitated by electron-withdrawing
nitrogen (compare Sec. 31.10).

31.20 Quinoline, SO_3, H_2SO_4; separate 8-isomer from undesired 5-isomer;
OH^-, strong heat; acidify.

31.21 Conjugate addition of amine to crotonaldehyde or acrolein (formed
from glycerol); ring closure; aromatization by dehydrogenation.

31.22 Glycerol $\longrightarrow HOCH_2CH=CHOH$; this tautomerizes to $HOCH_2CH_2CHO$,
which loses water $\longrightarrow$ acrolein. (See Prob. 27.5, page 867).

31.23 (a) 8-Nitroquinoline; (b) 8-hydroxyquinoline (8-quinolinol);

(c) 4,5-diazaphenanthrene;   (d) 1,5-diazaphenanthrene;
(e) 6-methylquinoline.

31.24   6-Bromoquinoline: p-BrC$_6$H$_4$NH$_2$, glycerol, Skraup conditions.
8-Methylquinoline: o-CH$_3$C$_6$H$_4$NH$_2$, glycerol, Skraup conditions.

31.25   (a) CH$_3$CHO undergoes aldol condensation to give CH$_3$CH=CHCHO;
conjugate addition of PhNH$_2$, followed by Skraup ring closure, gives
2-methylquinoline (compare Prob. 31.21).   (b) 4-Methylquinoline.
(c) 2-Phenyl-4-quinolinecarboxylic acid.

31.26   Conjugate addition of PhNH$_2$ to enol (also an α,β-unsaturated ketone)
of acetylacetone, followed by Skraup ring closure.

31.27   (a) Nitrogen-containing ring is deactivated (as in quinoline); thus
substitution takes place in less deactivated ring at an α-position.
(b) Nucleophilic substitution facilitated "*ortho*" to nitrogen (compare
Sec. 31.10). Attack at 1-position permits other ring to retain aromaticity, and is therefore favored over attack at 3-position (compare
Sec. 30.13).   (c) Anion formed by removal of proton from methyl
group of 1-methylisoquinoline is stabilized because nitrogen can help
accommodate the negative charge without disruption of aromatic
sextet of benzenoid ring. This is not possible with the 3-methyl
isomer.

31.28   Electrophilic aromatic substitution or acid-catalyzed carbonyl addition, depending upon viewpoint.

31.29   Toluene, Cl$_2$, heat; CN$^-$; 2H$_2$, Ni; acetic anhydride.

1.   (a) 3-Bromopyridine;   (b) 3-pyridinesulfonic acid;   (d) 3-nitropyridine;
(e) 2-aminopyridine;   (f) 2-phenylpyridine;   (g) pyridinium chloride
(pyridine hydrochloride);   (k) N-ethylpyridinium bromide;
(l) N-benzylpyridinium chloride;   (m) pyridine N-oxide;
(n) 4-nitropyridine N-oxide;   (o) piperidine. No reaction: c, h, i, j.

2.   (a) 2-Thiophenesulfonic acid;   (b) 2-acetylthiophene;
(c) 2-acetylthiophene;   (d) 2-nitrothiophene;   (e) 2-aminothiophene;
(f) 2-bromothiophene;   (g) 2-thiophenecarboxylic acid;
(h) 2-pyrrolesulfonic acid;   (i) p-(2-pyrrylazo)benzenesulfonic acid;
(j) 2-aminopyrrole;   (k) pyrrolidine;   (l) furfurylideneacetone;
(m) 5- and 8-nitroquinoline;   (n) 4-nitroquinoline N-oxide;
(o) 1-(n-butyl)isoquinoline.

3.   (a) Possible: double bond between C-2 and C-3, or between C-3 and C-4;

(b) pyrroline actually has double bond between C-3 and C-4;
A, $HN(CH_2COOH)_2$; B, H_2NCH_2COOH (or $^+H_3NCH_2COO^-$).

4. (a) C, acetonylacetone, 2,5-hexanedione. (b) Protonation of oxygen; hydrolytic cleavage of protonated "ether" link; enol-to-keto tautomerization to give diketone.

5. Porphin, with same ring skeleton as in hemin, page 1152.

6. D, 2-COOH; E, 3-COOH; F, 4-COOH.

7. (a) 5- or 7-methylquinoline; (b) G, 7-methylquinoline; H, 8-amino-7-methylquinoline.

8. (a) $PhCH_2CH_2NH_2$ (page 735), PhCOCl (page 590); P_2O_5, heat; Pd, heat. (b) $PhCH_2COOH$ (page 587), $SOCl_2$; $PhCH_2CH_2NH_2$ (page 735); P_2O_5, heat; Pd, heat. (c) $o\text{-}CH_3C_6H_4CN$ (page 766), H_2O, H^+, heat; $SOCl_2$; $LiAlH(Bu\text{-}t)_3$; CH_3NO_2, OH^- (see Problem 21.22a, page 714); $4H_2$, Ni (reduction of nitro group and double bond); CH_3COCl; P_2O_5, heat; Pd, heat. (d) p-Nitroaniline (page 760), glycerol, Skraup conditions. (e) p-Nitrobenzoic acid (page 345), Fe, H^+; crotonaldehyde, Doebner-von Miller conditions. (f) p-Nitroaniline (page 760), Sn, H^+; double Skraup reaction.

9. (a) 3-Aminopyridine (Problem 31.12), HONO; CuCN. (b) CH_3Li; $3H_2$, Ni. (c) HNO_3, H_2SO_4; separate 5-isomer from 8-isomer; Fe, H^+. (d) Tollens' reagent; HNO_3, H_2SO_4; EtOH, H^+. (e) Acetic anhydride, NaOAc (Perkin reaction). (f) $NaBH_4$; acidify; conc. HCl, heat. (g) $CHCl_3$, OH^-, heat (Reimer-Tiemann reaction).

10. (See below for parent ring systems.) I, 2,4,6-trihydroxy-1,3-diazine; J, 3,6-dimethyl-4,5-dihydro-1,2-diazine; K, 3,6-dimethyl-1,2-diazine; L, 3,5-dimethyl-1,2-diazole; M, 2,3-dimethyl-1,4-diazanaphthalene; N, 1,3-dioxolan-2-one (ethylene carbonate); O, $o\text{-}HOOCC_6H_4NHCH_2COOH$; P, 3-indolol (3-hydroxyindole); Q, 2,5-dimethyl-3,6-dihydro-1,4-diazine; R, 2,5-dimethyl-1,4-diazine; S, 1,3-diazolid-2-one (2-imidazolidone, ethyleneurea); T, 4,5-benzo-2-methyl-1,3-diazole (2-methylbenzimidazole); U, $o\text{-}EtOOCC_6H_4NHCOCH_2COOEt$; V, ethyl 2,4-dihydroxy-3-quinolinecarboxylate (or the diketo tautomer); W, 2,4-dihydroxyquinoline; X, $PhCH(CN)CH_2COPh$; Y, $PhCH(COOMe)CH_2COPh$; Z, 6-hydroxy-1,3,5-triphenyl-1,4-dihydro-1,2-diazine (or keto form); AA, $HOOCCH_2CH_2NHNH_2$; BB, 1,2-diazolid-3-one (3-pyrazolidone); CC, 4,5-diazaphenanthrene; DD, 1,2-dibromo-1,2-di(o-nitrophenyl)ethene;

EE, diamine from DD;   FF, 3-bromo-2-(*o*-aminophenyl)indole;
GG, two indole units fused 2,3 to 3′,2′;
HH, N-methyl-1,2,3,4-tetrahydroquinoline;   II, 2-phenylbenzoxazole;
JJ, the benzene ring of II completely hydrogenated.   (s) *cis*-I cannot get
into the *anti* diaxial conformation needed for displacement of the tosy-
late anion.

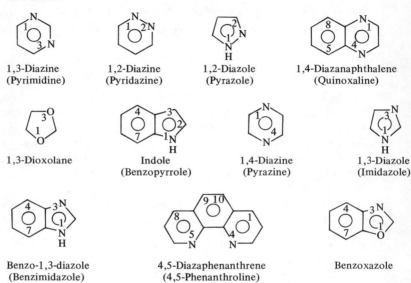

| 1,3-Diazine (Pyrimidine) | 1,2-Diazine (Pyridazine) | 1,2-Diazole (Pyrazole) | 1,4-Diazanaphthalene (Quinoxaline) |

| 1,3-Dioxolane | Indole (Benzopyrrole) | 1,4-Diazine (Pyrazine) | 1,3-Diazole (Imidazole) |

| Benzo-1,3-diazole (Benzimidazole) | 4,5-Diazaphenanthrene (4,5-Phenanthroline) | Benzoxazole |

11. KK, 3,4-$(MeO)_2C_6H_3CH_2CN$;   LL, 3,4-$(MeO)_2C_6H_3CH_2CH_2NH_2$;
MM, 3,4-$(MeO)_2C_6H_3CH_2COOH$;   NN, 3,4-$(MeO)_2C_6H_3CH_2COCl$;
OO, amide from LL and NN;   PP, a 1-substituted-7,8-dimethoxy-
3,4-dihydroisoquinoline.

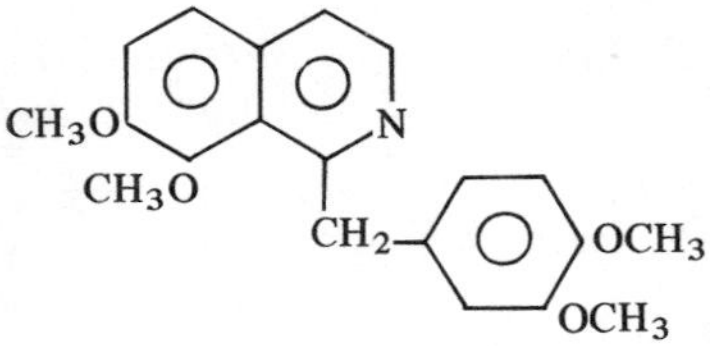

Papaverine

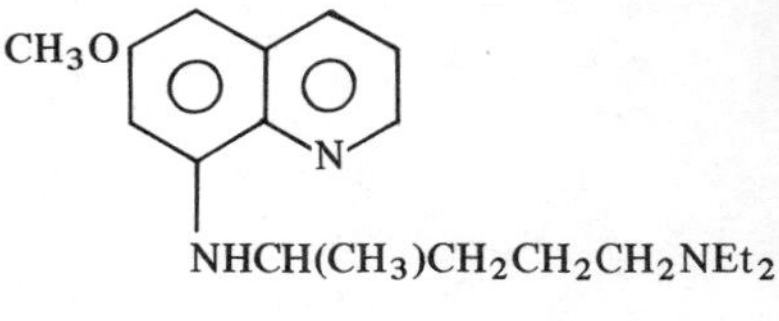

Plasmochin

12. QQ, $Et_2NCH_2CH_2OH$;   RR, $Et_2NCH_2CH_2Cl$;
SS, $Et_2NCH_2CH_2CH(COOEt)COCH_3$;   TT, $Et_2NCH_2CH_2CH_2COCH_3$;
UU, $Et_2NCH_2CH_2CH_2CHOHCH_3$;   VV, $Et_2NCH_2CH_2CH_2CHBrCH_3$;
WW, 8-nitro-6-methoxyquinoline;   XX, 8-amino-6-methoxyquinoline.

13. YY, 3-pyridylCOCH$_2$CH$_2$CH$_2$OEt;
    ZZ, 3-pyridylCH(NH$_2$)CH$_2$CH$_2$CH$_2$OEt;
    AAA, 2-(3-pyridyl)pyrrolidine;   BBB and CCC, diastereomeric salts of
    nicotine and (+)-tartaric acid; nicotine, 2-(3-pyridyl)-N-methylpyrrolidine
    (see page 1004).

14. (a) DDD, *o*-hydroxybenzalacetophenone;   (b) DDD forms a cyclic
    hemiketal, which is aromatized by loss of the —OH group; the resulting
    aromatic structure is a cation.   (c) Oxygen contributes a pair of elec-
    trons to complete the aromatic sextet, thus giving a system analogous to
    that of naphthalene.

15. (a) 2-COOH-5-CH$_2$COOH-N-methylpyrrolidine and N-methyl-2,6-
    piperidinedicarboxylic acid are possible;   (b) tropinic acid is actually
    2-COOH-5-CH$_2$COOH-N-methylpyrrolidine.

16. Reduction of keto group; dehydration of alcohol; double exhaustive
    methylation.

17.

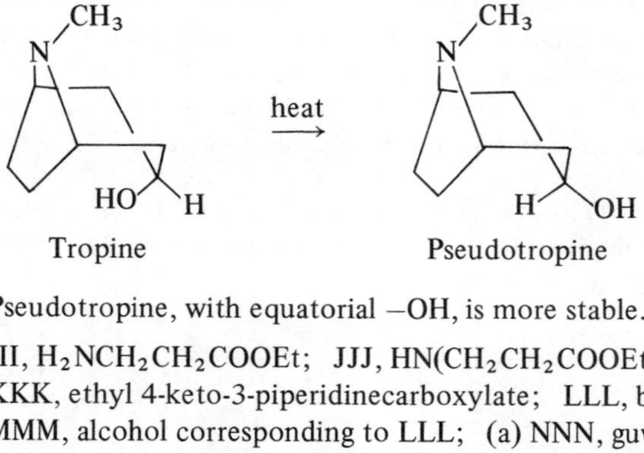

Tropine →(heat) Pseudotropine

Pseudotropine, with equatorial —OH, is more stable.

18. III, H$_2$NCH$_2$CH$_2$COOEt;   JJJ, HN(CH$_2$CH$_2$COOEt)$_2$;
    KKK, ethyl 4-keto-3-piperidinecarboxylate;   LLL, benzamide of KKK;
    MMM, alcohol corresponding to LLL;   (a) NNN, guvacine,
    1,2,5,6-tetrahydro-3-pyridinecarboxylic acid; arecaidine,
    N-methylguvacine;   (b) nicotinic acid.

19.

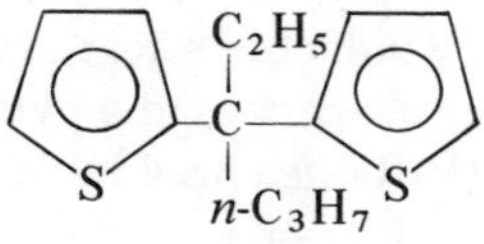

OOO

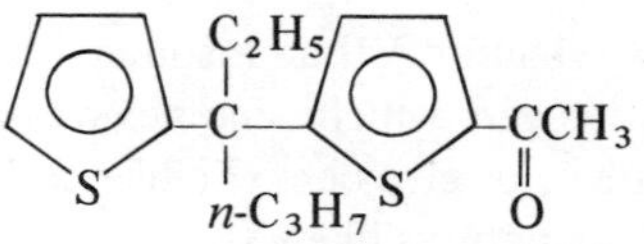

PPP

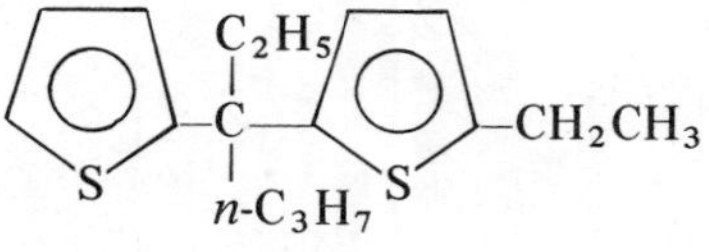

QQQ

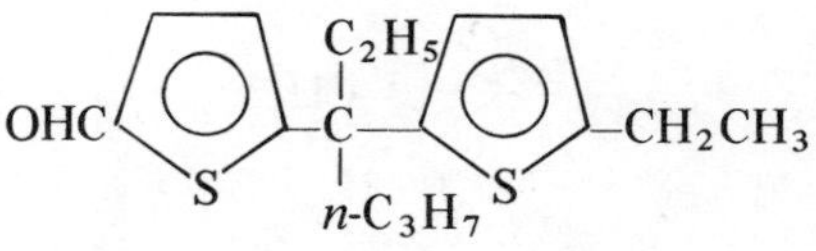

RRR

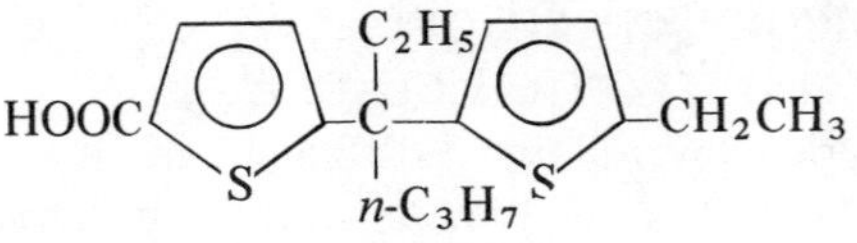

SSS

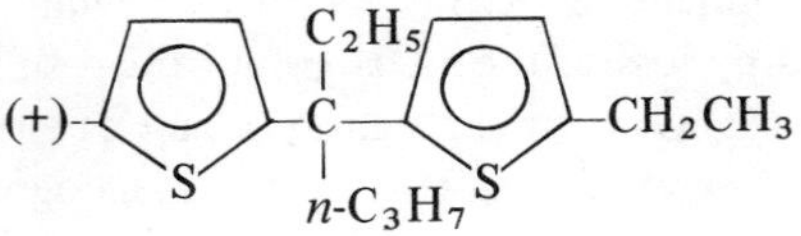

TTT

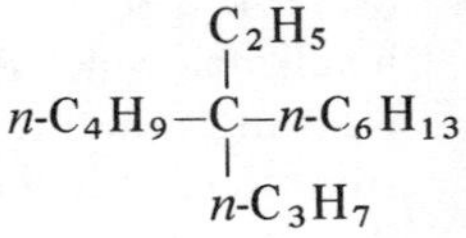

$$n\text{-}C_4H_9\text{---}\overset{\displaystyle C_2H_5}{\underset{\displaystyle n\text{-}C_3H_7}{C}}\text{---}n\text{-}C_6H_{13}$$

UUU

One enantiomer

Chirality does not necessarily lead to measurable optical activity (see Sec. 4.13).

20. (a) "Pyrrole" nitrogen (—NH—) contributes two π electrons, other atoms contribute one each (including "pyridine" nitrogen), to give the aromatic sextet. Valence-bond description like that of pyrrole (Sec. 31.2), with "pyridine" nitrogen taking the place of a carbon.   (b) Aliphatic $NH_2 >$ "pyridine" N $>$ "pyrrole" NH. Unshared pair is in, respectively, an sp^3 orbital, an sp^2 orbital, and the π cloud (see Secs. 31.2 and 31.11).

21. (a) Dipolar ion (VI) loses CO_2 to form carbanion (VII) stabilized by positive charge on nitrogen. N-methyl derivative necessarily exists entirely as dipolar ion.

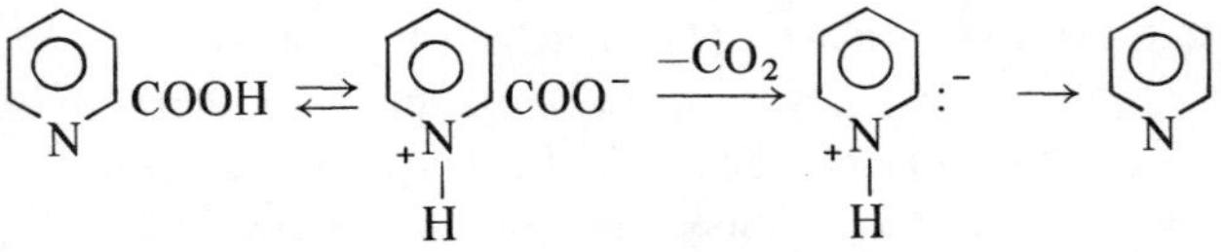

VI   VII

(b) Carbanion VII and isomers stabilized by inductive effect of charge on nitrogen, which becomes weaker with distance. 2- and 4-pyridineacetic acids give benzylic-like carbanions (VIII) stabilized by resonance with structures like IX.

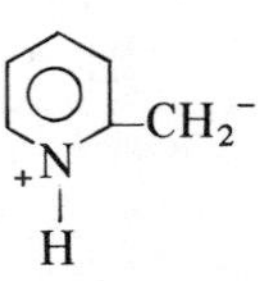

VIII 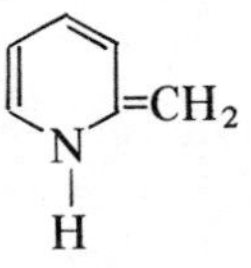   IX

CHAPTER 32

32.1   (a) Amide; see Sec. 32.7   (b) Amide; 6-aminohexanoic acid.
       (c) Ether; ethylene oxide.   (d) Chloroalkene; 2-chloro-1,3-butadiene.
       (e) Chloroalkane; 1,1-dichloroethene.

32.2   (a) Amide.   (b) Ester.   (c) Acetal.   (d) Acetal.

32.3   1,2- and 1,4-addition.

32.4   Combination.

32.5   Relative ease of abstraction of atoms.   (a) H: aryl, $1°$, $1°$ benzylic,
       $2°$ benzylic, $3°$ benzylic.   (b) H: $2°$, allylic.   (c) X: C—Br bond
       weaker than C—Cl.

32.6   (a) Polymer is transfer agent.   (b) Intramolecular chain-transfer:
       growing radical attacks itself.

32.7   (a) Similar to those on page 1035. Butadiene carries partial positive
       charge, acrylonitrile partial negative charge.   (b) Greater reactivity
       of butadiene toward any radical.

32.8   (a) Polybutadiene still contains double bonds, undergoes vinyl
       copolymerization with styrene.   (b) Free radicals formed by abstrac-
       tion of hydrogen from poly(vinyl chloride), add to methyl
       methacrylate.

32.9   (a) Chain-transfer.   (b) $CH_3OCH_2CH_2OH$.

31.10 Terminal group: (a) —H;   (b) —COOH;   (c) —CH_2CH_2OH;
       (d) —$(CH_2CH_2O)_nH$.

32.11 (a) $1°$ groups esterified more rapidly than $2°$ groups;   (b) cross-linking
       involves esterification of $2°$ alcohol groups in different linear poly-
       mers by single phthalic anhydride molecule.

32.12   ⟿OCH_2CH_2O—CO—NH—⟨O⟩—CH_3
                                        NH—CO—OCH_2CH_2O⟿

32.13 (a) Hot acid or base;   (b) hot acid or base;   (c) aqueous acid;
       (d) aqueous acid.

32.14 (a) Transesterification to give methyl acetate and poly(vinyl alcohol);
       the hypothetical monomer, vinyl alcohol, exists in keto form, acetal-
       dehyde.   (b) Formation of a cyclic acetal, with adjacent —OH's of
       poly(vinyl alcohol) serving as two alcohol molecules.

32.15 The poly(vinyl chloride) is atactic. Poly(vinylidene chloride) has two identical substituents on carbon, and chains fit together well.

32.16 (a) Chains are irregularly substituted, fit together poorly; intermolecular forces are weak. (b) Abstraction of $-H$ from polymer generates free radicals, which combine; cross-links are carbon—carbon bonds.

1. More stable particle formed in each step, with same orientation.

2. Acid-catalyzed polymerization of alkene easily formed from $2°$ or $3°$ alcohol.

3. Because of symmetry of isobutylene units, there is no chance for stereoisomeric polymers; structure of 1-butene, however, permits stereoisomeric polymers.

4. Nucleophilic carbonyl addition to give $(-CH_2O-)_n$. Chain-reaction polymerization.

5. Hydrolysis gives diamines, diols, and CO_2.

6. $PhCH=CH_2$, stability of benzylic radical being formed. For rest of series, polar effect: electron-withdrawal by Ph or Cl deactivates toward electrophilic CCl_3 radical.

7. Competition between alkene (addition) and CX_4 (abstraction) for intermediate radicals. (a) The radical produced in Step (3) of the CCl_4 sequence on page 205 adds to $RCH=CH_2$, and the new radical so formed then attacks CCl_4 in the manner of Step (4). (b) Abstraction from CBr_4 is easier than from CCl_4. All radicals formed in Step (3) react with CBr_4 instead of with $RCH=CH_2$. (c) Growing radicals (benzylic, and highly selective) add to this *highly reactive* alkene instead of abstracting from CCl_4.

8. (a) Ethylene oxide, limited amount of aqueous OH^-; $2,4\text{-}(OCN)_2C_6H_3CH_3$. (b) Ethylene glycol, maleic anhydride; styrene, free-radical initiator. (c) Propylene oxide, limited amount of $NH_2CH_2CH_2NH_2$. (d) Styrene, Na, naphthalene; kill living polymer with ethylene oxide. (e) Vinyl chloride, vinyl acetate, free-radical initiator; methyl methacrylate, benzoyl peroxide.

9. β-propiolactone + :Base $\longrightarrow$ $^-OCH_2CH_2COBase$
   $^-OCH_2CH_2COBase$ + β-propiolactone $\longrightarrow$
   $$^-OCH_2CH_2CO-OCH_2CH_2OBase, \textit{etc.}$$

10. $NH_2CH_2CH(Ph)\sim\sim CH_2CH(Ph)^- + NH_3 \longrightarrow$
    $$NH_2CH_2CH(Ph)\sim\sim CH_2CH_2Ph$$

11. Cleavage indicates occasional vicinal OH grouping, and hence vicinal $OOCH_3$ grouping. Evidently, *some* head-to-head polymerization has taken place.

12. (a)

$$\sim\!\!\sim N(CH_2)_5 \underset{\underset{O}{\|}}{C}\!-\!N(CH_2)_5 \underset{\underset{O}{\|}}{C}\!\sim\!\!\sim$$

with H on each N

(b) Caprolactam + :Base $\longrightarrow$ $^-NH(CH_2)_5COBase$
caprolactam + $^-NH(CH_2)_5COBase$ $\longrightarrow$
$^-NH(CH_2)_5CONH(CH_2)_5COBase$, *etc.*

13. Cyclohexanone.

14. *Para* isomer gives straight, symmetrical chains that fit together well.

15. Compounds are ionic, due to stability of benzylic anions.

16. A, *meso,* resembles isotactic; B, racemic, resembles syndiotactic.

17. C, $HOCH_2CH_2OCO(CH_2)_4COO\sim\!\!\sim CH_2CH_2OH$;
D, $p\text{-}OCNC_6H_4C_6H_4NHCOOCH_2CH_2OCO(CH_2)_4COO\sim\!\!\sim CH_2CH_2O\text{-}$
$CONHC_6H_4C_6H_4NCO\text{-}p$
E, $H_2NC_6H_4C_6H_4NHCOOCH_2CH_2OCO(CH_2)_4COO\sim\!\!\sim CH_2CH_2O\text{-}$
$CONHC_6H_4C_6H_4NH_2 + CO_2$
CO_2 formed in last step is dispersed in polymer to give a foam.

18. Monomer (which can lose hydrogen atom to give allylic free radical) serves as chain-transfer agent. Abstraction of deuterium is more difficult, and labeled ester is poorer chain-transfer agent.

19. Oxygen abstracts hydrogen atoms to form allylic free radicals, $R\cdot$. These combine with oxygen to give $-O-O-$ cross-links; gain in weight due to gain of oxygen. Mechanism seems to be:

$R\cdot + O_2 \longrightarrow RCOO\cdot$
$2RCOO\cdot \longrightarrow ROOR + O_2$

20. (a) Use excess epichlorohydrin to have epoxide groups at both ends.
$$H_2C\!-\!CHCH_2O(A\!-\!OCH_2CHOHCH_2O)_nA\!-\!OCH_2CH\!-\!CH_2$$
with epoxide O bridges at both ends

Cement $(A = -C_6H_4-C(CH_3)_2-C_6H_4-)$

(b) $\sim\!\!\sim NHCH_2CH_2NCH_2CH_2NHCH_2\underset{\underset{OH}{|}}{C}HCH_2O\text{-}$
$(A\!-\!OCH_2CHOHCH_2O)_nA\!-\!OCH_2\underset{\underset{OH}{|}}{C}HCH_2NH\sim\!\!\sim$

(c) Excess phenol, acetone, acid or base (compare page 1043).

21. F, syndiotactic; G, isotactic. Methylene protons are equivalent in F (*b*) and non-equivalent in G (*b* and *c*).

CHAPTER 33

33.1 Decarboxylation. Fatty acids could be precursors of petroleum hydro-carbons.

33.2 (a) Isoprene unit. (b) Likely that petroleum comes from green plants.

33.3 Tung oil contains high proportion of eleostearic acid; abstraction of hydrogen atom (see answer to Problem 19, page 1052) gives allylic free radical with delocalization over three double bonds.

33.4 Alkoxide is poor leaving group.

33.5 Preserves semiliquidity of membranes in colder part of body.

1. Nervonic acid, *cis*- or *trans*-$CH_3(CH_2)_7CH=CH(CH_2)_{13}COOH$ (actually, *trans*).

2. Transesterification to more random distribution of acyl groups among glyceride molecules.

3. Hybrid (allylic) free radical is intermediate.

4. Weakly basic 2,4-dinitrophenoxide ion is good leaving group.

5. Spermaceti, *n*-hexadecyl *n*-hexadecanoate.

6. Cleavage of monoanion as dipolar ion (or with simultaneous transfer of proton) easiest because of (a) protonation of alkoxy group and (b) double negative charge on other oxygens:

$$R\overset{+}{-}O-PO_3^{--} \overset{H_2O}{\longrightarrow} ROH + H_2PO_4^-$$
$$|$$
$$H$$

7. C, $CH_3(CH_2)_4CH_2C\equiv CH$; D, $CH_3(CH_2)_4CH_2C\equiv CCH_2(CH_2)_7CH_2Cl$; E, $CH_3(CH_2)_4CH_2C\equiv CCH_2(CH_2)_7CH_2CN$; F, $CH_3(CH_2)_4CH_2C\equiv CCH_2(CH_2)_7CH_2COOH$; vaccenic acid, *cis*-$CH_3(CH_2)_4CH_2CH=CHCH_2(CH_2)_7CH_2COOH$.

8. G, *n*-$C_{13}H_{27}CH_2CH(COOEt)_2$; H, *n*-$C_{13}H_{27}CH_2CH(COOEt)COOH$; I, *n*-$C_{13}H_{27}CH_2CH(COOEt)COOTHP$;

J, *cis-n-*$C_6H_{13}CH=CH(CH_2)_7COCl$;

K, *cis-n-*$C_{13}H_{27}CH_2C(COOEt)(COOTHP)CO(CH_2)_7CH=CHC_6H_{13}-n$;

L, *cis-n-*$C_{13}H_{27}CH_2CH(COOEt)CO(CH_2)_7CH=CHC_6H_{13}-n$;

M, *cis-n-*$C_{13}H_{27}CH_2CH(COOEt)CHOH(CH_2)_7CH=CHC_6H_{13}-n$;

corynomycolinic acid,

cis-n-$C_{13}H_{27}CH_2CH(COOH)CHOH(CH_2)_7CH=CHC_6H_{13}-n$.

9. N, *n-*$C_8H_{17}CHBrCH_3$;   O, *n-*$C_8H_{17}CH(CH_3)CH_2COOH$;

P, *n-*$C_8H_{17}CH(CH_3)CH_2COCl$;   Q, *n-*$C_8H_{17}CH(CH_3)CH_2COOEt$;

R, *n-*$C_8H_{17}CH(CH_3)CH_2CH_2OH$;   S, *n-*$C_8H_{17}CH(CH_3)CH_2CH_2Br$;

T, *n-*$C_8H_{17}CH(CH_3)CH_2CH_2CO(CH_2)_5COOEt$;

U, *n-*$C_8H_{17}CH(CH_3)CH_2CH_2CH_2(CH_2)_5COOEt$;

tuberculostearic acid, 10-methyloctadecanoic acid.

10. C_{27}-phthienoic acid,

$CH_3(CH_2)_{17}CH(CH_3)CH_2CH(CH_3)CH=C(CH_3)COOH$;

V, $CH_3(CH_2)_{17}CH(CH_3)CH_2CH(CH_3)COOH$;

W, $CH_3(CH_2)_{17}CH(CH_3)CH_2CH(CH_3)C(OH)Ph_2$;

X, $CH_3(CH_2)_{17}CH(CH_3)CH_2C(CH_3)=CPh_2$;

Y, $CH_3(CH_2)_{17}CH(CH_3)CH_2COCH_3$;

Z, $CH_3(CH_2)_{17}CH(CH_3)CH_2CBr(CH_3)COOH$;

AA, $CH_3(CH_2)_{17}CH(CH_3)CH=C(CH_3)COOH$.

11. CC, octadecanoic acid;   DD, 2-methylheptadecanoic acid.

12. $(CH_3O)_2PO-$, like a second $-COOCH_3$, increases acidity of α-H.

EE, $C_2H_5C(CH_3)(OH)CH(COOCH_3)PO(OCH_3)_2$;

FF, *(Z)-*$C_2H_5(CH_3)C=CHCOOCH_3$;

GG, *(Z)-*$C_2H_5(CH_3)C=CHCH_2OH$;   HH, *(Z)-*$C_2H_5(CH_3)C=CHCH_2Br$;

II, *(Z)-*$C_2H_5(CH_3)C=CHCH_2CH(COOEt)COC_2H_5$;

JJ, *(Z)-*$C_2H_5(CH_3)C=CHCH_2CH_2COC_2H_5$;

KK, *(Z)-*$C_2H_5(CH_3)C=CHCH_2CH_2C(OH)(C_2H_5)CH(COOCH_3)-$

$PO(OCH_3)_2$;

LL, *(Z,E)-*$C_2H_5(CH_3)C=CHCH_2CH_2(C_2H_5)C=CHCOOCH_3$;

MM, *(Z,E)-*$C_2H_5(CH_3)C=CHCH_2CH_2(C_2H_5)C=CHCH_2OH$;

NN, *(Z,E)-*$C_2H_5(CH_3)C=CHCH_2CH_2(C_2H_5)C=CHCH_2Br$;

OO, *(Z,E)-*$C_2H_5(CH_3)C=CHCH_2CH_2(C_2H_5)C=CHCH_2CH(COOEt)COCH_3$;

PP, *(Z,E)-*$C_2H_5(CH_3)C=CHCH_2CH_2(C_2H_5)C=CHCH_2CH_2COCH_3$;

QQ, *(Z,E)-*$C_2H_5(CH_3)C=CHCH_2CH_2(C_2H_5)C=CHCH_2CH_2C(OH)-$

$(CH_3)CH(COOCH_3)PO(OCH_3)_2$;

RR, *(Z,E,E)-*$C_2H_5(CH_3)C=CHCH_2CH_2(C_2H_5)C=CHCH_2CH_2(CH_3)C=$

$CHCOOCH_3$;

juvenile hormone,

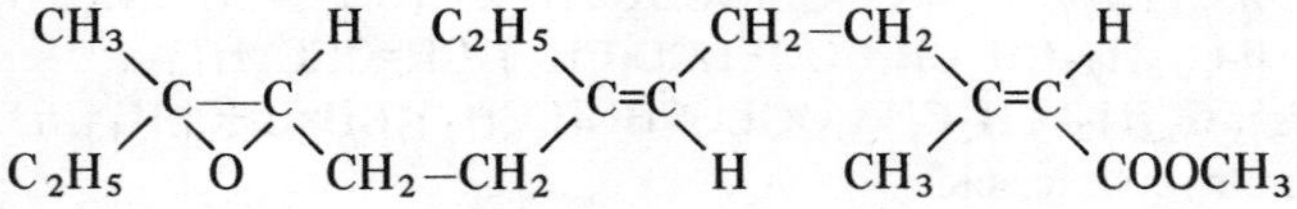

$$CH_3 \quad H \quad C_2H_5 \quad CH_2{-}CH_2 \quad H$$

$$C_2H_5 \quad O \quad CH_2{-}CH_2 \quad H \quad CH_3 \quad COOCH_3$$

with C—C, C=C, C=C linkages as shown.

CHAPTER 34

34.1 Starting at the top: $-CO-$; $-CHO$; $-CHO$ and $-CH_2OH$; five $-OH$'s; C–C–C–C–C–C; C–C–C–C–C–CHO.

34.2 Formulas I-VIII, page 1082.

34.3 (a) 3; (b) 8;

(c)

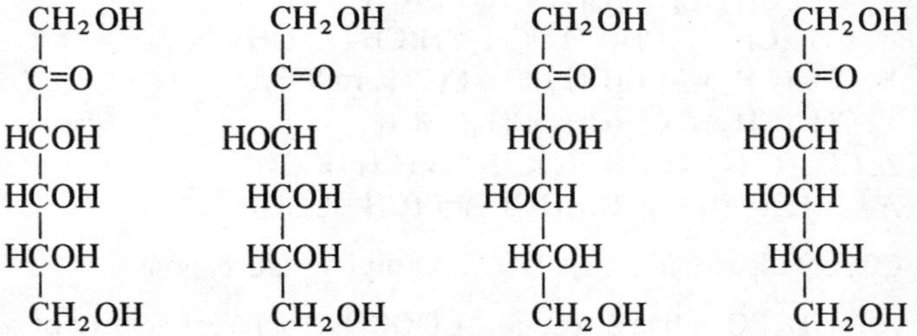

CH_2OH	CH_2OH	CH_2OH	CH_2OH
C=O	C=O	C=O	C=O
HCOH	HOCH	HCOH	HOCH
HCOH	HCOH	HOCH	HOCH
HCOH	HCOH	HCOH	HCOH
CH_2OH	CH_2OH	CH_2OH	CH_2OH

34.4 Glucose + $5HIO_4 \longrightarrow 5HCOOH + HCHO$.

34.5 A, gluconic acid; B, glucitol; C, glucaric acid; D, glucuronic acid.

34.6 Fructose. Aldose $\longrightarrow$ osazone $\longrightarrow$ osone $\longrightarrow$ 2-ketose.

34.7 Identical in configuration at C-3, C-4, and C-5.

34.8 Excess of $NaBH_4$ reduces to alditol.

34.9 (a) 2 tetroses; (b) 4 pentoses; 8 hexoses (see Prob. 34.2). The lowest chiral carbon has $-OH$ on right, as this configuration is undisturbed in building up from (+)-glyceraldehyde.

34.10 (a) Mesotartaric acid and D-tartaric acid (page 1090). (b) Test tartaric acid from each for optical activity.

34.11 I, (+)-allose; II, (+)-altrose; VI, (−)-idose; VII, (+)-galactose; VIII, (+)-talose.

34.12 Compare with pages 1086-1087, and Prob. 34.11.

34.13 CH$_2$OH
     |
    C=O
     |
  HOCH
     |
    HCOH
     |
    HCOH
     |
    CH$_2$OH
  D-(−)-Fructose

34.14 Mirror images of III and IV (page 1085) and of structure in Prob. 34.13.

34.15 (a) R; (b) R; (c) S; (d) R.

34.16 A, CH$_3$CHOHCOOEt; B, CH$_3$CHOHCH$_2$OH; C, CH$_3$CHOHCH$_2$Br;
D, CH$_3$CHOHCH$_2$CN; E, CH$_3$CHOHCH$_2$COOH;
F, CH$_3$CHOHCH$_2$COOMe; G, CH$_3$CHOHCH$_2$CH$_2$OH;
H, CH$_3$CHOHCH$_2$CH$_2$I. The absolute configuration of (+)-2-butanol is given on page 678. It is (S)-(+)-2-butanol.

34.17 (a) S,S-; (b) R,R-; (c) R,S-.

34.18 (a) Chiral center already present in reactants; transition states, like products, are diastereomeric and of different stabilities. (b) The proportions of the cyanohydrins will be 1:3. Except for one of the tartaric acids (*meso* isomer), all products will be optically active. (c) Inactive because the enantiomeric cyanohydrins will be formed in equal amounts. The isomer favored in the L-series will be the mirror image of the isomer favored in the D-series.

34.19 A, monolactone involving C-3 and C-6; B, monolactone involving C-1 and C-4; C, −COOH at C-1; D, lactone involving C-1 and C-4; E, −COOH at C-6; F, lactone involving C-3 and C-6; L-(+)-gulose, mirror image of V (page 1085).

34.20 (a) 36.2% α, 63.8% β. (b) In the β-form, the anomeric −OH group is equatorial.

34.21 Protonation of ring oxygen; ring opening to give protonated aldehyde; loss of proton to give open-chain aldose; then reverse of these steps. Loss of configuration only at C-1.

34.22 Ring of cyclic α- and β-pentaacetates not easily cleaved to give aldehydo form.

34.23 (a) MeOH, HOOC−CHO, and D-glyceric acid; (b) (+)-glucose gave the same glyceric acid as obtained by oxidation of (+)-glyceraldehyde, hence C-5 has –OH on right.

34.24 HCHO instead of HCOOH.

34.25 (a) Six-membered ring; (b) HCOOH, OHC–CHO, and HOCH$_2$CHO.

34.26 (a) Six-membered ring; (b) enantiomer.

34.27 (a) Five-membered ring; (b) optically active, L-family; (c) enantiomer.

34.28 (a) Like I, page 1104, except for axial –OH on C-3; (b) like I, page 1104, except for axial –OH's on C-3 and C-4; (c) like I, page 1104, except for –H in place of –CH$_2$OH on C-5; (d) shape of II, page 1104, with equatorial –OH's except on C-4, and –H in place of –CH$_2$OH on C-5; (e) mirror image of I, page 1104.

(f)

β-D-(–)-Fructopyranose

1. (a) D-Galactosoxime; (b) D-galactosazone; (c) D-galactonic acid; (d) galactaric acid (mucic acid); (e) 5HCOOH + HCHO; (f) penta-O-acetyl-D-galactose; (g) penta-O-benzoyl-D-galactose; (h) methyl α- and β-D-galactoside; (i) methyl α- and β-2,3,4,6-tetra-O-methyl-D-galactoside; (j) 2,3,4,6-tetra-O-methyl-D-galactose; (k) 2,3,4-tri-O-methyl-L-arabaric acid; (l) galactitol; (m) galactitol; (n) two epimeric heptoses; (o) D- and L-galactonic acid; (p) D-talose (and D-galactose); (q) D-galactosone; (r) a D-2-ketohexose; (s) D-lyxose; (t) no reaction; (u) product on page 1099 from α-isomer; β-isomer gives opposite configuration at C-1; (v) HOOC–CHO and D-glyceric acid.

2. (a) MeOH, HCl. (b) Product a, Me$_2$SO$_4$, OH⁻. (c) Product b, dil. HCl. (d) Br$_2$(aq); pyridine, warm; H⁺ (lactone formation); NaBH$_4$. (e) HNO$_3$, heat; H⁺ (monolactone formation); NaBH$_4$, reduction to glyconic acid; H⁺ (lactone formation); NaBH$_4$, reduction to aldose. (f) Br$_2$(aq); CaCO$_3$; H$_2$O$_2$, Fe⁺⁺⁺. (g) Product f, Br$_2$(aq); CaCO$_3$; H$_2$O$_2$, Fe⁺⁺⁺; HNO$_3$, heat. (h) NaBH$_4$; acidify; acetic anhydride, H⁺.

(i) $PhNHNH_2$; PhCHO, H^+ (osone formation); Zn, HOAc. (j) CN^-, H^+; H_2O, H^+, warm; separate the two lactones; $NaBH_4$.

3. (a) See Problem 34.3(a). (b) One gives the same osazone as D-allose or D-altrose; this is D-psicose. Another gives the same osazone as D-gulose or D-idose; this is D-sorbose. The third gives the same osazone as D-galactose or D-talose; this is D-tagatose.

4. A, $ClCH_2CHOHC\equiv CCHOHCH_2Cl$, mainly *meso*; B, diepoxide from A; C, $CH_2OHCHOHC\equiv CCHOHCH_2OH$, *meso*; D, $CH_2OHCHOHCH=CHCHOHCH_2OH$, *cis, meso*; E and E', allitol and galactitol, both *meso* compounds; F, glucitol (or gulitol), racemic modification; G, $CH_2OHCHOHCH=CHCHOHCH_2OH$, *trans*, 2 diastereomers; H, glucitol (or gulitol), racemic modification; I and I', allitol and galactitol, both *meso* compounds; J, $HC\equiv CCHOHCHOHCH_2OH$, racemic modification (*erythro*); K, $CH_2=CHCHOAcCHOAcCH_2OAc$, racemic modification (*erythro*); L and M, $BrCH_2CHOHCHOAcCHOAcCH_2OAc$, 2 pairs of enantiomers; N, ribitol, *meso* compound; O, arabitol (or lyxitol), racemic modification. (c) Erythritol: H_2, Lindlar's catalyst; $KMnO_4$. Or Na, NH_3; HCO_2OH. DL-Threitol: H_2, Lindlar's catalyst; HCO_2OH. Or Na, NH_3; $KMnO_4$. (d) Nucleophilic carbonyl addition.

5. (a) P: in structure IVc or Vc, page 1094, replace $-CH_3$ by $-R$ and $-CH_2OH$ by $-COOH$ (P is actually β); (b) like V (page 1105) and IV (page 1105), with $-CH_2OH$ replaced by $-COOH$; (c) $-COOH$ at C-1 or C-6 of D-fructose. The C-1 acid gives D-gluconic and D-mannonic acids. The C-6 acid gives L-gulonic and D-mannonic acids. (d) The C-1 acid related to D-fructose, $HOCH_2(CHOH)_3COCOOH$.

6. Rate-determining step involves OH^- before reaction with Cu^{++}; probably abstraction of proton leading to formation of enediol.

7. (a) 5 carbons, five-membered ring; (b) C-1 and C-4; (c) Q, methyl α-D-arabinofuranoside.

8. Salicin, *o*-(hydroxymethyl)phenyl β-D-glucopyranoside.

9. Bio-inonose, the pentahydroxycyclohexanone in which successive $-OH$ groups are *trans* to each other. R and S, diastereomeric hexahydroxycyclohexanes which differ in configuration of only one carbon atom.

10. (a) C-1, then C-2; C-6; C-3; CO_2 from C-3 and C-4, HCOOH from C-2 and C-5, CHI_3 from C-1 and C-6. (b) $HOCH_2COOH$ from C-1 and C-2, HCOOH from C-3 and C-4, HCHO from C-5; HCHO from C-1 and C-5, HCOOH from C-2, C-3, and C-4; HCHO from C-5, HCOOH from C-4, osazone from C-1, C-2, and C-3.

11. T, D-ribose; U, D-arabinose; V, 3-ribityl phosphate; W, ribitol; X, ribityl pentaacetate; Y, 2,3,5-tri-O-methyl-D-ribose; (c) see Figure 37.5, page 1179.

12. Z and AA are ketals: Z, furanose with acetone bridging C-1 to C-2 and C-5 to C-6; AA, pyranose, with acetone bridging C-1 to C-2.

13. Either reactant converted into a mixture of glyceraldehyde and dihydroxyacetone; aldol and crossed-aldol condensations yield final products.

14. S_N1-type, with separation of relatively stable oxonium ion (see Sec. 19.15).

15. (a) Proton on C-1 most deshielded by two oxygens. (b) JJ, β-anomer; KK, α-anomer; axial H absorbs upfield from equatorial, has large coupling constant with axial H on C-2. (c) LL, β-anomer; MM, α-anomer; same reasoning as in (b). (d) NN, α-mannose; OO, β-mannose; PP, β-glucose; QQ, α-glucose; $J = 3$ indicates axial−equatorial coupling, $J = 8$ indicates axial−axial coupling; equatorial H farther downfield than axial H.

16.

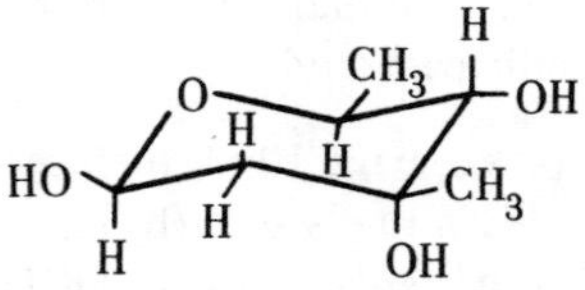

L-(−)-Mycarose.

(e) α-glycoside;   (f) β-anomer.

17. (a) Anomeric effect (Sec. 34.20) stabilizes the α-anomer. (b) Anomeric effect stabilizes diaxial chlorines.

18. (a) On steric grounds, neither; anomeric effect would favor axial OAc on C-1. (b) Tells nothing: in either conformation two OAc groups are equatorial, two are axial. (c) The $e{:}a$ peak area ratio would be 2:1 if the OAc group on C-1 were all axial, 1:1 if half axial, 0.5:1 if none axial. Ratio of 1.46:1.00 shows that the OAc group on C-1 is axial in 79% of the molecules.

CHAPTER 35

35.1 Differs from I in configuration in right-hand glucose moeity.

35.2 Di-O-methyl-L-tartaric acid and methoxyacetic acid; methoxymalonic acid and di-O-methyl-D-glyceric acid.

35.3 2,3,4,6-Tetra-O-methyl-D-glucose and 2,3,6-tri-O-methyl-D-glucose. One ring is six-membered; other ring could be 5- or 6-membered, attached at C-5 or C-4 to other ring. (Compound could, of course, be either α- or β-anomer.) If oxidize first (to maltobionic acid), and then methylate and hydrolyze, the point of attachment (and with it, the ring size) is revealed.

35.4 D-Glucose and D-erythrose; indicates ring attachment is at C-4 of reducing moiety of maltose.

35.5 Less chance of breaking the glycosidic linkage with formation of monosaccharides.

35.6 Similar to the oxidation-methylation-hydrolysis sequence with maltose, except that cellobiose is used. Final methylated monosaccharides are the same as from maltose.

35.7 (a) Similar to the oxidation-methylation-hydrolysis sequence with maltose, except that lactose is used. Final methylated monosaccharides are 2,3,4,6-tetra-O-methyl-D-galactose and 2,3,5,6-tetra-O-methyl-D-gluconic acid.
(b) 2,3,4-Tri-O-methyl-L-arabinaric (or -L-lyxaric) acid and di-O-methyl-L-tartaric acid; di-O-methyl-L-tartaric acid and di-O-methyl-D-glyceric acid.

35.8 D-Galactose and D-erythrose.

35.9 $(-92.4° + 52.7°)/2 = -19.9°$. Divided by 2 since g/cc based on combined wt of the two (isomeric) compounds.

35.10 $C_{12}H_{20}O_{10}$, non-reducing.

35.11 Probably the glucose unit has the α-configuration, and sucrose is an α-glucoside.

35.12 (a) 2,3,4,6-Tetra-O-methyl-D-glucose and 1,3,4,6-tetra-O-methyl-D-fructose;   (b) tri-O-methylxylaric acid and di-O-methyl-L-tartaric acid; di-O-methyl-D-tartaric acid.

35.13 1 (0.0025%); 3 (0.0075%); 9 (0.022%).

35.14 (a) A large group in an axial position.   (b) Largest groups attached are other glucose units at C-1 and C-4; these, as well as $-CH_2OH$ at C-5, would occupy quasi-equatorial positions in twist-boat conformation (at, say, positions marked 1, 4, and 5, respectively, on page 296).

34.15   (a) 3 molecules of HCOOH per molecule of amylose: HCOOH from
terminal non-reducing unit; no small cleavage products from non-
terminal units; 2HCOOH and 1HCHO from terminal reducing unit.
(b) Moles HCOOH/3 = moles amylose; wt. amylose/moles amylose =
mol. wt. amylose; mol. wt. amylose/wt. (of 162) per glucose unit =
glucose units per molecule of amylose.   (c) 950.

34.16   A poly-α-D-glucopyranoside; chain-forming unit, attachment at C-1
and C-6; chain-linking unit, attachment at C-1, C-3, and C-6; chain-
terminating unit, attachment at C-1.

34.17   A poly-β-D-xylopyranoside; chain-forming unit, attachment at C-1
and C-4; chain-linking unit, attachment at C-1, C-3, and C-4; chain-
terminating unit, attachment at C-1.

1.   Gentiobiose, 6-O-(β-D-glucopyranosyl)-D-glucopyranose.

2.   (a) Trehalose, α-D-glucopyranosyl α-D-glucopyranoside;
(b) isotrehalose, α-D-glucopyranosyl β-D-glucopyranoside;
neotrehalose, β-D-glucopyranosyl β-D-glucopyranoside.

3.   Ruberythric acid is actually 2-(1-hydroxy-9,10-anthraquinonyl)
β-6-O-(β-D-xylopyranosyl)-D-glucopyranoside. From data, uncertainties
are: (a) which —OH of alizarin is involved; methylate ruberythric acid,
hydrolyze, and see which —OH is unmethylated (glycoside linkages
cleaved under conditions where phenolic ether linkage is preserved);
(b) whether glycosidic linkages (between alizarin and C-1 of glucose
unit, and between C-6 of glucose unit and C-1 of xylose unit) are *alpha*
or *beta*; study enzymatic hydrolysis of ruberythric acid and of
primeverose.

4.   Raffinose, α-D-galactosyl unit attached at C-6 of glucose unit of
sucrose; melibiose, 6-O-(α-D-galactopyranosyl)-D-glucopyranose.

5.   (a) Melezitose, α-D-glucopyranosyl unit attached at C-3 of fructose unit
of sucrose; turanose, 3-O-(α-D-glucopyranosyl)-D-fructofuranose.
(b) HCHO would be given by a 3-ring or 4-ring structure for fructose
unit, and by a 3-, 4-, or 5-ring structure for glucose unit.   (c) 3HIO$_4$
and 2HCOOH per ring, or 6HIO$_4$ and 4HCOOH for the two rings;
(d) 5HIO$_4$ and 3HCOOH for the two rings;   (e) 4HIO$_4$ and 2HCOOH
for the two rings;   (f) glucose rings must both be pyranose rings because
only 4HIO$_4$ were actually consumed and 2HCOOH formed;
(g) pyranose, 1HIO$_4$; furanose, no HIO$_4$;   (h) fructose unit must have
furanose ring, because all the HIO$_4$ was used up by the glucose units

($4HIO_4$) and the fructose ring actually found therefore consumed no HIO_4; (i) yes.

6. (a) 3 monosaccharide (glucose) units arranged 2 different ways: either C-4 or C-6 of middle unit could be involved in one glycoside linkage, and C-1 of middle unit could be linked to either C-6 or C-4 of reducing moiety. (b) Panose, α-D-glucopyranosyl unit attached at C-6 of non-reducing moiety of maltose. Isomaltose, 6-O-(α-D-glucopyranosyl)-D-glucopyranose.

7. (a) $-CH_2OH$ groups of cellulose structure (page 1126) oxidized to $-COOH$; (b) D-glucuronic acid; (c) D-xylose.

8. (a) Araban, poly-L-arabinofuranoside; chain-forming unit, attachment at C-1 and C-5; chain-linking unit, attachment at C-1, C-2, and C-5; chain-terminating unit, attachment at C-1. (b) Mannan, poly-D-mannopyranoside; one chain-forming unit, attachment at C-1 and C-3; another chain-forming unit, attachment at C-1 and C-2; a third chain-forming unit, attachment at C-1 and C-6; chain-linking unit, attachment at C-1, C-2, and C-6; chain-terminating unit, attachment at C-1.

9. Furfural (page 1007); A, 2-furoic acid (page 1008); B, furan (page 1007); C, tetrahydrofuran (page 1008); D, 1,4-dichlorobutane; E, adiponitrile (page 736); F, adipic acid.

10. (a) Alginic acid, poly-β-D-galacturonic acid; six-membered rings attached at C-1 and C-4. (b) Pectic acid, poly-α-D-galacturonic acid; six-membered rings attached at C-1 and C-4. (c) Agar, polygalacto-pyranoside; six-membered rings attached at C-1 and C-3. About every tenth unit is L-galactose, esterified by sulfuric acid on C-6; six-membered ring attached to chain at C-1 and C-4. Rest of units are D-galactose.

11. Polycellobiuronic acid; six-membered rings; chain-forming attachment at C-1 of D-glucose unit and at C-3 of D-glucoronic acid unit.

12. G, polymeric dialdehyde (see Problem 35.15a); H, polymeric diacid corresponding to G; I, D-CH_2OHCHOHCHOHCOOH; J, HOOC—CHO.

13. (a) 3 molecules of HCOOH per molecule of cellulose; (b) see Problem 35.15b; (c) 1390 glucose units.

CHAPTER 36

36.1 $-NH_2 > -COO^-$; proton goes to $-NH_2$ to form $^+H_3NCHRCOO^-$.

36.2 $-COOH > -NH_3^+$; $-COOH$ gives up proton to form $^+H_3NCHRCOO^-$.

36.3 K_b for aromatic amines is quite low, so that $-NH_2$ is not neutralized by $-COOH$. But $-SO_3H$ is strongly acidic and can neutralize an aromatic $-NH_2$ group.

36.4 (a) Esterify amino acids in strongly acidic solutions; (b) acylate amino acids in strongly alkaline solutions.

36.5 (a) On acid side; (b) on basic side; (c) more acidic and more basic than for glycine.

36.6 Sulfanilic acid gives up proton to OH^- to form water-soluble sulfonate; but $-SO_3^-$ does not take up a proton, and hence sulfanilic acid is unchanged in acid.

36.7 Differential migration at different pH's; or differences in solubility at different pH's; or precipitate acidic amino acids as salts with certain bases, and basic amino acids as salts with certain acids.

36.8 L-Threonine is

. There are 3 other stereoisomers.

36.9 CyS—SCy, one *meso*, 2 enantiomers; Hylys, 2 pairs of enantiomers; Hypro, 2 pairs of enantiomers; Ileu, 2 pairs of enantiomers.

36.10 Direct ammonolysis: HVZ reaction, followed by excess NH_3. Gly, acetic acid; Ala, propionic acid; Val, isovaleric acid; Leu, isocaproic acid; Asp, succinic acid. Gabriel synthesis: K phthalimide and α-halo ester, followed by hydrolysis of the substituted imide. Gly, ethyl chloroacetate; Leu, ethyl α-chloroisocaproate. Malonic ester synthesis: sodiomalonic ester and alkyl halide, followed by saponification, acidification, α-bromination, decarboxylation, excess NH_3. Val, *iso*-PrBr; Ileu, *sec*-BuBr. Phthalimidomalonic ester method: K phthalimide and bromomalonic ester; Na; alkylation; saponification, acidification, decarboxylation; hydrolysis of substituted imide. Glu, ethyl β-bromopropionate; Asp, ethyl bromoacetate; Ser, phthalimido-malonic ester, HCHO, OH^-.

36.11 Intermediate for Ala is $CH_3CH(NH_2)CN$. Gly, HCHO; Leu, isovaleraldehyde from isopentyl alcohol; Ileu, α-methyl-*n*-butyraldehyde from 2-methyl-1-butanol; Val, isobutyraldehyde from *iso*-BuOH; Ser, $EtOCH_2CHO$ from $EtOCH_2CH_2OH$ (see page 564), with cleavage of ether in final step after the Strecker reaction.

36.12 (a) A, $(CH_3)_2CHCH(COOEt)COCOOEt$; B, $(CH_3)_2CHCH_2COCOOEt$;

(b) Ala: ethyl oxalate, ethyl acetate, NaOEt; crossed Claisen condensation; ketonic cleavage of β-keto ester to give $HOOCCOCH_3$; NH_3, H_2, Pd, heat. Glu: ethyl oxalate, ethyl succinate, NaOEt, crossed Claisen condensation; ketonic cleavage of β-keto ester to give $HOOCCOCH_2CH_2COOH$; NH_3, H_2, Pd, heat.

36.13 (a) $H_2NCH_2COO^-Na^+$; (b) $Cl^{-+}H_3NCH_2COOH$;
(c) $PhCONHCH_2COOH$; (d) $CH_3CONHCH_2COOH$;
(e) $HOCH_2COOH + N_2$; (f) $HSO_4^{-+}H_3NCH_2COOEt$;
(g) $C_6H_5CH_2OCONHCH_2COOH$.

36.14 (a) $PhCONHCH_2COCl$; (b) $PhCONHCH_2CONH_2$;
(c) $PhCONHCH_2CONHCH(CH_3)COOH$; (d) $PhCONHCH_2COOEt$;
(e) disubstitution *ortho* to $-OH$; (f) $^-OOCCH_2CH(NH_2)COO^-$;
(g) N,N-dimethylproline, a betaine (dipolar ion containing a quaternary ammonium group); (h) $p\text{-}CH_3OC_6H_4CH_2CH(NMe_3^+)COO^-$;
(i) $Na^{+-}OOCCH_2CH_2CH(NH_3^+)COO^-$;
(j) $EtOOCCH_2CH_2CH(COOEt)NH_3^+HSO_4^-$.

36.15 (a) 22.4 cc; (b) 44.8 cc; (c) no N_2.

36.16 Minimum mol.wt. = 114; could be valine.

36.17 (a)
$$-C\!\!=\!\!\overset{\ddot{}}{O}: \qquad -C\!\!=\!\!\overset{\ddot{}}{O}:^-$$
with $\overset{\ddots}{N}-$, H and $\overset{+}{N}-$, H respectively

(b) overlapping of p orbital of N with π orbital of C=O.

36.18 (a)

$H-C(=O)(CH_3)N\text{-}CH_3$ structure and $H-C(-O^-)(CH_3)\overset{+}{N}\text{-}CH_3$ structure. Partial double-bond char-

acter of carbon-nitrogen bond, with accompanying hindered rotation, gives rise to diastereomeric $-CH_3$ groups. Signals coalesce at high temperature as methyls become equivalent through rapid rotation.
(b) Confirm partial double-bond character of carbon-nitrogen bond in peptide linkage.

36.19 Salmine, $AlaArg_{50}Gly_4IleuPro_6Ser_7Val_3$. Weights add up to more than 100 g because of water taken up in hydrolysis of peptide links.

36.20 Same as empirical formula (preceding problem).

36.21 70300.

36.22   (a) 16700;   (b) 4.

36.23   A sulfonamide, which is more resistant to hydrolysis than carboxa-mides (see Sec. 23.6).

36.24   (a) Phe. Val. Asp. Glu.His;   (b) His. Leu.CySH.Gly.Ser.His.Leu;
(c) Tyr.Leu.Val.CySH.Gly.Glu.Arg.Gly.Phe.Phe.

36.25   (a) Cbz.Gly.Ala, $SOCl_2$; Phe; H_2, Pd.   (b) $PhCH_2OCOCl$, Ala; $SOCl_2$; Gly; H_2, Pd.

36.26   The following groups are attached to the rings of polystyrene:
A, $-CH_2Cl$;   B, $-CH_2OCOCH_2NHCOOCH_2Ph$;
C, $-CH_2OCOCH_2NH_2$;
D, $-CH_2OCOCH_2NHCOCH(CH_3)NHCOOCH_2Ph$;
E, $-CH_2OCOCH_2NHCOCH(CH_3)NH_2$;   G, $-CH_2Br$.
F is alanylglycine.

1.   (a) $PhCH_2Cl$, sodiomalonic ester; saponify, acidify, $-CO_2$; Br_2, P; excess NH_3.   (b) $PhCH_2Cl$, sodiomalonic ester; saponify, acidify, $-CO_2$; Br_2, P; EtOH, H^+; K phthalimide; hydrolysis.   (c) $PhCH_2Cl$, sodiomalonic ester; saponify, acidify; Br_2; heat, $-CO_2$; excess NH_3.   (d) Bromo-malonic ester, K phthalimide; Na; $PhCH_2Cl$; conc. HCl, heat; base. (e) $PhCH_2COOH$ (page 587), $SOCl_2$; $LiAlH(Bu\text{-}t)_3$; KCN, NH_4Cl; H_2O, H^+, heat.   (f) $PhCH_2CN$ (page 587), EtOH, H^+ (to give ester); ethyl oxalate, NaOEt, crossed Claisen cond.; ketonic cleavage of $PhCH(COOEt)COCOOEt$ (β-keto ester); NH_3, H_2, Pd, heat.

2.   (a) A, phthalimidomalonic ester;   B, α-H of A replaced by $-CH_2CH_2CH_2Br$;   C, $-Br$ of B replaced by $-OOCCH_3$; D, $HOCH_2CH_2CH_2CH(NH_3^+)COO^-$;   E, $-OH$ of D replaced by $-Cl$; E undergoes intramolecular alkylation to give proline.   (b) Phthalimido-malonic ester, NaOEt; 1,4-dibromobutane (displacement of only one $-Br$); excess NH_3; hydrolysis.

3.   (a) F, $CH_3CONHC(COOEt)_2CH_2CH_2CHO$;   G, cyanohydrin from F; H, unsaturated nitrile from G;
I, $CH_3CONHC(COOEt)_2CH_2(CH_2)_2CH_2NH_2$;
J, $CH_3CONHC(COOEt)_2CH_2(CH_2)_2CH_2NHCOCH_3$;
(b) K, $NCCH_2CH_2CH(COOEt)_2$;   L, $H_2NCH_2CH_2CH_2CH(COOEt)_2$;
M, ethyl 2-keto-3-piperidinecarboxylate;
N, ethyl 2-keto-3-chloro-3-piperidinecarboxylate;
O, $^+H_3NCH_2CH_2CH_2CHClCOO^-$;   (c) acrolein, CN^-, conjugate addn.;
KCN, NH_4Cl; H_2O, H^+, heat.

4. (a) Diketopiperazine, cyclic diamide; (b) unsaturated acid;
   (c) γ-lactam, 5-ring amide; (d) δ-lactam, 6-ring amide.

5. (a) Proton goes to most basic nitrogen. (b) $^+H_3N(CH_2)_4CH(NH_2)COO^-$
   and $H_2N(CH_2)_4CH(NH_3^+)COO^-$. α-NH_2 weakened as base by nearby
   $-COO^-$, so that more distant ϵ-NH_2 is more basic.
   (c) $HOOCCH_2CH(NH_3^+)COO^-$ and $^-OOCCH_2CH(NH_3^+)COOH$. α-NH_2
   strengthens adjacent $-COOH$; more distant $-COOH$ less affected.
   (d) Position of proton shown in Table 36.1 gives the most stable cation
   (compare guanidinium ion, Problem 20.24, page 686); other 3 nitrogens
   less basic. (e) p-$HOC_6H_4CH_2CH(NH_3^+)COO^-$ and
   p-$^-OC_6H_4CH_2CH(NH_3^+)COOH$. $-COOH$ much stronger acid than
   phenolic $-OH$.

6. (a) Betaine, $^+Me_3NCH_2COO^-$; (b) P, N-methylammonium iodide of
   methyl nicotinate (methyl 3-pyridinecarboxylate); trigonelline,
   N-methylpyridinium-3-carboxylate (dipolar ion).

7. As water content of solvent is lowered, hydrophobic parts no longer
   hide themselves.

8. Gly.Ala: K phthalimide, $BrCH_2COOEt$; H_2O, OH^-, gentle warming (to
   hydrolyze the ester group); $SOCl_2$; alanine; N_2H_4, heat. Ala.Gly: same
   procedure except use $CH_3CHBrCOOEt$ first, then glycine.

9. Minimum mol. wt. = 13000; minimum of one Fe and six S atoms.

10. (a) Approx. 32 $-CONH_2$ groups; (b) 395–398 peptide links plus
    $-CONH_2$ groups; (c) 367–370 amino acid residues.

11. (a) Leu_2Orn_2-D-$Phe_2Pro_2Val_2$; (b) ring structure;

    (c) Val.Orn.Leu.Phe

    ·Pro·　　　　·Pro·

    Val.Orn.Leu.Phe

    Gramicidin S

    Cyclic decapeptide

12. (a) One hexapeptide, 5 tetrapeptides, 2 tripeptides; (b) one octapeptide,
    one hexapeptide, one pentapeptide, 2 tetrapeptides, missing Leu, Phe,
    Phe, Tyr; (c) see (f) below; (d) one nonapeptide, one octapeptide, one
    tripeptide, one dipeptide, none missing; (e) see (f) below;

(f) Beef insulin:

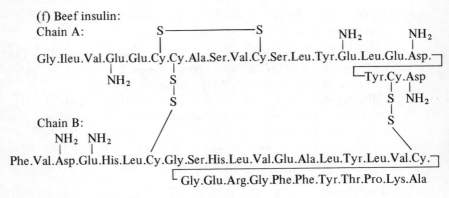

(g) DNP.NH(CH$_2$)$_4$CH(NH$_3^+$)COO$^-$ from ϵ-amino group of Lys. If Lys had been terminal, would have gotten a double DNP derivative of it, and no DNP.Phe.

CHAPTER 37

1. CO_2 becomes the —COOH of malonyl—CoA in reaction (1), Sec. 37.6; this is the carbon lost in reaction (4).

2. Slow (rate-determining) formation of a tetrahedral intermediate (see Sec. 20.17) followed by fast loss of OR or SR.

3. (b) Guanine and cytosine, 3 H-bonds per pair; adenine and thymine, only 2.

4. (a) Aldol-like condensation between ester and keto group of oxaloace-tate. (b) Aldol-like condensation between ester and keto group of acetoacetyl—CoA; reduction of ester to 1° alcohol by hydride transfer.

5. A, $C_2H_5OOCCH_2CH_2NHCONH_2$; B, a dihydroxydihydro-1,3-diazine (see page 1206 for parent diazine ring system);
C, a dihydroxydihydro-5-bromo-1,3-diazine; D, 2,4-dichloro-1,3-diazine;
E, 2-chloro-4-amino-1,3-diazine; F, 4-chloro-2-amino-1,3-diazine;
G, 2-methoxy-4-amino-1,3-diazine. (d) The structure shown on page 1179, and five others in which one or two protons have been transferred from nitrogen to oxygen and hence have dipolar character.

6. Biological oxidation of fatty acids removes 2 carbons at a time, starting at carboxyl end: "*beta*-oxidation."

7. *Retro* (reverse) aldol condensation.

8. (a) Direct transfer of a hydride ion from C-1 of ethanol to C-4 of pyri-
    dine ring of NAD⁺. There are now two hydrogens on C-4 (see Sec. 36.15)
    and, if one of them is D, C-4 is chiral center. (Because of chirality of rest
    of NADD molecule, these are *diastereotopic* hydrogens; see Sec. 13.7.)
    Of the two hydrogens on C-4, *only* the one originally received from
    ethanol in part (a) is transferred back to aldehyde, indicating transfer in
    both directions is stereospecific.   (c) Transfer to D-glucose of only the
    other hydrogen on C-4, indicating stereospecificity opposite to that in
    (b).   (d) Chemical reduction is not stereospecific, and gives mixture of
    diastereomeric NADD molecules.   (e) X and Y are the two enantiomers
    of CH₃CHDOH. Transfer is stereospecific not only with regard to which
    hydrogen on C-4 is transferred, but with regard to which face of
    acetaldehyde it becomes attached to. If D becomes attached to that
    face, X is formed; if H becomes attached, Y is formed.

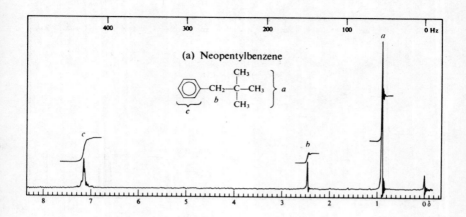

(a) Neopentylbenzene

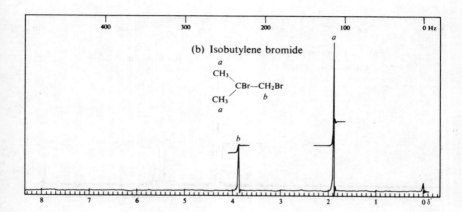

(b) Isobutylene bromide

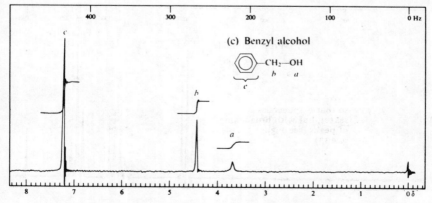

(c) Benzyl alcohol

Figure 13.7. Nmr spectra for Problem 13.9, p. 425.

175

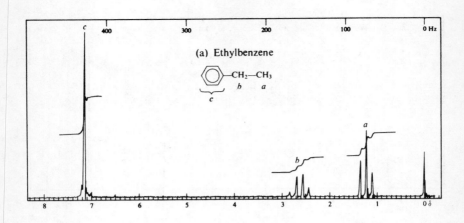

(a) Ethylbenzene

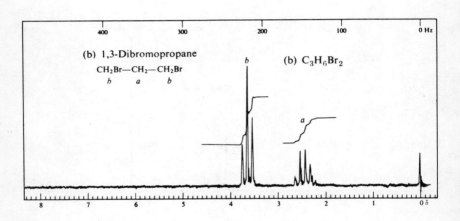

(b) 1,3-Dibromopropane

$CH_2Br—CH_2—CH_2Br$
  b   a   b

(b) $C_3H_6Br_2$

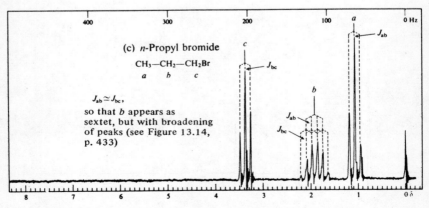

(c) n-Propyl bromide

$CH_3—CH_2—CH_2Br$
  a   b   c

$J_{ab} \simeq J_{bc}$,

so that b appears as
sextet, but with broadening
of peaks (see Figure 13.14,
p. 433)

J_{bc}

J_{ab}

J_{ab}

J_{bc}

Figure 13.16. Nmr spectra for Problem 13.12, p. 435.

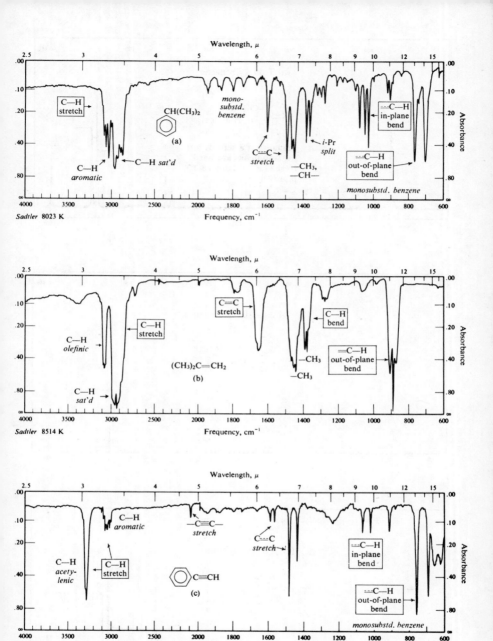

Figure 13.19. Infrared spectra for Problem 10, p. 447.

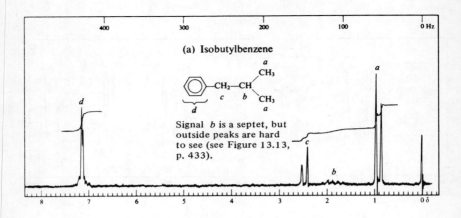

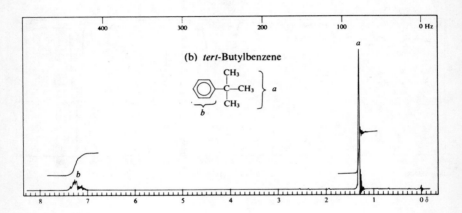

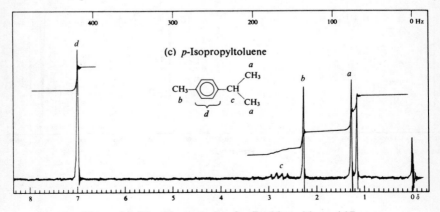

Figure 13.20. Nmr spectra for Problem 11, p. 447.

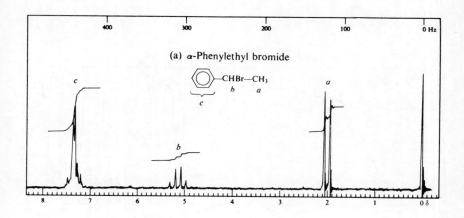

(a) α-Phenylethyl bromide

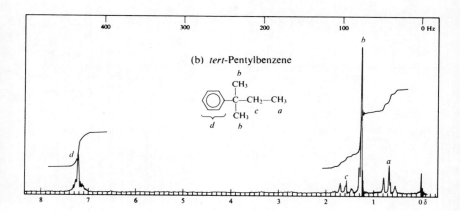

(b) *tert*-Pentylbenzene

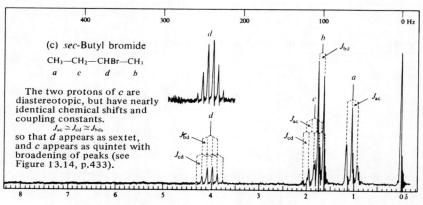

(c) *sec*-Butyl bromide

CH₃—CH₂—CHBr—CH₃
a   c   d   b

The two protons of *c* are diastereotopic, but have nearly identical chemical shifts and coupling constants.

$J_{ac} \simeq J_{cd} \simeq J_{bd}$,

so that *d* appears as sextet, and *c* appears as quintet with broadening of peaks (see Figure 13.14, p.433).

Figure 13.21. Nmr spectra for Problem 12, p. 447.

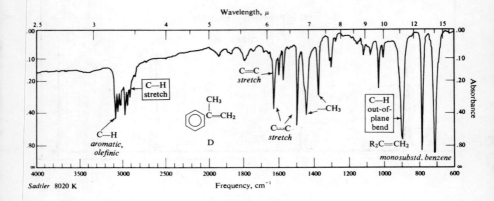

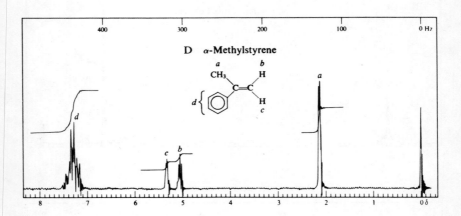

Figure 13.22. Infrared and nmr spectra for compound D, Problem 13, p. 447.

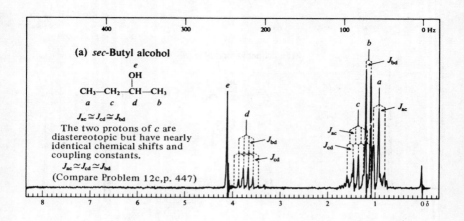

(a) *sec*-Butyl alcohol

$$\begin{array}{c} \overset{e}{\text{OH}} \\ | \\ \text{CH}_3\!-\!\text{CH}_2\!-\!\text{CH}\!-\!\text{CH}_3 \\ \; a \quad\;\; c \quad\;\; d \quad\;\; b \end{array}$$

$J_{ac} \simeq J_{cd} \simeq J_{bd}$

The two protons of *c* are diastereotopic but have nearly identical chemical shifts and coupling constants.

$J_{ac} \simeq J_{cd} \simeq J_{bd}$
(Compare Problem 12c, p. 447)

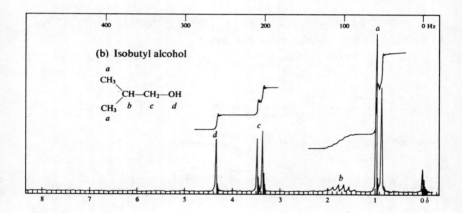

(b) Isobutyl alcohol

$$\begin{array}{c} \overset{a}{\text{CH}_3} \\ \diagdown \\ \quad\;\; \text{CH}\!-\!\text{CH}_2\!-\!\text{OH} \\ \diagup\; b \quad\;\; c \quad\;\; d \\ \text{CH}_3 \\ \;\; a \end{array}$$

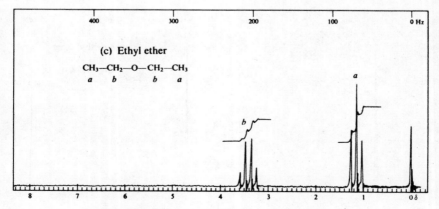

(c) Ethyl ether

$$\text{CH}_3\!-\!\text{CH}_2\!-\!\text{O}\!-\!\text{CH}_2\!-\!\text{CH}_3$$
$$\;\; a \qquad\; b \qquad\quad\; b \qquad\;\; a$$

Figure 16.2. Nmr spectra for Problem 22, p. 546.

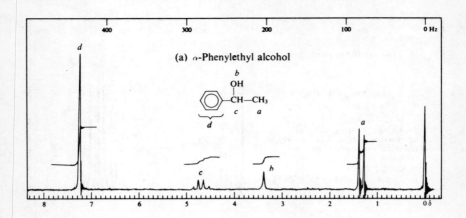

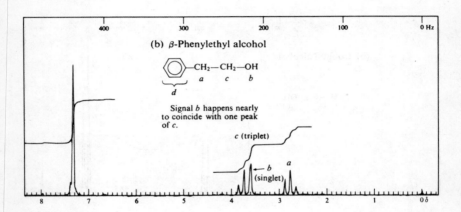

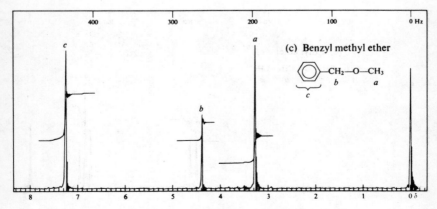

Figure 16.3. Nmr spectra for Problem 23, p. 546.

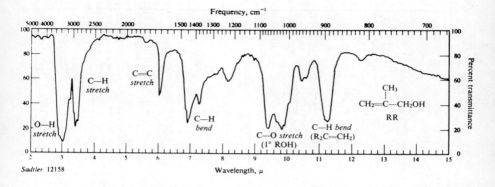

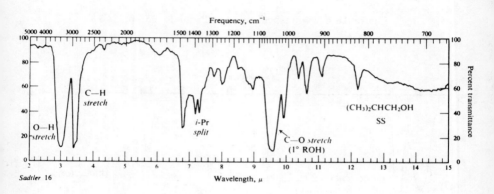

Figure 16.4. Infrared spectra for Problem 24, p. 546.

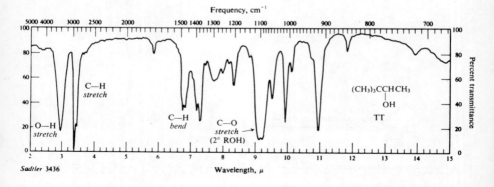

Figure 16.5. Infrared spectrum for Problem 25, p. 546.

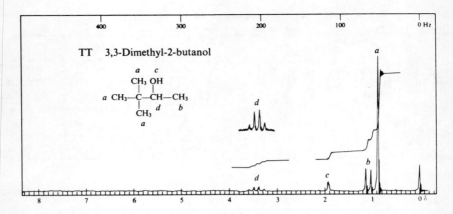

Figure 16.6 Nmr spectrum for Problem 25, p. 546

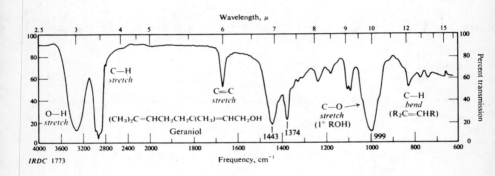

IRDC 1773

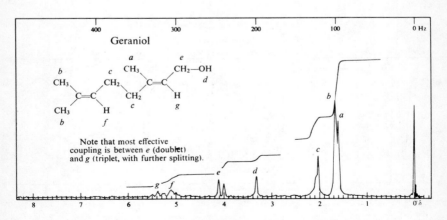

Figure 16.7. Infrared and nmr spectra for Problem 26, p. 546.

184

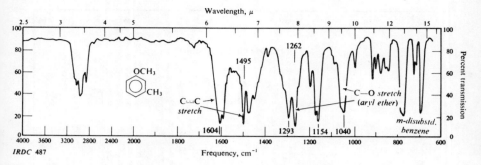

Figure 17.2. Infrared spectra for Problem 16, p. 574

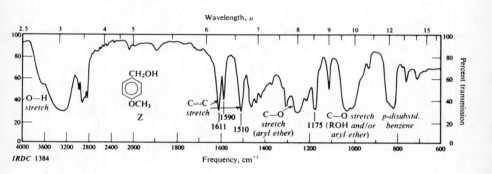

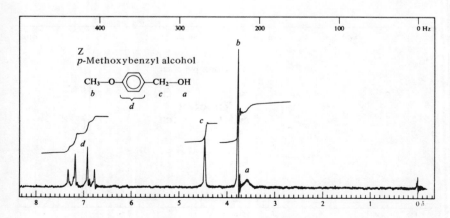

Figure 17.3. Infrared and nmr spectra for Problem 17, p. 574.

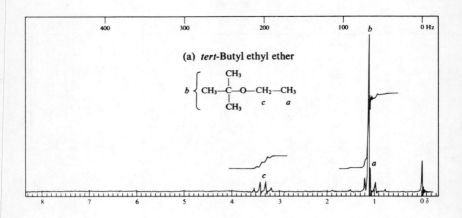

(a) *tert*-Butyl ethyl ether

$$CH_3 - \underset{\underset{CH_3}{|}}{\overset{\overset{CH_3}{|}}{C}} - O - CH_2 - CH_3$$
$$\qquad\qquad c \qquad a$$

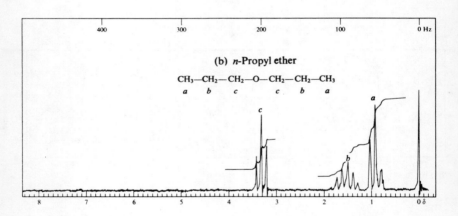

(b) *n*-Propyl ether

$$CH_3 - CH_2 - CH_2 - O - CH_2 - CH_2 - CH_3$$
$$\ \ a \qquad b \qquad c \qquad\quad c \qquad b \qquad a$$

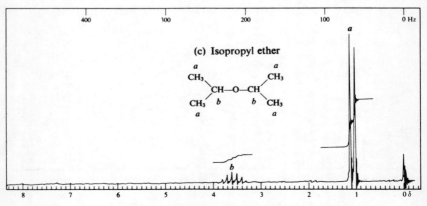

(c) Isopropyl ether

$$\underset{\underset{CH_3}{a}}{\overset{\overset{CH_3}{a}}{CH_3}}\underset{b}{CH} - O - \underset{b}{CH}\underset{\underset{CH_3}{a}}{\overset{\overset{CH_3}{a}}{CH_3}}$$

Figure 17.4. Nmr spectra for Problem 18, p. 574.

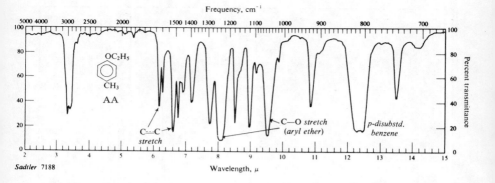

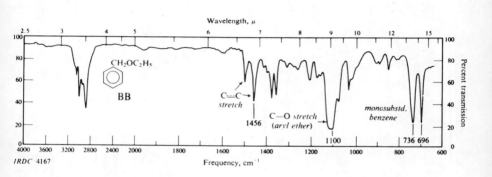

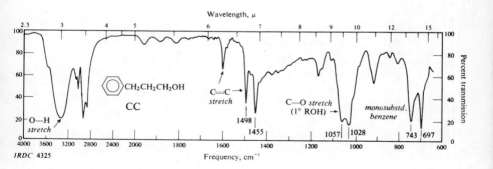

Figure 17.5. Infrared spectra for Problem 19, p. 574.

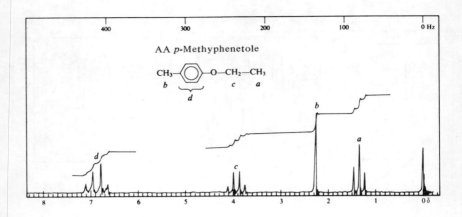

AA *p*-Methyphenetole

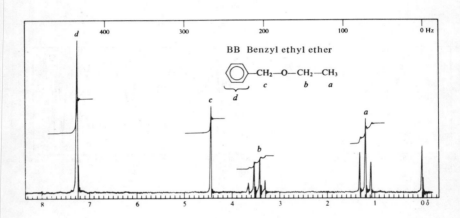

BB Benzyl ethyl ether

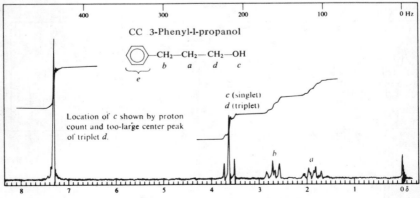

CC 3-Phenyl-1-propanol

Location of *c* shown by proton
count and too-large center peak
of triplet *d*.

c (singlet)
d (triplet)

Figure 17.6.   Nmr spectra for Problem 19, p. 574.

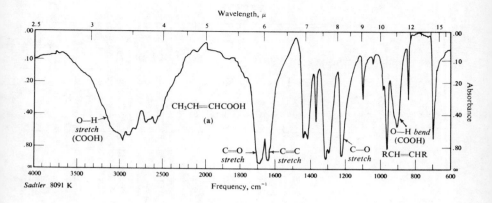

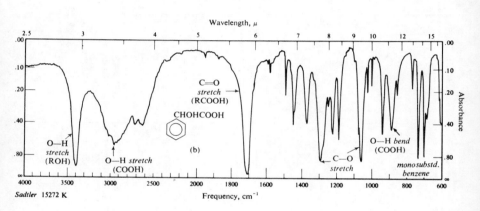

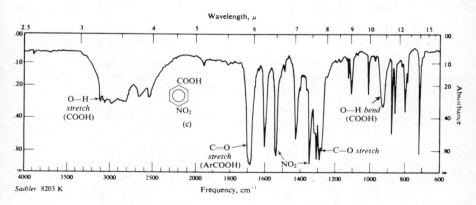

Figure 18.5. Infrared spectra for Problem 30, p. 615.

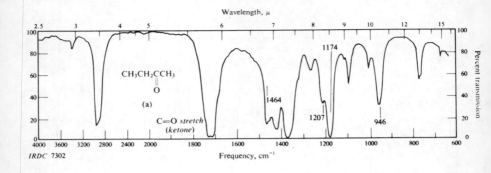

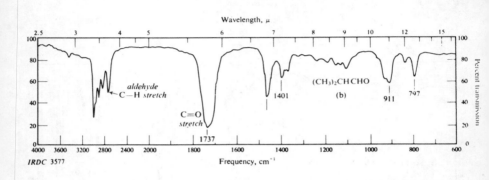

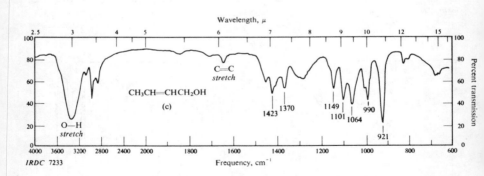

Figure 19.2. Infrared spectra for Problem 28, p. 653.

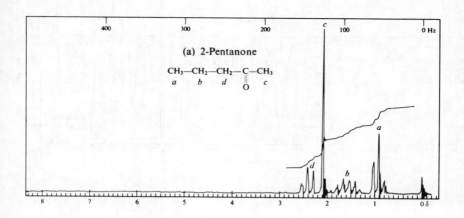

(a) 2-Pentanone

$$CH_3{-}CH_2{-}CH_2{-}C{-}CH_3$$
$$a \quad b \quad d \quad \underset{O}{\|} \quad c$$

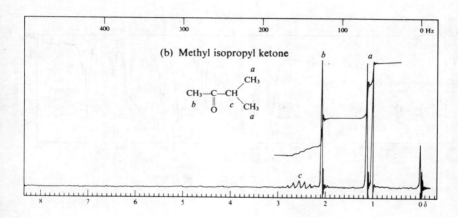

(b) Methyl isopropyl ketone

$$
\begin{array}{c}
\qquad\qquad\quad a \\
\qquad\qquad\ CH_3 \\
CH_3{-}C{-}CH \\
b\ \ \underset{O}{\|}\ \ \ c\ \ CH_3 \\
\qquad\qquad\quad a
\end{array}
$$

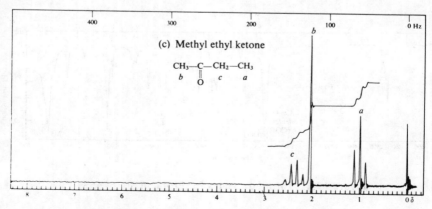

(c) Methyl ethyl ketone

$$CH_3{-}C{-}CH_2{-}CH_3$$
$$b\ \ \underset{O}{\|}\ \ c\ \ \ a$$

Figure 19.3. Nmr spectra for Problem 29, p. 653.

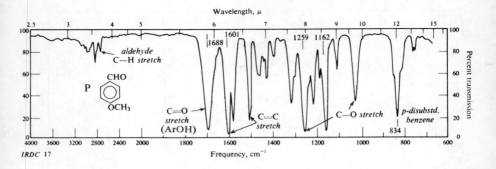

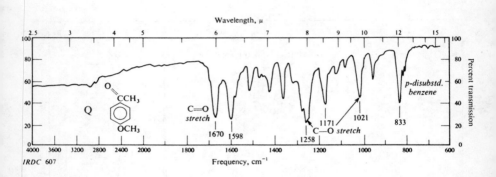

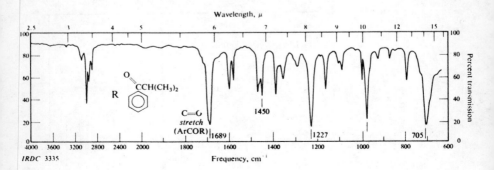

Figure 19.4. Infrared spectra for Problem 30, p. 653.

192

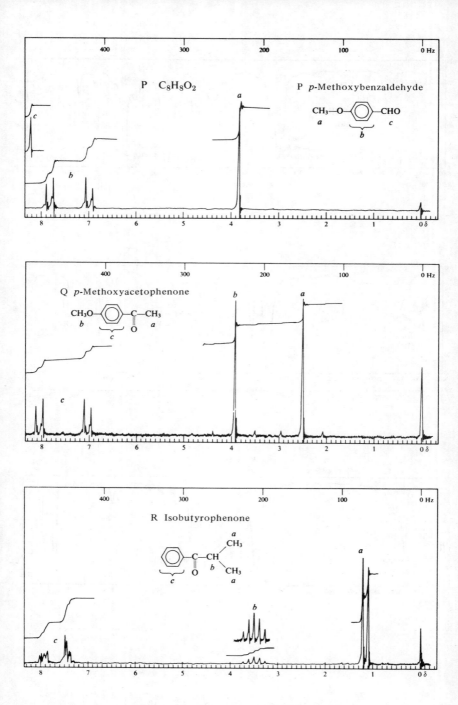

Figure 19.5. Nmr spectra for Problem 30, p. 653.

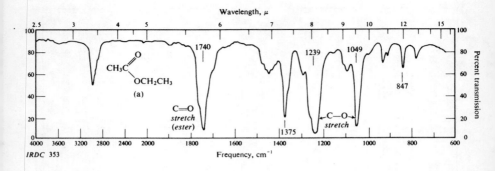

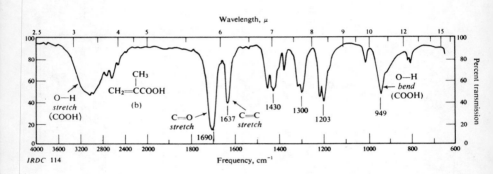

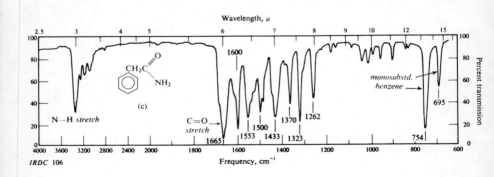

Figure 20.2. Infrared spectra for Problem 23, p. 694.

194

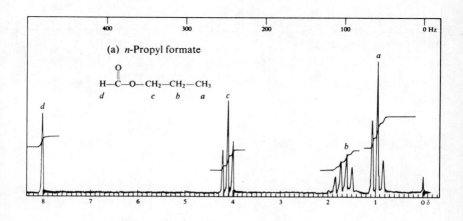

(a) *n*-Propyl formate

(b) Methyl propionate

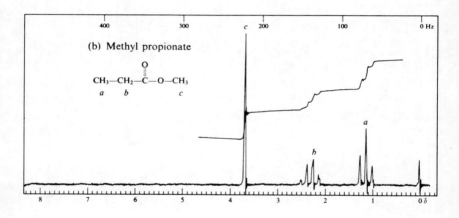

(c) Ethyl acetate

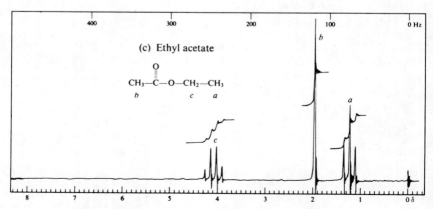

Figure 20.3. Nmr spectra for Problem 24, p. 694.

195

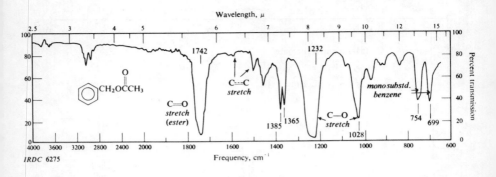

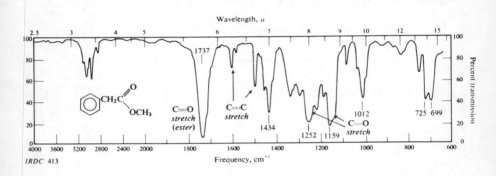

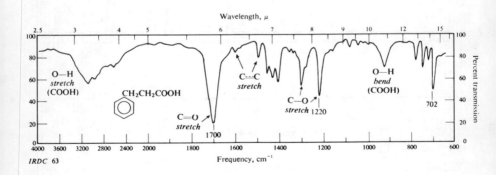

Figure 20.4. Infrared spectra for Problem 25, p. 694.

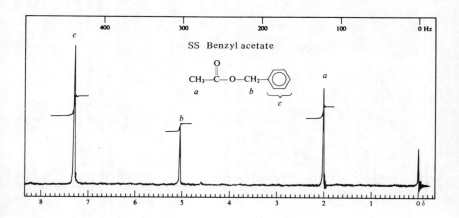

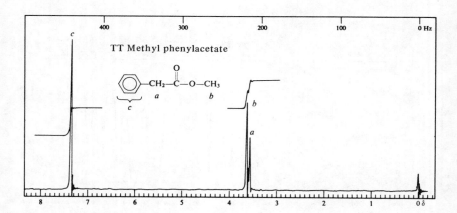

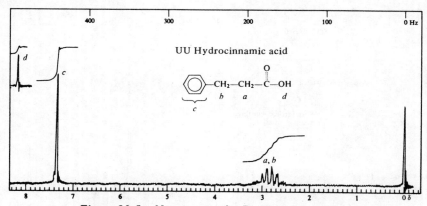

Figure 20.5. Nmr spectra for Problem 25, p. 694.

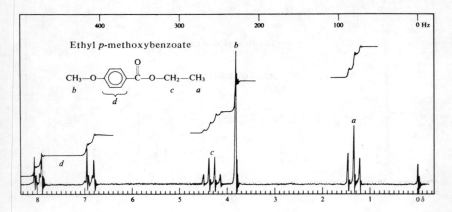

Figure 20.6. Nmr spectrum for Problem 26, p. 694.

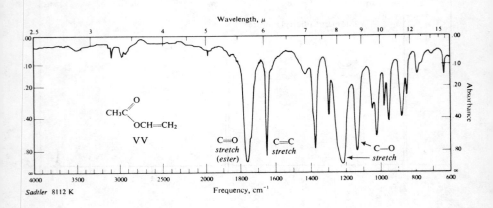

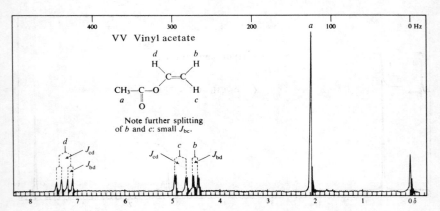

Figure 20.7. Infrared and nmr spectra for Problem 27, p. 694.

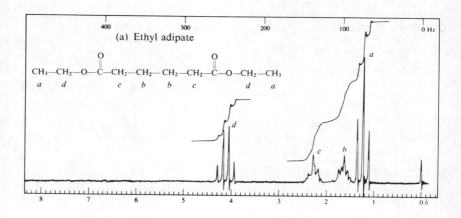

(a) Ethyl adipate

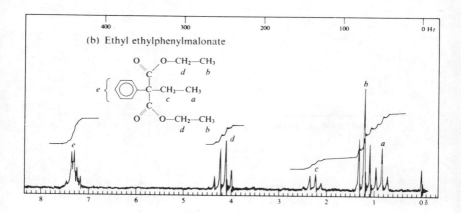

(b) Ethyl ethylphenylmalonate

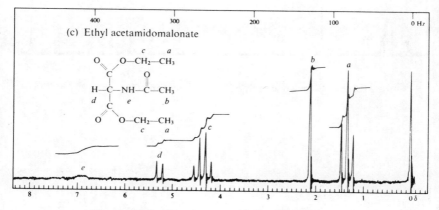

(c) Ethyl acetamidomalonate

Figure 20.8. Nmr spectra for Problem 28, p. 694.

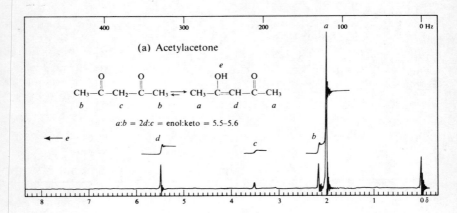

Figure 21.1(a). Nmr spectrum of acetylacetone (Problem 23, p. 725).

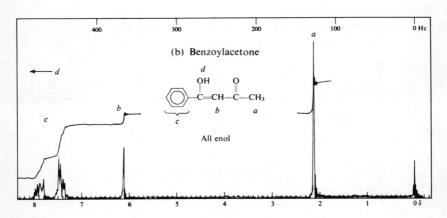

Figure 21.1(b). Nmr spectrum of benzoylacetone (Problem 23, p. 725).

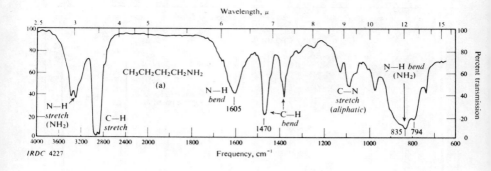

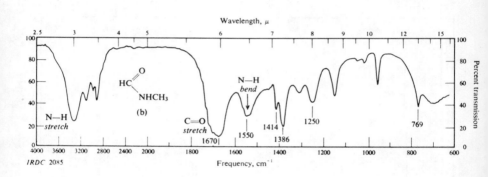

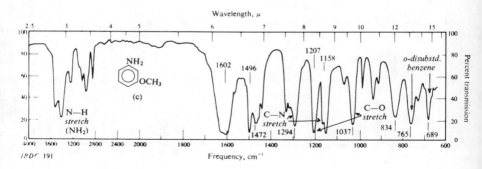

Figure 23.3. Infrared spectra for Problem 26, p. 782.

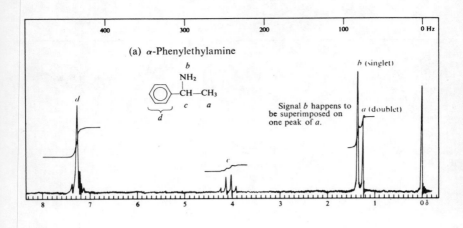

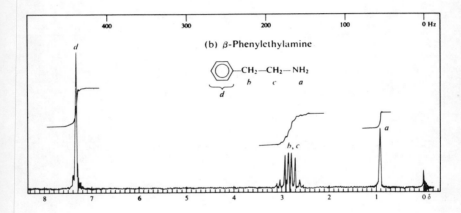

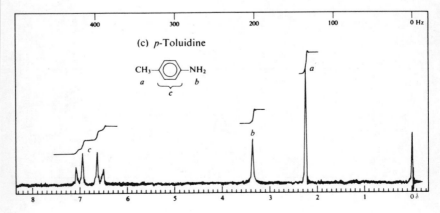

Figure 23.4. Nmr spectra for Problem 27, p. 782.

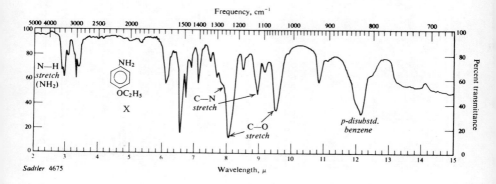

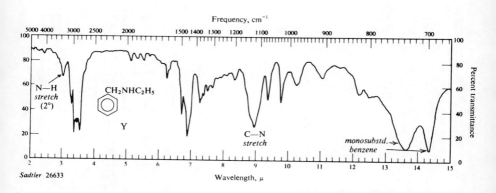

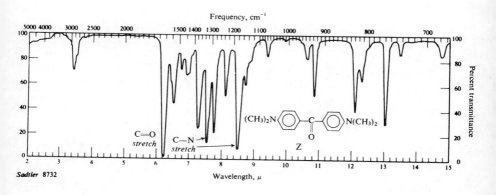

Figure 23.5. Infrared spectra for Problem 28, p. 782.

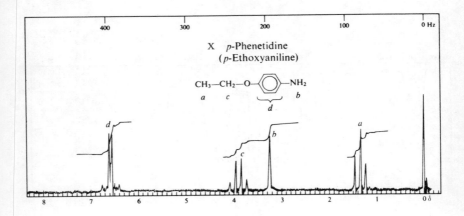

X *p*-Phenetidine
(*p*-Ethoxyaniline)

CH₃—CH₂—O—⟨ ⟩—NH₂
 a   *c*   *d*   *b*

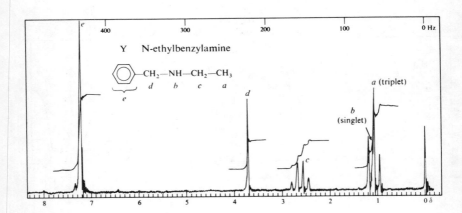

Y N-ethylbenzylamine

⟨ ⟩—CH₂—NH—CH₂—CH₃
 e   *d*   *b*   *c*   *a*

a (triplet)

b (singlet)

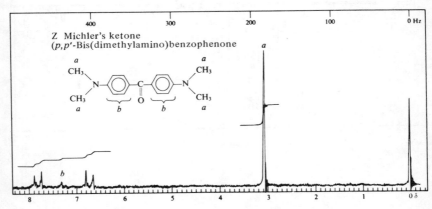

Z Michler's ketone
(*p,p'*-Bis(dimethylamino)benzophenone)

Figure 23.6. Nmr spectra for Problem 28, p. 782.

204

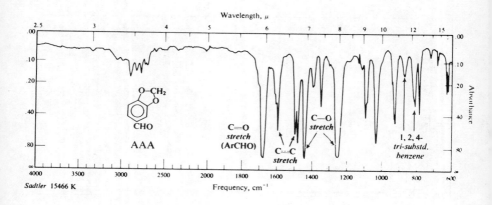

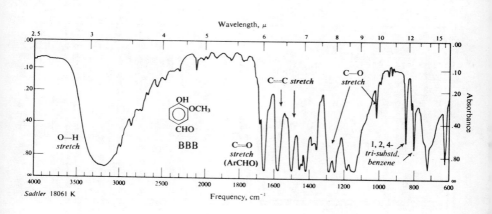

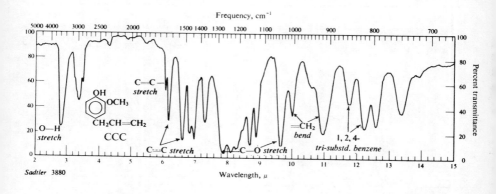

Figure 24.3. Infrared spectra for Problem 28, p. 811.

205

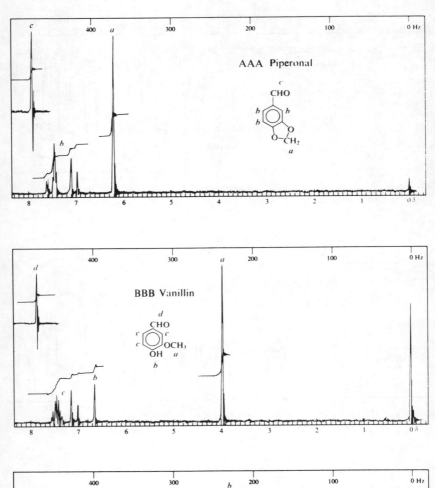

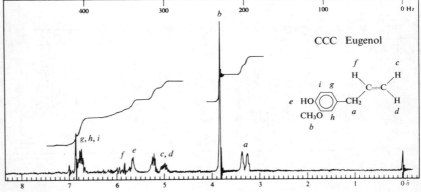

Figure 24.4. Nmr spectra for Problem 28, p. 811.

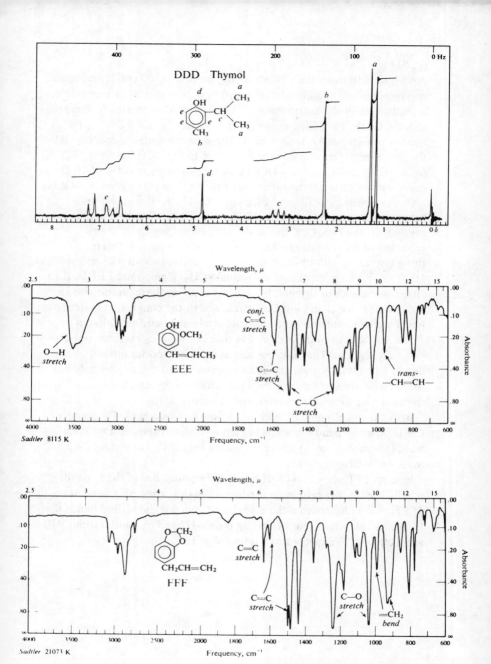

Figure 24.6. Infrared spectra for Problem 28, p. 811.

28. (p. 811)

AAA and BBB show the C=O stretching band at 1700 cm^{-1}, and must be piperonal and vanillin, the only carbonyl compounds of the set; this is confirmed by the far downfield —CHO proton absorption in their nmr spectra. Of the two, BBB shows O—H stretching at 3200 cm^{-1}, and hence is vanillin; AAA is piperonal. These assignments are confirmed by the nmr spectra: proton counting (relative to the —CHO) reveals —OCH$_3$ (plus —OH) in contrast to —OCH$_2$O—; the two oxygens of —OCH$_2$O— cause a much stronger downfield shift than the single oxygen of —OCH$_3$.

Of the remaining, CCC and EEE show O—H stretching, and must belong to the group of unassigned phenols: eugenol, isoeugenol, and thymol. Of the two, CCC shows the C=C stretching at 1650 cm^{-1} expected of an unconjugated C=C, and hence is eugenol; this is confirmed by the C—H out-of-plane bending bands at about 915 and 1000 cm^{-1}, characteristic of a terminal =CH$_2$. Compound EEE is, then, either isoeugenol or thymol. In contrast to thymol, isoeugenol has an unsaturated side chain, but C=C stretching in the conjugated system might well be hidden by the aromatic stretching band at 1600 cm^{-1}.

The nmr spectrum of DDD shows that it can be, of all seven possibilities, only thymol. The large doublet at δ 1.25 is too far upfield to be due to any allylic, vinylic, or alkoxy protons, and can be due only to the six β-protons of the isopropyl side chain of thymol. Inspection shows the entire spectrum to fit this structure neatly.

With thymol eliminated, EEE must now be isoeugenol. The shape of the 1600-cm^{-1} band hints at a hidden C=C absorption, and we see a band (about 965 cm^{-1}) where we would expect C—H bending for a *trans* —CH=CH—.

Finally, FFF shows no O—H band, and so must be, of the remaining possibilities, either safrole or anethole. The C=C stretching band at 1650 cm^{-1} indicates that the side chain is unconjugated, and hence that FFF is safrole; this is confirmed by the C—H bending bands (about 920 and 1000 cm^{-1}) expected of a terminal =CH$_2$.